D0983139

Inorganic
Syntheses

Volume VII

Inorganic Syntheses

Volume VII

McGraw-Hill Book Company, Inc.

New York   San Francisco   Toronto   London

INORGANIC SYNTHESES, VOLUME VII

II

35030

To
Herman Irving Schlesinger
(1882–1960)

PREFACE

The present volume of INORGANIC SYNTHESES contains sixty-five contributions covering a wide range of compounds and emanating from a large number of laboratories both in this country and abroad. As in previous volumes of this series, each synthesis has been carefully checked in a laboratory other than that from which it was submitted. Also in accordance with established practice, the syntheses in Volume VII are arranged on the basis of the Mendeleev periodic classification, with subdivision into A and B groups. The author, subject, and formula indexes in this volume are cumulative for all seven volumes.

Contributions for Volume VIII of this series are invited, and manuscripts, in triplicate and in the conventional style, should be submitted to the editor-in-chief of that volume, Professor Henry F. Holtzclaw, Jr., Department of Chemistry, University of Nebraska, Lincoln, Nebraska. The services of competent checkers are always desired, and those persons interested in performing this invaluable function are urged to communicate with Professor Holtzclaw.

Since the appearance of Volume VI, four new members have been elected to the Editorial Board. They include Professor William L. Jolly of the University of California (Berkeley); Dr. Earl L. Muetterties of E. I. du Pont de Nemours and Co.; Dr. Morris L. Nielsen of the Monsanto Chemical Co.; and Professor Robert W. Parry of the University of Michigan.

The editor-in-chief is deeply grateful to his associates on the Editorial and Advisory Boards for their most valuable assistance in the preparation of Volume VII. He is particularly indebted to Miss Janet D. Scott for handling all the problems of nomenclature and indexing, and for her participation in the final editing of the manuscript. Finally, the editor wishes to acknowledge the splendid efforts of Miss Julia Jeffery, Miss Judith Ann Kleinberg, and Mrs. Alberta Rogers in typing the manuscript.

The editors welcome suggestions and criticisms pertinent to this and other volumes of INORGANIC SYNTHESES. The comments of the readers of the series have always been most useful.

Jacob Kleinberg

CONTENTS

CHAPTER IA

See also: Sodium hydrogen sulfide, synthesis 35
Potassium octacyanotungstate(IV) 2-hydrate, synthesis 40
Sodium fluoride(F[18]), synthesis 42
Potassium hexachlororhenate(IV) and potassium hexabro-
morhenate(IV), synthesis 51
Sodium salts of carbonyl hydrides prepared in ethereal media,
synthesis 53

1. LITHIUM HYDROXIDE AND LITHIUM OXIDE

SUBMITTED BY JUSTO BRAVO*
CHECKED BY JOHAN H. DE GROOT†

Anhydrous lithium hydroxide was first obtained by Troost[1] by thermally dehydrating the monohydrate in a vacuum for several weeks. De Forcrand[2] obtained the anhydrous product by passing pure dry hydrogen over the hydrated crystals for an hour at a temperature not exceeding 140°. By fusion of the hydrate, Gmelin[3] produced an anhydrous product.

The thermal decomposition of lithium hydroxide has been effected by Dittmar[4] by holding it at red heat under a hydrogen atmosphere for 4 hours. The decomposition pressures along with the corresponding temperatures have been published in the International Critical Tables.[5]

* Foote Minera Company, Berwyn, Pa.
† Research Associate with the Joint Committee on Chemical Analysis by Powder Diffraction Methods, American Society for Testing Materials, National Bureau of Standards, Washington, D.C.

1

A. ANHYDROUS LITHIUM HYDROXIDE

$$LiOH \cdot H_2O \rightarrow LiOH + H_2O$$

Procedure

A laboratory roaster (Fig. 1) is provided with a tube to supply a positive pressure of carbon dioxide–free dry air

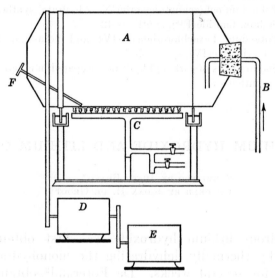

FIG. 1. Apparatus for the preparation of anhydrous lithium hydroxide.
  A—Stainless-steel rotating drum, 8 in. in diameter and 14 in. long.
  B—Tube supplying carbon dioxide–free dry air.
  C—Air-blast gas burner.
  D—Reducer drive.
  E—110-voltmeter.
  F—Metal thermometer.

inside the drum. The drum is heated by an air-blast gas burner. It is charged with 876.8 g. (20.9 mols) of lithium hydroxide 1-hydrate (99.5% $LiOH \cdot H_2O$, 0.50% Li_2CO_3). The gas burner is lighted and the drum is rotated. A temperature of 130 to 150°, measured by a metal thermometer inserted at the front end of the drum, is maintained by adjusting the gas and air pressure. Within one hour the disappearance of the water vapor is observed, and a granulated dry lithium hydroxide is obtained. The drum is cooled by shutting off the gas. When the temperature reaches about 50°, the product is scooped into a bottle. (NOTE: The transfer of all material is carried out in a dry-box which contains carbon dioxide–free dry air.) The bottle is sealed and a sample analyzed. The yield of 500.0 g. is nearly quantitative. *Product analysis:* 99.0% LiOH, 1.0% Li_2CO_3.

Properties

Anhydrous lithium hydroxide is white, granular, and free flowing. It readily absorbs both carbon dioxide and water from the atmosphere. Both the hydroxide and the monoxide have a marked irritating effect on the skin. The hydroxide has a density of 2.54 g./cc.

B. LITHIUM OXIDE*

$$2LiOH \rightarrow Li_2O + H_2O$$

Procedure

In a carbon dioxide–free dry-box, 200.0 g. (8.35 mols) of anhydrous lithium hydroxide is placed in a nickel trough, 12 in. long, $3\frac{1}{2}$ in. in diameter, $\frac{1}{16}$ in. thick, lined with silver foil 16 in. long, 6 in. wide, and 0.002 in. thick. The trough is placed in a tube furnace (Fig. 2). The furnace is heated to $675° \pm 10°$ and maintained at this temperature by a temperature controller. The open end of the furnace is closed with a rubber stopper connected with a glass tube and rubber tubing to a Dry Ice–acetone trap, which is directed to a vacuum pump. The pressure is maintained at about 0.5 in. The process is allowed to proceed for half an hour at the temperature indicated, after which

---

* An alternative method for the preparation of this compound has been given by A. J. Cohen, INORGANIC SYNTHESES, **5**, 5 (1957).

the pump and heat are shut off. The rubber tubing is clamped for vacuum tightness. When the temperature is about 50°, the vacuum is released by the introduction of carbon dioxide–free dry air. The stopper is removed and the trough quickly transferred into the dry-box. The

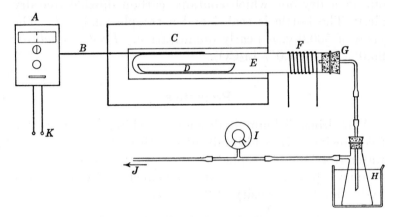

Fig. 2. Apparatus for the preparation of lithium oxide.
A—Temperature controller.
B—Thermocouple connection.
C—Tube furnace.
D—Nickel trough lined with silver foil.
E—Four-inch-diameter quartz tube.
F—Cooling coil (water circulation).
G—Rubber stopper.
H—Dry Ice–acetone trap.
I—Vacuum gage.
J—To vacuum pump.
K—220-volt power source.

lithium oxide is removed by peeling off the silver foil. The product is crushed, bottled, and sealed. The yield of 125 g. is quantitative. *Product analysis:* 98% Li_2O, 2.0% Li_2CO_3.

Properties

Lithium oxide is obtained as a white crusty material. It readily absorbs both carbon dioxide and water from the atmosphere. At elevated temperature it attacks glass, silica, and many metals. The high-temperature heat content and entropy have been evaluated.[6]

References

1. L. TROOST: *Ann. chim. phys.*, [3], **51**, 115 (1857).
2. R. DE FORCRAND: *Compt. rend.*, **146**, 802 (1908).
3. C. G. GMELIN: *Ann.*, **62**, 399 (1899).
4. W. DITTMAR: *J. Soc. Chem. Ind.*, **7**, 730 (1888).
5. "International Critical Tables," E. W. Washburn (ed.), McGraw-Hill Book Company, New York, 1926–1930.
6. C. H. SHOMATE and A. J. COHEN: *J. Am. Chem. Soc.*, **77**, 285 (1955).

2. 1-PHENYLBIGUANIDE-*p*-SULFONIC ACID COMPLEXES OF COPPER(II)

Submitted by Priyadaranjan RâУ*
Checked by Sam N. Holter† and W. Conard Fernelius†

Two modifications (green and red) of the copper derivative of phenylbiguanide-*p*-sulfonic acid (*N*-(amidinoamidino)sulfanilic acid) are known.[1,2] Both are formed by the careful neutralization of the acid by ammonia in the presence of copper ion. The two modifications have almost the same magnetic moment and they dissolve in alkali to give the same red solution. Although only a few cis-trans isomers of copper(II) are known, infrared spectra indicate that the two forms of the present complex are cis-trans isomers.[3]

A. 1-PHENYLBIGUANIDE-*p*-SULFONIC ACID

$$HO_3SC_6H_4NH_2 \cdot H_2O + NCNHC(=NH)NH_2 \rightarrow$$
$$HO_3SC_6H_4NHC(=NH)NHC(=NH)NH_2 + H_2O$$

Phenylbiguanide-*p*-sulfonic acid is prepared by the usual reaction for the synthesis of *N*-substituted biguanides: i.e., the addition of dicyanodiamide (cyanoguanidine) to an amine.[1]

Procedure

A mixture of 2.0 g. (0.0104 mol) of sulfanilic acid, 1.2 g. (0.0142 mol) of dicyanodiamide, and 30 ml. of water is

* University College of Science, Calcutta, India.
† The Pennsylvania State University, University Park, Pa.

heated at reflux for about 2 hours, during which a silky white solid separates. When the mixture has cooled, the solid is filtered and washed with 50 ml. of water. Yield (based on sulfanilic acid): 2.0 g. (74%). For purification, the product is recrystallized from 170 ml. of boiling water. Yield: 1.8 g. (67%); m.p. 265 to 268° (decomp.). *Anal.* Calcd. for $HO_3SC_6H_4C_2N_5H_6$: N, 27.20; S, 12.45. Found: N, 26.90; S (by peroxide fusion), 12.60.

Properties

Phenylbiguanide-*p*-sulfonic acid forms silky white crystals which are very slightly acid to litmus. The substance is nearly insoluble in cold water and organic solvents such as alcohol, ether, and acetone, but is soluble in strong acids as well as dilute alkalies and ammonia.

B. COPPER COMPLEXES OF 1-PHENYLBIGUANIDE-*p*-SULFONIC ACID

$$2HSO_3C_6H_4C_2N_5H_6 + Cu^{++} + 2NH_3 \rightarrow$$
$$[Cu(HO_3SC_6H_4C_2N_5H_5)_2] + 2NH_4^+$$

1. Red-violet modification. A mixture of 2.05 g. (0.008 mol) of phenylbiguanide-*p*-sulfonic acid and 150 ml. of water is acidified with 1.5 ml. of concentrated hydrochloric acid (35%) and warmed to 60°. To this solution is added 1 g. (0.004 mol) of copper(II) sulfate 5-hydrate dissolved in 10 ml. of water. The resulting solution is then treated with dilute (12%) ammonia water drop by drop until the solution becomes just alkaline and the red-violet crystals of the copper complex separate. About 4 ml. of ammonia is required. The crystals are filtered, washed first with 100 ml. of water and finally with 15 ml. of ethanol, and dried in air. Yield: 2.2 g. (93% based on copper taken). *Anal.* Calcd. for $[Cu(HO_3SC_6H_4C_2N_5H_5)_2] \cdot H_2O$: N, 23.59; Cu, 10.71; H_2O, 3.04. Found: N, 23.66; Cu, 10.61, 10.64; H_2O (loss at 90°), 3.0.

2. Green modification. A mixture of 3 g. (0.0117 mol) of phenylbiguanide-*p*-sulfonic acid and 150 ml. of water is acidified with 2.5 ml. of concentrated hydrochloric acid (35%) and warmed to 60°. To this solution is added 1 g. (0.004 mol) of copper(II) sulfate 5-hydrate dissolved in 10 ml. of water. The resulting mixture is then treated with concentrated ammonia water (24%) until the red-violet precipitate first formed goes into solution with a deep blue color. About 200 ml. of ammonia solution is required. The blue solution is heated with stirring on a water bath (80°) for 10 minutes with the addition of concentrated ammonia water from time to time to replace what has boiled off. During the latter part of the heating dark green crystals begin to separate on the side of the container. After heating for about an hour, the crystals are filtered and washed with water. They may be purified by dissolution in 15 ml. of warm dilute hydrochloric acid (5.8%), reprecipitation from hot solution with 100 ml. of concentrated ammonia water, and digestion on the water bath as before. Yield: 2.2 g. (93% based on copper taken). *Anal.* Calcd. for $[Cu(HO_3SC_6H_4C_2N_5H_5)_2]\cdot1.5H_2O$: N, 23.23; Cu, 10.54. Found: N, 23.56; Cu, 10.68.

Properties

Both modifications of the copper derivative of phenyl-biguanide-*p*-sulfonic acid are insoluble in water but dissolve in alkali to form a red solution from which red-violet crystals separate on neutralization with acid in the cold. The red form changes to the green form on warming with ammonia solution. The magnetic moments are: red-violet, $\mu = 1.85$ Bohr magnetons; green, $\mu = 1.84$ Bohr magnetons.

References

1. P. RÂY and S. K. SIDDHANTA: *J. Indian Chem. Soc.*, **20**, 250 (1943).
2. P. RÂY and R. K. DUTT: *ibid.*, **25**, 563 (1948).
3. P. RÂY: unpublished observations.

3. TETRAKIS[IODO(TRI-*n*-BUTYLPHOSPHINE)-COPPER(I)] AND IODO-(2,2'-BIPYRIDINE)-(TRI-*n*-BUTYLPHOSPHINE)COPPER(I)

SUBMITTED BY GEORGE B. KAUFFMAN* AND LARRY A. TETER*
CHECKED BY T. C. ICHNIOWSKI† AND A. F. CLIFFORD†

Tertiary alkylphosphines or -arsines combine in equimolar amounts with gold(I) chloride, silver(I) iodide, or copper(I) iodide to form crystalline nonelectrolytic compounds insoluble in water but very soluble in most organic solvents. X-ray diffraction of the solids as well as ebullioscopic and cryoscopic measurements of solutions have shown the copper(I) iodide derivatives to be tetramers which dissociate only slightly in solution.[1] In these structures the four copper atoms are situated at the apexes of a regular tetrahedron with the iodine atoms at the centers, but above the planes of the tetrahedral faces, while each phosphorus or arsenic atom lies beyond each copper atom on a line extending from the center of the tetrahedron through the corresponding copper atom. The stability of these compounds can thus be attributed to the attainment by copper of a coordination number of four and an effective atomic number equal to the atomic number of the nearest inert gas, krypton. When acetone solutions of tetrakis[iodo(tri-*n*-butylphosphine)copper(I)] and 2,2'-bipyridine (dipyridyl) are mixed, the tetrameric structure is ruptured, yielding iodo-(2,2'-bipyridine)(tri-*n*-butylphosphine)copper(I), in which the monomolecular structure is stabilized by chelation of 2,2'-bipyridine with consequent achievement of a coordination number of four by copper.

The stabilities and melting points of the copper(I) iodide derivatives of tertiary phosphines fall rapidly, and their solubilities in organic solvents increase as the size

* Fresno State College, Fresno, Calif.
† Purdue University, Lafayette, Ind.

of the alkyl group increases. The tetramer of copper(I) iodide with triethylphosphine was first prepared by Arbusow.[2]

Procedure

A. TETRAKIS[IODO(TRI-*n*-BUTYLPHOSPHINE)COPPER(I)]

$$4(n\text{-}C_4H_9)_3P + 4CuI \rightarrow [CuI\{(n\text{-}C_4H_9)_3P\}]_4$$

Thirteen and fifteen-hundredths grams (0.069 mol) of copper(I) iodide* is dissolved with stirring in a solution of 130 g. of potassium iodide in 100 ml. of water. If the resulting solution is not colorless, it is shaken for several minutes with 1 g. of decolorizing charcoal and filtered.† The colorless solution is next shaken vigorously for five minutes with 12.5 ml. (10.15 g. = 0.050 mol)‡ of *freshly distilled* tri-*n*-butylphosphine§ (density = 0.812 g./ml.) in a 250-ml. glass-stoppered Erlenmeyer flask until the initially formed greasy mass becomes crystalline. The white crystals are collected on a 6-cm. Büchner funnel and washed free of any occluded copper(I) iodide with several 10-ml. portions of saturated potassium iodide solution. They are then similarly washed with distilled water and 95% ethanol, and air-dried. The yield of crude product is 19.0 g. (96.7% based on tri-*n*-butylphosphine).

The product may be purified by recrystallization from a solvent pair such as ethanol and isopropyl alcohol or ethanol and acetone. The crystals are dissolved in a hot mixture of 115 ml. of ethanol and 75 ml. of isopropyl

---

* Either commercially available copper(I) iodide or that prepared according to the directions of Kauffman and Pinnell[3] may be used.

† This technique may also be used to purify copper(I) iodide which has become discolored on standing. Upon dilution of the filtered solution with water, pure white copper(I) iodide precipitates.

‡ Since excess tri-*n*-butylphosphine may give an oily product, copper(I) iodide is used in excess.

§ Either commercially available tri-*n*-butylphosphine or that prepared according to the directions of Kauffman and Teter[4] may be used.

alcohol, and the solution is first cooled *slowly* without shaking before being placed in an ice bath, so that crystals rather than a fine powder are obtained. Several such recrystallizations, each with a percentage recovery of about 85%, are required to give a product with a melting point of 75°. For example, after four recrystallizations the yield of ethanol-washed and air-dried product is *ca.* 9.82 g. (*ca.* 50%).

B. IODO-(2,2'-BIPYRIDINE)- (TRI-*n*-BUTYLPHOSPHINE)COPPER(I)

$$[CuI\{(n\text{-}C_4H_9)_3P\}]_4 + 4(C_5H_4N)_2 \rightarrow 4[CuI(C_5H_4N)_2(n\text{-}C_4H_9)_3P]$$

A solution of 1.00 g. (0.0064 mol) of 2,2'-bipyridine in 20 ml. of cold acetone is stirred into a solution of 2.50 g. (0.00158 mol) of tetrakis[iodo(tri-*n*-butylphosphine)copper(I)] (Procedure A) in 20 ml. of cold acetone. The resulting deep red solution is evaporated at room temperature by directing a stream of air across the surface until the volume has been reduced to about 15 ml. The mixture is *quickly* heated to boiling on a water bath, filtered *immediately* by suction and cooled in an ice bath.* The resulting orange-red crystals are collected on a 5-cm. sintered-glass funnel and air-dried. The yield is 2.30 g. (66.3%). The compound may be recrystallized from about 10 ml. of hot acetone, but the loss is severe as the compound is very soluble in this solvent. Unless refrigerated, the compound decomposes in the course of several weeks.

Analysis

A 1-g. sample of tetrakis[iodo(tri-*n*-butylphosphine)-copper(I)] is decomposed by heating with 5 g. of sodium

---

* Delay and excessive heating cause extensive decomposition with formation of insoluble red di-μ-iodo-bis(2,2'-bipyridine)copper(I). This compound is removed by the filtration.

carbonate, the residue evaporated to dryness with 30 ml. of nitric acid and dissolved in 200 ml. of water, 5 ml. of sulfuric acid added, and copper determined by electrolytic reduction.   Calcd.   for $[CuI\{(n\text{-}C_4H_9)_3P\}]_4$:   Cu,   16.18. Found: Cu, 16.00.

Properties[1]

Tetrakis[iodo(tri-*n*-butylphosphine)copper(I)] forms white rhombic crystals which melt at 75°, but the melting point is greatly lowered by even traces of impurities. It is extremely soluble in chloroform, benzene, toluene, and ethyl ether, and moderately soluble in ethanol and water.   Unless refrigerated, it decomposes in several days to a green viscous syrup.   On heating *in vacuo* it liberates tri-*n*-butylphosphine, leaving a crystalline residue of copper(I) iodide.   In acetone solution it reacts with 2,2'-bipyridine to give orange-red iodo-(2,2'-bipyridine)-(tri-*n*-butylphosphine)copper(I) (m.p., 123°).   On heating the latter compound *in vacuo*, 2,2'-bipyridine first sublimes and then tri-*n*-butylphosphine distills, leaving a crystalline deposit of copper(I) iodide; in boiling ethanol, benzene, or acetone solution, it loses tri-*n*-butylphosphine and deposits insoluble deep red di-μ-iodo-bis[2,2'-bipyridinedi-

$$[(C_5H_4N)_2Cu \overset{\displaystyle I}{\underset{\displaystyle I}{\diamondsuit}} Cu(C_5H_4N)_2]$$

copper(I)], $[(C_5H_4N)_2Cu \diamondsuit Cu(C_5H_4N)_2]$,   a compound

first prepared by Tartarini.[5]

References

1. F. G. MANN, D. PURDIE, and A. F. WELLS: *J. Chem. Soc.*, **1936**, 1503.
2. A. E. ARBUSOW: *J. Russ. Phys. Chem. Soc.*, **38** ii, 293 (1906).
3. G. B. KAUFFMAN and R. P. PINNELL: INORGANIC SYNTHESES, **6**, 3 (1960).
4. G. B. KAUFFMAN and L. A. TETER: *ibid.*, **6**, 87 (1960).
5. G. TARTARINI: *Gazz. chim. ital.*, **63**, 597 (1933).

CHAPTER IIA

See also: Pentacalcium monohydroxyorthophosphate, synthesis 17

4. BARIUM IODATE 1-HYDRATE

$$Ba(NO_3)_2 + 2KIO_4 + 2CH_3CHOHCOOH \rightarrow Ba(IO_3)_2 \cdot H_2O$$
$$+ 2KNO_3 + 2CH_3CHO + 2CO_2 + H_2O$$

SUBMITTED BY JACK L. LAMBERT AND STANLEY K. YASUDA*
CHECKED BY H. SCHAUBLE†

Barium iodate 1-hydrate in granular form is obtained by the reaction in solution of barium ion with iodate ion formed by the slow reduction of periodic acid by lactic acid at room temperature. Periodic acid is a specific oxidant for glycols and α-hydroxy aldehydes, ketones, and acids, but the rate of oxidation is very slow for α-hydroxy acids.[1] Thus the barium iodate 1-hydrate crystals are slowly formed from a dilute solution of iodate ion which is being formed as a reaction product.

Procedure

Barium nitrate, 3.75 g. (0.0143 mol), potassium metaperiodate (tetraoxoiodate(VII)), KIO_4, 5.80 g. (0.0256 mol), and 85% lactic acid, 100 ml. (all reagent grade) are added to 2 l. of distilled water at room temperature in a

* Kansas State University, Manhattan, Kan.
† University of Illinois, Urbana, Ill.

190 × 100-mm. crystallizing dish. The solution is stirred until all the crystals dissolve, as they do with difficulty; then the dish is covered and allowed to stand at room temperature for 48 hours. Crystals begin to form in several hours and grow to 0.015 cm. and larger in size as shown by retention of a large portion of the product on a 100-mesh sieve screen. The yield is about 5.2 g. or 82% of theoretical, based on the potassium metaperiodate; if the solubility of barium iodate is taken into account, the yield is probably over 90%. Barium nitrate is present in excess of the equivalent amount so that at the beginning the solution is nearly saturated with the two salts.

Analysis

Gravimetric determination of the barium in 0.5000-g. samples of the iodate monohydrate by precipitation and ignition as barium sulfate indicated 100.2% purity. The weighed samples were dried at 50° and dissolved in dilute hydrochloric acid containing a slight excess of iodide ion, and the iodine produced was driven off by gentle boiling before sulfuric acid was added to precipitate barium sulfate. Titration with 0.1039 N thiosulfate solution to the starch-iodine end point of the iodine formed by reaction of 0.1000-g. samples of the barium iodate 1-hydrate with excess iodide ion in dilute hydrochloric acid solution indicated 99.9% purity. A qualitative test for carbonaceous material in the monohydrate crystals by ignition and absorption of the gaseous products in calcium hydroxide solution was negative.

Properties

The product obtained consists of compact single crystals having a relatively small surface area per unit weight. No loss in weight occurred after washing a sample three times each with ethanol and ethyl ether, followed by drying 5 to 10 minutes in a vacuum desiccator. Loss in weight after heating one hour at 50° was 0.1%.

Solutions of barium iodate thermally equilibrated with excess barium iodate monohydrate by stirring approximately one hour in a constant-temperature bath were titrated with 0.01043 N thiosulfate solution after reaction with excess potassium iodide in acid solution. Solubilities in grams per liter calculated from four or more determinations at each temperature were as follows: 20°, 3.70 $\times$ 10^{-1}; 25°, 4.25 $\times$ 10^{-1}; 30°, 4.83 $\times$ 10^{-1}; 35°, 5.42 $\times$ 10^{-1}. The increase in solubility is very nearly linear with increase in temperature. The solubility product constant for temperatures between 20 and 35° can be found from the equation:

$$K_{sp} = [2.24 \times 10^{-10}(t - 20)] + 1.58 \times 10^{-9}$$

where t is the temperature in degrees Centigrade.

Reference

1. R. L. SHRINER and R. C. FUSON: "The Systematic Identification of Organic Compounds," 3rd ed., p. 115, John Wiley & Sons, Inc., New York, 1948.

CHAPTER IIIA

5. GALLIUM(III) NITRIDE

$$Ga_2O_3 + 2NH_3 \xrightarrow{900°} 2GaN + 3H_2O$$

SUBMITTED BY RICHARD C. SCHOONMAKER* AND CLAUDIA E. BURTON*
CHECKED BY J. LUNDSTROM† AND J. L. MARGRAVE†

Gallium(III) nitride has been previously prepared by the reaction of ammonia with liquid gallium at 1000°,[1,2,3] and by decomposition of ammonium hexafluorogallate(III) in an atmosphere of ammonia at 900°.[3] The former reaction proceeds slowly under these conditions and the product, while analyzing as relatively high-purity GaN,[1] is inhomogeneous in color.[1,3] The method described here involves passage of ammonia over gallium oxide heated to 850 to 900°.‡ The reaction proceeds rapidly and there is complete conversion of gallium oxide to the nitride.

* Oberlin College, Oberlin, Ohio.
† University of Wisconsin, Madison, Wis.
‡ A procedure similar to the one reported here has been developed independently by M. R. Lorenz (private communication).

Procedure

The apparatus employed in the synthesis is shown in Fig. 3. The combustion tube (24 in. long and $1\frac{1}{4}$ in. o.d.) is made of fused quartz and the sample boats (3 in. long, $\frac{1}{2}$ in. wide, and $\frac{1}{2}$ in. deep) are of high-purity alumina. Pure gallium(III) oxide (1.5057 g.; 0.00803 mol), obtained

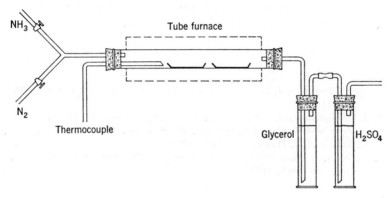

FIG. 3. Apparatus for the preparation of gallium(III) nitride.

both commercially and by synthesis in the laboratory, is placed in the sample boats, and dry nitrogen is swept through the combustion tube to remove atmospheric contaminants. The temperature of the gallium(III) oxide is then raised to approximately 900°. After stabilization of the temperature, the flow gas is changed from nitrogen to ammonia. The reaction is allowed to proceed for approximately one hour. At the end of this period the conversion of white gallium(III) oxide to a homogeneous pale yellow powder, GaN, is apparently complete. The yield is 1.3089 g. (97%). To assure completion of the reaction, however, the yellow powder is removed from the furnace, stirred up, and replaced for a second run during which the previously described procedure is repeated.

Analysis and Properties

X-ray powder patterns of GaN produced by the present method are in excellent agreement with those reported[4] for a sample which was analyzed as 99.9% pure GaN and which was prepared by the older technique. The crystal parameters for the Wurtzite structure agree very closely with those tabulated by Wyckoff[5] for GaN. The nitride is stable toward water and most acids, but when heated in air is slowly transformed to the oxide.

References

1. W. C. JOHNSON, J. B. PARSONS, and M. C. CREW: *J. Phys. Chem.*, **36**, 2651 (1932).
2. J. C. MARGRAVE and R. J. SIME: *J. Phys. Chem.*, **60**, 810 (1956).
3. R. JUZA and H. HAHN: *Z. anorg. u. allgem. Chem.*, **244**, 111 (1940).
4. R. JUZA and H. HAHN: *ibid.*, **239**, 282 (1938).
5. R. W. G. WYCKOFF: "Crystal Structures," p. 31, Interscience Publishers, Inc., New York, 1953.

6. INDIUM(I) BROMIDE

$$2In + HgBr_2 \rightarrow Hg + 2InBr$$

SUBMITTED BY R. J. CLARK,* ERNEST GRISWOLD,† AND JACOB KLEINBERG†
CHECKED BY RICHARD D. BARNES‡ AND JOHN D. CORBETT‡

Previous methods[1-7] for the preparation of indium(I) bromide, as well as other indium monohalides and the dihalides, have utilized two main approaches. Either the metal was halogenated with free halogen or hydrogen halide under the appropriate conditions, or indium tri-

* Iowa State University, Ames, Iowa.
† University of Kansas, Lawrence, Kan.
‡ Iowa State University, Ames, Iowa.

halide was reduced by means of hydrogen or indium metal. These methods offer a number of difficulties. Some of the chemicals are troublesome to handle, either because of their high vapor pressures or their hygroscopic nature. Also, in some cases rigorous control of experimental conditions is necessary in order to obtain the appropriate composition of the final product.

The procedure described below for the preparation of indium(I) bromide is extremely simple. Moreover, by appropriate variation of the stoichiometry of the reactants, it can be used for the preparation of indium dibromide. The preparation consists of the reaction of indium metal with mercury(II) bromide at an elevated temperature in a sealed evacuated tube. Mercury(I) bromide can be used in place of the mercury(II) compound. The same method can also be used for the synthesis of the chlorides and iodides of lower-valent indium.[8]

Procedure

The reaction is carried out in a 20×0.8-cm. piece of thick-walled Pyrex tubing* which has a small well of 8-mm. tubing sealed about 6 cm. from the closed end of the tube. One and fifteen-hundredths grams (0.01 mol) of indium† and 1.80 g. (0.005 mol) of mercury(II) bromide are weighed into the reaction tube. The tube is then evacuated to a pressure of 10 to 15μ, sealed, and heated to 350° in a muffle furnace for about 30 minutes. The mercury set free is separated from the molten indium(I) bromide by removing the tube from the furnace and carefully tilting it so that the mercury runs into the well. To ensure complete

---

* The checkers report that it is not necessary to use thick-walled tubing. The reaction can be initiated in well-evacuated tubing of ordinary thickness with perfect safety by means of a hand torch, provided part of the tube is left cool enough for condensation if the initial reaction becomes too vigorous.

† (Source, Fairmount Chemical Co., New York, cited purity, 99.999%.) The checkers recommend the use of excess indium (6 to 7%) beyond the stoichiometric quantity to ensure completion of reaction.

removal of the mercury, the end of the tube containing the indium halide product is placed in a tube furnace at 350° for about 2 hours, while the portion to which the well is attached is maintained at room temperature. The yield is quantitative, except for mechanical losses.*

A series of preparations gave products having the following bromide to indium† atomic ratios: 1.01, 1.06, 1.07, 1.03, 1.00.

Properties

Some of the physical properties of the halides of lower-valent indium are listed in Table I.

TABLE I

Compound	Color of solid	Color of melt	M.p., °C.	B.p., °C.
InCl	Deep red	Red to black	225	*ca.* 600
InCl$_2$	White	Yellow	*	
InBr	Deep red	Red to black	. . .	662
InBr$_2$	White	Yellow	. . .	632
InI	Brownish red	Black	365	*ca.* 700
InI$_2$	Chartreuse	Black	224	

* There is some question as to whether material of the composition InCl$_2$ is a compound melting sharply at 235°,[6] an incongruently melting compound,[9] or indeed a true compound at all.[8]

These halides are generally unstable toward water and undergo disproportionation in this medium. The ultimate products are indium metal and trihalide. The rate of disproportionation varies considerably from halide to halide.

References

1. W. Klemm: *Z. anorg. u. allgem. Chem.*, **152**, 252 (1926).
2. W. Klemm and F. Dierks: *ibid.*, **219**, 42 (1934).

* The initial reaction, once started, is so vigorous that it is unsafe to scale the reaction up without use of proper safety precautions.

† According to the checkers, the most satisfactory method for the determination of indium is by EDTA titration, as described by H. Flaschka and H. Abdine, *Chemist-Analyst*, **45**, 58 (1956).

3. L. F. Nilson and O. Pettersson: *Z. physik. Chem.*, **2**, 657 (1888).
4. A. Thiel: *Z. anorg. Chem.*, **40**, 280 (1904).
5. A. Thiel and H. Koelsch: *ibid.*, **66**, 288 (1910).
6. J. K. Aiken, J. B. Haley, and H. Terrey: *Trans. Faraday Soc.*, **32**, 1617 (1936).
7. M. Wehrli and E. Miescher: *Helv. Phys. Acta*, **7**, 298 (1934).
8. R. J. Clark, E. Griswold, and J. Kleinberg: *J. Am. Chem. Soc.*, **80**, 4764 (1958).
9. W. Klemm and W. Tilk: *Z. anorg. u. allgem. Chem.*, **207**, 175 (1932).

CHAPTER IVA

salts, and a note on the recovery of rhodium wastes, synthesis 57

7. HEXACHLORODISILOXANE

$$4SiCl_4 + O_2 \rightarrow 2Si_2OCl_6 + 2Cl_2$$

SUBMITTED BY B. A. GRIGOR* AND C. J. WILKINS*
CHECKED BY A. T. BRAULT† AND R. J. ANGELICI†

Methods given in the literature for the preparation of hexachlorodisiloxane include the reaction of heated silicon with a mixture of oxygen and chlorine,[1] the controlled hydrolysis of silicon tetrachloride in dilute solution,[2] and the high-temperature reaction between silicon tetrachloride vapor and oxygen.[3] Although each method has its advantages and preference could depend upon availability of materials and equipment, the procedure for the last is described here as offering ease in the preparation of small samples and suitability for scaling to larger quantities.[4] Details of the equipment recommended depend upon the scale of operation.

* University of Canterbury, Christchurch, New Zealand.
† Northwestern University, Evanston, Ill.

Procedure

SMALL-SCALE PREPARATION

The assembly shown in Fig. 4 is set up in a fume hood. Oxygen dried with a sulfuric acid bubbler is passed through 500 g. (2.94 mols) of silicon tetrachloride in a 500-ml. distillation flask maintained in a water bath at 50°. The

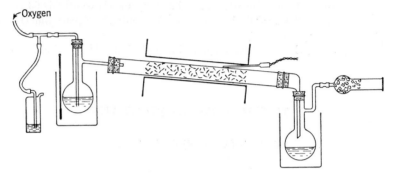

FIG. 4. Apparatus for small-scale preparation of Si_2OCl_6.

oxygen and entrained silicon tetrachloride vapor pass through a preheated silica tube loosely packed with chips (15 mm.) of unglazed porcelain. (This packing increases the reaction rate about sixfold.) The issuing vapors are condensed in a 500-ml. distillation flask with an upswept sidearm, immersed in an ice-salt freezing mixture. With a silica tube 90 cm. long and 3.0 cm. i.d., heated to 960 to 990° in a furnace 45 cm. long, an oxygen flow of 18 to 20 l. per hour is appropriate. Almost all of the silicon tetrachloride will pass through the furnace in the course of two hours, and a yield of 25 to 30 g. of hexachlorodisiloxane may be expected. With a smaller reaction tube the oxygen flow should be reduced in proportion.*

* Attention must be drawn to several experimental points. The porcelain packing must be heated to reaction temperature before use; this removes moisture which would cause hydrolysis and contribute to possible blockage. It is most convenient to do this preheating in the silica tube under a slow stream of oxygen (*before* introducing silicon tetrachloride) and *without* the adapter fitted over the rubber sealing ring. The delivery tube from the

Separation of the hexachlorodisiloxane (b.p. 137°) from unreacted silicon tetrachloride is accomplished by distillation. A 40-cm. fractionating column packed with glass helixes and provided with a heating jacket is suitable. The distillation is started cautiously since much dissolved chlorine is expelled initially. (*Care.* Use a fume hood!) Silicon tetrachloride (b.p. 57°) will pass up the column with little or no heat applied to the jacket. When the bulk of the tetrachloride has passed over, the heat to the flask and the column jacket is increased carefully so that distillation continues steadily. The product passing over at 135 to 138° is collected and redistilled if desired. The recovered silicon tetrachloride may be recirculated.

If desired, the crude reaction product may be returned to the volatilization flask without fractional distillation. In this case, the liquid is transferred to the flask before the water bath is heated in order to avoid rapid expulsion of dissolved chlorine. (*Caution!*) Not more than about three-quarters of the liquid is volatilized since it now contains high-boiling material. However, after 90 minutes the temperature of the water bath may be raised progressively to 60°.

LARGER-SCALE PREPARATION

If larger quantities of hexachlorodisiloxane, say more than 60 g., are desired, it is better to use apparatus providing automatic circulation of silicon tetrachloride (Fig. 5). Details of equipment recommended are as follows (though sizes and flow rates may be scaled somewhat). The silica

---

adapter should have a diameter of 10 to 12 mm. as an added precaution against blockage by any solid which might form during the initial stages of the reaction. This delivery tube should extend about one-third of the distance into the bulb of the collecting flask. The effluent gas is discharged through a large loosely packed calcium chloride tube. On a branch from the oxygen line, a trap is provided containing a 5-mm. head of mercury to act as a safety valve.

Glassware coated with silica may be cleaned by leaving for half an hour in hot alkali.

tube, 90 × 3.0 cm., should be heated to 1000° over a length
of 45 cm. The heated section must be loosely packed
with dry unglazed porcelain (as for the small-scale preparation). A silicon tetrachloride boiler of 1000 to 1200 ml.
takes a charge of 1000 g. (5.88 mols). The fractionating
column, 30 × 2.0 cm., should be sealed to the flask and
must be packed with glass helixes. The flow of silicon

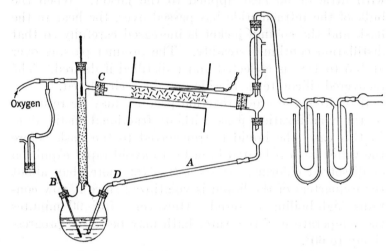

Fig. 5. Apparatus for larger-scale preparation of Si_2OCl_6.

tetrachloride should be regulated to 200 to 280 g. per hour
(4 to 5 drops per second) and the oxygen flow to 15 to
20 l. per hour. The condensing traps should have a liquid
capacity of at least 150 ml. to the bottom of the center
tube. The first trap will fill with liquid in about three
hours. The initial temperature rise of the liquid in the
boiler will be 1 to 2° per hour, with a final rise of 25° in
10 to 12 hours. The oxychloride formed and most of the
unreacted tetrachloride are retained by the reflux condenser and returned to the boiler by way of the tube A,
which must reach close to the bottom of the flask.*

* Residual silicon tetrachloride vapor carried through the condenser is
retained in the two Dry Ice–acetone traps. This silicon tetrachloride

The progress of the reaction is indicated by the thermometer B, which measures the temperature of the liquid in the boiler. When this temperature has risen to 80 to 85°, the reaction is stopped. The boiler is disconnected at C and D and the liquid removed to a distillation flask with a 40-cm. fractionating column and heating jacket. The fractional distillation is then continued as described for the small-scale preparation.*

The total weight of liquid remaining in the boiler when the reaction is stopped is usually 500 to 600 g., comprising 250 g. of hexachlorodisiloxane, 50 to 70 g. of higher oxychlorides, and the balance silicon tetrachloride.†

Properties

Hexachlorodisiloxane is a colorless liquid boiling at 137°. It is the first member of the open-chain series of oxyhalides of general composition $Si_nO_{n-1}Cl_{2n+2}$. The reactivity of the silicon-chlorine bond in the molecule is

---

should be returned eventually to the boiler, but since it is heavily contaminated with dissolved chlorine it is better to replenish the boiler with an equivalent quantity of fresh tetrachloride. This may be added carefully through the top of the condenser without interrupting the process. The silicon tetrachloride from the traps should be allowed to warm to room temperature (either in the traps or in some other vented vessel, to permit escape of chlorine) and may be added to the *cold* boiler at the start of a subsequent run.

* Accumulated high-boiling residues left after the distillation of hexachlorodisiloxane afford a source of the higher members of the oxychloride series $Si_nO_{n-1}Cl_{2n+2}$ and of the cyclic members $Si_nO_nCl_{2n}$. For information on their separation reference 5 should be consulted.

† Rubber hardens in contact with silicon tetrachloride vapor and this can lead to slight leakage of vapor where disconnections are made between runs. The yields quoted include such losses. It is recommended that the outlet be fitted with an *unpacked* calcium chloride tube, because packing impedes escape of gas and can increase leakage loss. To avoid breaking seals at C and D the product may be drawn into a tap funnel inserted through the thermometer port. Ground joints should not be used on the main apparatus, because lubricants do not prevent seizing. Ground joints on the cold traps are satisfactory (though not essential), and should be greased with silicone.

similar to the reactivity of this bond in silicon tetrachloride. Thus the compound hydrolyzes vigorously and completely, reacts with Grignard reagents,[4] and undergoes halogen-exchange fluorination.[6] The last reaction is accompanied by disproportionation to silica and silicon tetrahalide.

References

1. W. C. SCHUMC and D. F. HOLLOWAY: *J. Am. Chem. Soc.*, **63**, 2753 (1941).
2. J. GOUBEAU and R. WARNECKE: *Z. anorg. Chem.*, **259**, 109 (1949); W. C. SCHUMB and A. J. STEVENS: *J. Am. Chem. Soc.*, **72**, 3178 (1950).
3. H. RHEINBOLDT and W. WISFELD: *Ann.*, **517**, 197 (1935). (This paper contains earlier references to the method.)
4. H. J. EMELÉUS and D. S. PAYNE: *J. Chem. Soc.*, **1947**, 1590.
5. D. W. S. CHAMBERS and C. J. WILKINS: *ibid.*, **1960**, 5088.
6. H. S. BOOTH and R. A. OSTEN: *J. Am. Chem. Soc.*, **67**, 1092 (1945).

8. TRICHLOROSILANETHIOL

$$SiCl_4 + H_2S \rightarrow SiCl_3SH + HCl$$

SUBMITTED BY D. J. PANCKHURST* AND C. J. WILKINS*
CHECKED BY A. T. BRAULT† AND R. J. ANGELICI†

Trichlorosilanethiol is the primary product of the high-temperature reaction between silicon tetrachloride and hydrogen sulfide,[1] which leads also to the formation of tetrachlorocyclodisilthiane, $Si_2S_2Cl_4$, sulfide dichloride polymer, $(SiSCl_2)_x$, and a little bis(trichlorosilyl) sulfide (hexachlorodisilthiane), $(SiCl_3)_2S$[2]. A satisfactory yield of the thiol may be obtained by passing silicon tetrachloride and hydrogen sulfide through a silica tube heated to 900 to 950°.

* University of Canterbury, Christchurch, New Zealand.
† Northwestern University, Evanston, Ill.

Procedure

The apparatus required is similar to that shown in Fig. 4 for the preparation of hexachlorodisiloxane, but with the addition of a tower (25 × 5 cm.) packed with granular calcium chloride to dry the incoming hydrogen sulfide, and of a condensing trap to retain silicon tetrachloride in the effluent gas, as in Fig. 5. The silica tube should be left unpacked. The whole assembly must be set up under a fume hood. The hydrogen sulfide is bubbled through the silicon tetrachloride (500 g.) held at 40° in the water bath. The reactants are then passed through the silica tube and the product is allowed to condense in the receiving flask cooled in ice. A hydrogen sulfide flow of 6 l. per hour and a silica tube, 60 × 2.5 cm., heated to 950° over a 30-cm. length are recommended.* Silicon tetrachloride will pass over at about 45 g. per hour and yield 6 g. of thiol per hour.

The condensing trap, having a liquid capacity of at least 100 ml., should be held at −40 to −50°. This trap retains residual silicon tetrachloride along with some hydrogen sulfide (b.p. −52°). The latter *must* be volatilized by allowing the trap to warm to room temperature before the tetrachloride is returned to the apparatus for a subsequent run.

The liquid from the condensing flask is fractionally distilled to separate the thiol, boiling at 95 to 96°, from unchanged silicon tetrachloride (b.p. 57.6°).†

---

* The checkers recommend that the portion of the exit end of the silica tube which is not heated be surrounded by a copper coil through which cold water is passed to ensure shock cooling of the product vapors.

† If instead of trichlorosilanethiol a high yield of tetrachlorocyclodisilthiane is desired, it is necessary to recirculate the thiol through the hot tube. This may be done without the need to isolate the thiol by using the kind of apparatus in Fig. 5, provided the column above the boiler carries no packing. For details on experimental conditions and the separation of the products reference 2 should be consulted.

Properties

Trichlorosilanethiol is a colorless liquid boiling at 95.5 to 95.6° at 759 mm. pressure. It hydrolyzes vigorously to hydrogen ch'oride, hydrogen sulfide, and silicic acid, and slowly deposits sulfur on exposure to air. The pure compound decomposes at 700° in approximate accord with the equation:

$$2SiCl_3SH \rightarrow H_2S + SiCl_4 + SiSCl_2 \text{ (as } Si_2S_2Cl_4 \text{ and polymer)}$$

At 80 to 100° aluminum chloride catalyzes this reaction together with a simultaneous decomposition to bis(trichlorosilyl) sulfide:

$$2SiCl_3SH \rightarrow (SiCl_3)_2S + H_2S$$

With bromine there occurs the reaction:

$$SiCl_3SH + Br_2 \rightarrow SiCl_3Br + HBr + S$$

References

1. I. PIERRE: *Ann. chim. phys.*, [3], **24**, 286 (1848); C. FRIEDEL and A. LADENBURG: *Ann.*, **145**, 179 (1867); *Compt. rend.*, **64**, 1295 (1867).
2. D. J. PANCKHURST, C. J. WILKINS, and P. W. CRAIGHEAD: *J. Chem. Soc.*, **1955**, 3396.

9. TRIS(ACETYLACETONATO)SILICON CHLORIDE HYDROCHLORIDE AND SOME DERIVATIVES

[Tris(2,4-pentanedionato)silicon chloride hydrochloride and some derivatives]

SUBMITTED BY REED F. RILEY,* ROBERT WEST,† AND ROBERT BARBARIN‡
CHECKED BY GEORGE SLUSARCZUK§ AND STANLEY KIRSCHNER§

The chelates which silicon forms with β-diketones (1,3-diketones)[1,2] and β-keto esters[3,4] are of interest as

* Polytechnic Institute of Brooklyn, Brooklyn, N.Y.
† University of Wisconsin, Madison, Wis.
‡ University of California at Los Angeles, Los Angeles, Calif.
§ Wayne State University, Detroit, Mich.

compounds in which silicon attains the relatively unusual coordination number (for silicon) of six. Furthermore, these hexacoordinate chelates represent the only firmly established examples of cationic species containing silicon. The acetylacetonato compound $[Si(C_5H_7O_2)_3]Cl \cdot HCl$ and two derivatives, $[Si(C_5H_7O_2)_3]FeCl_4$ and $[Si(C_5H_7O_2)_3]ZnCl_3$, may be prepared easily by a modification of the original method of Dilthey.[1]

Procedures

A. TRIS(ACETYLACETONATO)SILICON CHLORIDE HYDROCHLORIDE

$$SiCl_4 + 3C_5HO_2 \rightarrow [Si(C_5H_7O_2)_3]Cl \cdot HCl + 2HCl$$

A 300-ml. three-necked flask is equipped with a dropping funnel and with a short condenser, both isolated from atmospheric moisture by means of calcium chloride drying tubes. If the reaction is not to be carried out in a hood, a tube should lead from the drying tube at the top of the condenser to a trap for absorbing gaseous hydrogen chloride.

In the flask is placed 30 g. (0.0178 mol; 20.5 ml.) of silicon tetrachloride dissolved in 80 ml. of benzene,* and a boiling chip of porous porcelain is added. A solution of 17.7 g. (0.0178 mol; 18.1 ml.) of acetylacetone (2,4-pentanedione)† in 40 ml. of benzene is placed in the dropping funnel.

The acetylacetone solution is then added over a period of 10 minutes with occasional agitation of the flask and its contents. A light yellow oily layer appears immediately, accompanied by evolution of hydrogen chloride. Upon completion of the addition of the acetylacetone, the solution is brought to reflux and heated for thirty minutes, during which time the oily layer changes to an ivory-colored solid. The precipitate is removed by rapid filtration with suction

---

* Practical-grade reactants may be used without decrease in yield of product. The benzene should be dry.

† The molar proportion 1:1 is chosen because it yields the highest percentage of pure product, as judged from its color and melting point.

(best carried out in a hood). The crystalline product is then washed three times with ether and dried briefly *in vacuo* until a free-flowing material is obtained. The yield is approximately 23 g. or 97% based on the amount of acetylacetone present. Although Dilthey reports a melting point of 85 to 90°,[1] the authors found that the compound melts with decomposition in the range 171 to 174°. *Anal.* Calcd. for $[Si(C_5H_7O_2)_3]Cl\cdot HCl$: Cl, 17.9%. Found: Cl, 17.6%.

B. TRIS(ACETYLACETONATO)SILICON TETRACHLOROFERRATE(III)

$$[Si(C_5H_7O_2)_3]Cl\cdot HCl + FeCl_3 \rightarrow [Si(C_5H_7O_2)_3]FeCl_4 + HCl$$

Five grams (0.0125 mol) of $[Si(C_5H_7O_2)_3]Cl\cdot HCl$ is placed in a 250-ml. Erlenmeyer flask and is dissolved in 40 ml. of dry chloroform. Two and two-tenths grams (0.0138 mol, a 10% excess) of anhydrous iron(III) chloride* is then added and the mixture gently shaken until hydrogen chloride evolution ceases. The solution is vacuum-filtered to remove any insoluble hydrolysis products, and approximately 80 ml. of ether is added slowly to the filtrate. The solution is allowed to stand for 15 minutes, and the yellow-green needles are collected by vacuum filtration, washed three times with anhydrous ether, and dried briefly *in vacuo*. The yield is approximately 70% and the substance melts with decomposition in the range 184 to 186° (reported[1] 186 to 187°). *Anal.* Calcd. for $[Si(C_5H_7O_2)_3FeCl_4$: ($SiO_2 + Fe_2O_3$), 26.8%; Cl, 27.1%. Found: ($SiO_2 + Fe_2O_3$), 26.1%; Cl, 27.0%.

* The checkers report that the hydrated salt can be used.

C. TRIS(ACETYLACETONATO)SILICON TRICHLOROZINCATE

$$[Si(C_5H_7O_2)_3]Cl \cdot HCl + ZnCl_2 \rightarrow [Si(C_5H_7O_2)_3]ZnCl_3 + HCl$$

Two and seventeen-hundredths grams (0.0159 mol, a 10% excess) of zinc chloride which has been dried in a vacuum oven at 105° and 18-mm. pressure is slurried in 30 ml. of acetic acid to which 2.5 g. of acetic anhydride has previously been added. After addition of 5.5 g. (0.0138 mol) of $[Si(C_5H_7O_2)_3]Cl \cdot HCl$, the mixture is allowed to stand one-half hour with occasional shaking. Vacuum filtration of the mixture yields a precipitate which is dissolved in a minimum of boiling dry chloroform. The chloroform is then treated with twice its volume of anhydrous ether and the mixture allowed to stand for 15 minutes. The white crystalline solid is collected by vacuum filtration and washed three times with ether. The yield of dried $[Si(C_5H_7O_2)_3]ZnCl_3$ is over 80%. The substance does not melt but decomposes gradually above 190°. *Anal.* Calcd. for $[Si(C_5H_7O_2)]ZnCl_3$: $(SiO_2 + ZnO)$, 28.5%; Cl, 20.9%. Found: $(SiO_2 + ZnO)$, 27.8%; Cl, 20.8%.

Properties

All the compounds are soluble in chloroform, slightly soluble in carbon tetrachloride, and insoluble in ether and benzene. In water and alcohols rapid solvolysis of the M—Cl bonds and slower solvolysis of the Si—O bonds take place with the liberation of acetylacetone. Prolonged drying of $[Si(C_5H_7O_2)_3]Cl \cdot HCl$ *in vacuo* removes much of the hydrogen chloride, yielding a product which is much less hygroscopic.

References

1. W. DILTHEY: *Ber.*, **36**, 923 (1903).
2. W. DILTHEY: *ibid.*, 1595 (1903).
3. A. ROSENHEIM, W. LOEWENSTAMM, and L. SINGER: *ibid.*, 1833 (1903).
4. W. DILTHEY: *Ann.*, **344**, 304 (1906).

10. HYDRIDES OF GERMANIUM, TIN, ARSENIC, AND ANTIMONY

SUBMITTED BY WILLIAM L. JOLLY AND JOHN E. DRAKE*
CHECKED BY RALPH RUDOLPH† AND T. WARTIK†

Volatile hydrides may be prepared from ether solutions by the reaction of the appropriate chlorides with lithium tetrahydroaluminate.[1]   In this general method, it is necessary to work with strictly anhydrous reagents and solvents because of the great reactivity of lithium tetrahydroaluminate toward water.   The procedures described below are believed to be much more convenient because the reducing agent employed is potassium tetrahydroborate, which is relatively insensitive toward water.   Since only aqueous solutions are involved, there are no solvent-purification steps and there is no dissolution or contamination of stopcock grease, etc.

General Procedure‡

The apparatus shown in Fig. 6 may be used for the preparation of the hydrides of germanium, tin, arsenic,

* Department of Chemistry and Lawrence Radiation Laboratory, University of California, Berkeley 4, Calif.
† Pennsylvania State University, University Park, Pa.
‡ These syntheses are based in part on references 2 and 3.   For a discussion of general vacuum technique, see reference 4.

or antimony. Aqueous acid is placed in a 500-ml. three-necked round-bottomed flask equipped with a magnetic stirrer, an inlet tube for nitrogen or argon (dipping beneath the solution), a 100-ml. dropping funnel, and an outlet tube leading to a vacuum line. The flask is partially immersed in an ice-water bath. During a run, nitrogen

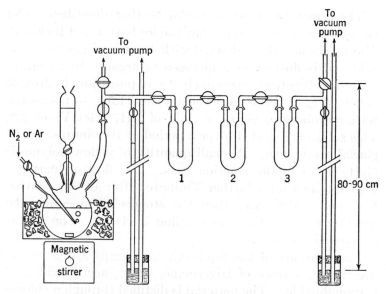

FIG. 6. Apparatus for the preparation of volatile hydrides.

or argon is continuously bubbled (at a rate of approximately 500 cc./min., S.T.P.) through the magnetically stirred acid solution and passed through a series of three traps (numbered 1, 2, and 3 in Fig. 6). The pressure in the system is maintained at approximately 100 mm. by adjustment of the stopcock leading to the vacuum pump on the right side of the line. Two of the traps are immersed in Dewar flasks containing liquid nitrogen.

A. GERMANE AND DIGERMANE

$$HGeO_3^- + BH_4^- + 2H^+ \rightarrow GeH_4 + H_3BO_3$$
$$8HGeO_3^- + 7BH_4^- + 15H^+ \rightarrow 4Ge_2H_6 + 7H_3BO_3 + 3H_2O$$

Procedure

The apparatus used is similar to that described under General Procedure except that the ice bath is not included. The reaction flask is charged with 120 ml. of glacial acetic acid and is flushed with nitrogen or argon. In 25 ml. of water are dissolved successively 2 g. of potassium hydroxide pellets, 1 g. of germanium dioxide, and 1.5 g. of potassium tetrahydroborate, giving a ratio of $BH_4^-/Ge(IV)$ of 2.9. This solution is added, over a period of 10 minutes, to the glacial acetic acid. A small quantity of yellow polymeric GeH_x forms in the reaction flask. The flow of inert gas is maintained for a further 5 minutes after all the solution has been added, and then the stopcock connecting the reaction flask to the vacuum line is closed. The line is evacuated thoroughly.

The contents of the liquid-nitrogen traps are germane, digermane, a trace of trigermane, water, acetic acid, and carbon dioxide. The material is distilled through a chloroform slush trap $(-63.5°)$ to remove trigermane, water, and acetic acid. The carbon dioxide is readily removed by passing the gases through successive traps of ascarite and magnesium perchlorate. Finally, by distilling the gases through a carbon disulfide slush bath $(-111.6°)$ to remove digermane, pure samples of both germane and digermane are obtained.

Typically, this procedure gives 0.007 mol, or about 160 cc. (S.T.P.), of pure germane, corresponding to a germanium conversion of 73%. The amount of digermane prepared is 0.00031 mol, or about 7 cc. (S.T.P.), corresponding to a germanium conversion of 6.5%. The yield of digermane is improved if a lower concentration of tetrahydroborate is used, the best result being a germanium conversion of 9.1% when the $BH_4^-/Ge(IV)$ ratio is 1.5. However, the yield of germane is decreased by any appreciable variation in the quoted amount of tetrahydroborate.

Properties

The germane prepared has a vapor pressure of 181 mm. at $-111.6°$ (literature, 182 mm.[5]). The infrared spectrum of the gas in the NaCl region shows the fundamental frequencies ν_3, ν_2, and ν_4 at 2105, 943, and 815 cm.$^{-1}$, respectively.[6] Germane is stored in a glass vessel with a greased stopcock.

The digermane prepared by this procedure has vapor pressures of 6 mm. at $-63.5°$, 77 mm. at $-22.9°$, and 221 mm. at 0° (literature, *ca.* 9 mm., *ca.* 85 mm., and 243 mm., respectively[7]). The infrared spectrum of the gas in the NaCl region shows the fundamental frequencies ν_5, ν_8, and ν_6 at 2069, 885, and 759 cm.$^{-1}$, respectively.[8] Digermane is absorbed by stopcock grease and should be kept in a vessel sealed with a mercury float valve or in an all-glass ampul. On heating it decomposes violently into its elements.

B. TRIGERMANE AND POLYMERIC GeH$_x$*

$$6HGeO_3^- + 5BH_4^- + 11H^+ \rightarrow 2Ge_3H_8 + 5H_3BO_3 + 3H_2O$$
$$8HGeO_3^- + (4 + x)BH_4^- + (12 + x)H^+ \rightarrow$$
$$8GeH_x + (4 + x)H_3BO_3 + (12 - 3x)H_2O$$

Procedure

The procedure described for the production of germane and digermane gives very poor yields of trigermane and polymeric GeH$_x$, and changes must be made in the procedure to obtain better yields of these last compounds.

* Where $x \approx 1.0$.

The apparatus used is identical to that described under General Procedure. The flask is charged with 120 ml. of 3 M sulfuric acid; the system is cooled in the ice bath, and the flask is flushed with nitrogen or argon. In 25 ml. of water are dissolved successively 2 g. of potassium hydroxide pellets, 1.0 g. of germanium(IV) oxide, and 3.0 g. of potassium tetrahydroborate, corresponding to a ratio of $BH_4^-/Ge(IV)$ of 5.8. This solution is added, over a period of 15 minutes, to the sulfuric acid. During the addition some foaming occurs and an appreciable amount of yellow polymeric GeH_x is deposited. On completing the addition, the flow of inert gas is maintained for a further 5 minutes before the line is thoroughly evacuated.

The trigermane and water present in the liquid-nitrogen traps can be separated from germane, digermane, and carbon dioxide by distilling the materials through a chloroform slush bath ($-63.5°$). The germane and digermane may be separated as described previously, but the yields are not as good as those obtained with acetic acid. The trigermane is easily separated from the water by passage through a trap containing magnesium perchlorate.

Typically, this procedure gives 0.00007 mol or 1.6 cc. (S.T.P.), of pure trigermane, corresponding to a germanium conversion of 2.2%.

The contents of the reaction flask are filtered immediately after the reaction is complete and the yellow polymeric GeH_x is thoroughly washed with water. It is then dried by pumping it on the vacuum line.

Typically, this procedure gives 0.0016 mol, or about 0.1 g. of polymeric GeH_x, corresponding to a germanium conversion of 17%.

Properties

The trigermane prepared has a vapor pressure of 9.5 mm. at 0° (literature, 14 mm.[7]). The infrared spectrum in the NaCl region shows two bands at 2041 and 794 cm.$^{-1}$.

Trigermane, like digermane, is absorbed by stopcock grease and should be kept in an all-glass ampul.

The polymeric GeH_x prepared is a yellow solid, which turns orange-brown without change of composition on treatment with concentrated alkali, but is decomposed by concentrated acids. It must be handled with care since on exposure to air it sometimes decomposes explosively into its elements. Both the yellow and the orange-brown materials explode on heating to give germanium, hydrogen, and a trace of germane. The value of x is usually close to unity (values between 0.95 and 1.10 are usually found); thus the product prepared by this procedure appears to resemble the polymeric compounds $(GeH)_n$ described by earlier workers.[9,10] The infrared spectrum (KBr pellet) in the NaCl region shows three main bands at 2062, 833, and 775 cm.$^{-1}$.

C. STANNANE AND DISTANNANE

$$4HSnO_2^- + 3BH_4^- + 7H^+ + H_2O \rightarrow 4SnH_4 + 3H_3BO_3$$
$$8HSnO_2^- + 5BH_4^- + 13H^+ \rightarrow 4Sn_2H_6 + 5H_3BO_3 + H_2O$$

Procedure

The apparatus is assembled as described under General Procedure. The reaction flask is charged with 150 ml. of 6 M hydrochloric acid and is flushed with nitrogen or argon. The solution to be added from the dropping funnel is prepared immediately before use as follows. An ice-cold solution of 36 g. of 85% potassium hydroxide in 60 ml. of water is added, with stirring, to an ice-cold solution of 15 g. of tin(II) chloride 2-hydrate in 60 ml. of water. A solution of 1.5 g. of potassium tetrahydroborate in 20 ml. of water is then added to the solution. The resulting stannate(II)-tetrahydroborate solution is added, over a period of about 30 minutes, to the stirred hydrochloric acid solution. During the reaction, a brown precipitate (which soon turns gray-black) forms in the flask. The flow of inert gas is continued for several minutes after the complete addition of the stannate(II)-tetrahydroborate solution. The stopcock connecting the reaction vessel with the vacuum line is then closed and the line is thoroughly evacuated.

During subsequent operations, it is best to keep the stopcock above the mercury manometers closed except when it is necessary that they be open for pressure measurements. The crude product is distilled into trap 3 preparatory to its purification by fractional condensation. If only stannane is sought, the material is distilled through a carbon disulfide slush trap ($-111.6°$) to remove both water and distannane. The stannane which passes through this trap is highly contaminated with carbon dioxide originating from the carbonate impurity in the potassium hydroxide. This impurity can be removed by distilling the stannane several times through a trap containing $\frac{1}{16}$-in. pellets of Linde Molecular Sieve, Type 4A,* at $0°$. A small amount of stannane decomposes in this process; so it is necessary to pump on the system during each distillation. Typically, 0.001 mol, or about 22 cc. (S.T.P.), of purified stannane is prepared by this procedure. This yield corresponds to 2.7% based on the hydroborate consumed.

If it is desired to isolate the distannane, the crude product is distilled through a chloroform slush trap ($-63.5°$) to collect water and through a carbon disulfide slush trap to collect distannane. The distillation must not be prolonged, or appreciable amounts of water will pass through the $-63.5°$ trap. Typically, 0.00002 mol, or about 0.4 cc. (S.T.P.), of distannane is prepared by this procedure. Slightly better yields may be obtained by making the stannate(II)-tetrahydroborate solution more concentrated.†

---

* Obtainable from the Linde Air Products Company, Division of Union Carbide Corporation. The molecular-sieve pellets should first be heated in the trap to $200°$ for several minutes while pumping to desorb highly volatile materials.

† It is possible to dissolve the reagents in a total of 110 ml., rather than 140 ml., of water.

Properties

Stannane, prepared as described, has a vapor pressure of 17 mm. at $-111.6°$, in good agreement with the literature value of 17.5 mm.[11] The melting and boiling points of stannane are reported as $-150°$ and $-51.8°$, respectively.[12] The infrared spectrum in the NaCl region shows a prominent triple band (the Sn-H stretching vibration,[13] ν_3) at 1900 cm.$^{-1}$, a medium band at 760 cm.$^{-1}$, and strong bands at 700 and 675 cm.$^{-1}$.[14] The presence of carbon dioxide in stannane may be readily determined from the infrared spectrum; carbon dioxide has a strong absorption band at 2300 cm.$^{-1}$. Stannane has been stored without decomposition in clean glass vessels in the absence of mercury for periods of several weeks. Traces of oxygen are reported to inhibit the decomposition.[15] Once started, decomposition is usually quite rapid and results in the formation of a beautiful tin mirror on the walls of the vessel. Stannane is best stored in a glass bulb with an extended tip immersed in liquid nitrogen.

Distannane is an extremely unstable substance which, when warmed to room temperature, completely decomposes into its elements, forming a mirror on the walls of the container. However, distannane may be readily distilled from a trap without decomposition if the distillation is carried out at very low pressures and if the trap is allowed to warm up very slowly.[3]

D. ARSINE

$$4As(OH)_4{}^- + 3BH_4{}^- + 7H^+ \rightarrow 4AsH_3 + 3H_3BO_3 + 7H_2O$$

Procedure

The apparatus is assembled as described under General Procedure. The reaction flask is charged with a solution of 25 ml. of concentrated sulfuric acid in 200 ml. of water and is flushed with nitrogen or argon. Four grams of sodium hydroxide, 8.0 g. of arsenic(III) oxide, and 2.0 g. of potassium tetrahydroborate are dissolved, in that order, in 20 ml. of water. This solution should be prepared immediately before its use, because it decomposes with evolution of arsine and precipitation of arsenic. The solution is added through the dropping funnel, over a period of 15 minutes, to the sulfuric acid solution. An orange precipitate of arsenic forms in the flask. A small amount of yellow polymeric As_2H forms at the entrance to each of the liquid nitrogen traps. This material forms as the result of the decomposition of diarsine, As_2H_4.[16] The flow of inert gas is continued for several minutes after the complete addition of the arsenite-tetrahydroborate solution. The stopcock connecting the reaction vessel with the vacuum line is then closed and the line is thoroughly evacuated.

The crude arsine is distilled into trap 1 (Fig. 6), a U-tube packed with ascarite is substituted for trap 2, and the arsine is then distilled through the ascarite into trap 3. Trap 2 is put back and immersed in a carbon disulfide slush bath ($-111.6°$), and the arsine is distilled into trap 1. Typically, 0.029 mol, or 650 cc. (S.T.P.), of purified arsine is prepared by this procedure. This corresponds to 59% yield, based on the tetrahydroborate consumed.

Properties

Arsine has a vapor pressure of 35 mm. at $-111.6°$,[17] a melting point of $-116.93°$,[18] and a boiling point of $-62.48°$.[18] The infrared spectrum in the NaCl region shows a triple band at 2122 cm.$^{-1}$ (ν_1 and ν_2) and bands at 1005 and 906 cm.$^{-1}$ (ν_4 and ν_3, respectively).[19] Arsine is a relatively stable gas, which may be stored in glass vessels for several months with less than 5% decomposition. Ordinary stopcock grease is blackened by prolonged exposure to the gas.

E. STIBINE

$$4Sb(OH)_4^- + 3BH_4^- + 7H^+ \rightarrow 4SbH_3 + 3H_3BO_3 + 7H_2O$$

Procedure

The apparatus is assembled as described under General Procedure. The reaction flask is charged with a solution of 25 ml. of concentrated sulfuric acid in 200 ml. of water and is flushed with nitrogen or argon. Twelve grams of 85% potassium hydroxide, 15 g. of potassium antimony tartrate, and 2.0 g. of potassium tetrahydroborate are dissolved, in that order, in 100 ml. of water. This solution is added through the dropping funnel, over a period of 15 minutes, to the sulfuric acid solution. A black precipitate of antimony forms in the flask The flow of inert gas is continued for several minutes after the complete addition of the antimonite-tetrahydroborate solution. The stopcock connecting the reaction vessel with the vacuum line is then closed and the line is thoroughly evacuated.

The crude stibine, with its impurities of water and carbon dioxide, is distilled into an ampul attached to the ball joint which was previously connected to the reaction vessel. Trap 1 is immersed in a toluene slush bath ($-95°$); trap 2 is immersed in an n-pentane slush bath ($-130°$), and trap 3 is immersed in liquid nitrogen. By slowly distilling the crude stibine through these traps, the water with traces of stibine is condensed out in the $-95°$ trap, pure stibine is collected in the $-130°$ trap, and the carbon dioxide with traces of stibine is collected in the liquid-nitrogen trap. With suitable precautions (because of the poisonous nature of stibine), the contents of traps 1 and 3 are discarded. Typically, 0.025 mol, or 560 cc. (S.T.P.), of purified stibine is prepared by this procedure. This corresponds to a 51% yield, based on the tetrahydroborate consumed.

Properties

Stibine has vapor pressures of 81 mm. and 224 mm. at the melting points of chloroform $(-63.5°)$ and chlorobenzene $(-45.2°)$, respectively.[20] The boiling point is $-18.4°$.[20] The infrared spectrum in the NaCl region shows a triple band at 1890 cm.$^{-1}$ (ν_1 and ν_3) and bands at 831 and 781 cm.$^{-1}$ (ν_4 and ν_2, respectively).[21] Stibine lies between arsine and stannane in its stability toward decomposition into the elements. If it is to be stored longer than two or three days, it should be kept frozen with liquid nitrogen.

References

1. T. WARTIK and H. I. SCHLESINGER: *J. Am. Chem. Soc.*, **75**, 835 (1953).
2. S. R. GUNN, W. L. JOLLY, and L. G. GREEN: *J. Phys. Chem.*, **64**, 1334 (1960).
3. W. L. JOLLY: *J. Am. Chem. Soc.*, **83**, 335 (1961).
4. R. T. SANDERSON: "Vacuum Manipulation of Volatile Compounds," John Wiley & Sons, Inc., New York, 1948.
5. A. E. FINHOLT, A. C. BOND, Jr., K. E. WILZBACH, and H. I. SCHLESINGER: *J. Am. Chem. Soc.*, **69**, 2692 (1947).
6. J. W. STRALEY, C. H. TINDAL, and H. H. NIELSEN: *Phys. Rev.*, **62**, 161 (1942).
7. L. M. DENNIS, R. B. COREY, and R. W. MOORE: *J. Am. Chem. Soc.*, **46**, 657 (1924).
8. D. A. DOWS and R. M. HEXTER: *J. Chem. Phys.*, **24**, 1029 (1956).
9. L. M. DENNIS and N. A. SKOW: *J. Am. Chem. Soc.*, **52**, 2369 (1930).
10. C. A. KRAUS and E. S. CARNEY: *ibid.*, **56**, 765 (1934).
11. S. R. GUNN and L. G. GREEN: *J. Phys. Chem.*, **65**, 779 (1961).
12. Natl. Bur. Standards (U.S.), Cir. 500, "Selected Values of Chemical Thermodynamic Properties," 1952.
13. G. R. WILKINSON and M. K. WILSON: *J. Chem. Phys.*, **25**, 784 (1956).
14. W. L. JOLLY: unpublished data.
15. H. J. EMELÉUS and S. F. A. KETTLE: *J. Chem. Soc.*, **1958**, 2444.
16. R. NAST: *Chem. Ber.*, **81**, 271 (1948).
17. W. C. JOHNSON and A. PECHUKAS: *J. Am. Chem. Soc.*, **59**, 2065 (1937).
18. R. H. SHERMAN and W. F. GIAUQUE: *ibid.*, **77**, 2154 (1955).
19. E. LEE and C. K. WU: *Trans. Faraday Soc.*, **35**, 1366 (1939).
20. L. BERKA, T. BRIGGS, M. MILLARD, and W. JOLLY: *J. Inorg. & Nuclear Chem.*, **14**, 190 (1960).
21. D. C. SMITH: *J. Chem. Phys.*, **19**, 384 (1951).

CHAPTER IVB

See also: Anhydrous metal chlorides, synthesis 45

11. TITANIUM(III) CHLORIDE

(Titanium Trichloride)

$$2TiCl_4 + H_2 \leftrightharpoons 2TiCl_3 + 2HCl$$

Submitted by W. L. Groeneveld,* G. P. M. Leger,* J. Wolters* and R. Waterman†
Checked by A. L. McClelland‡

Anhydrous titanium(III) chloride can be prepared according to several methods, most of which, however, give only low yields of an impure product. The present method is essentially the same as that described by Sherfey,[1] which consists in vapor-phase reduction of titanium(IV) chloride with hydrogen on or near the surface of a glowing tungsten wire. Some modifications have been introduced into the method, resulting in a much higher yield than that reported by Sherfey. The present method also employs more readily available laboratory glassware.

Procedure

The apparatus for the preparation is assembled as shown in Fig. 7. Standard ground-glass joints are used through-

* Leiden University, Netherlands.
† Technical University, Delft, Netherlands.
‡ E. I. du Pont de Nemours and Company, Wilmington, Del.

out.   Wherever these may come into contact with tita-
nium(IV) chloride, they should be lubricated with silicone
grease (other lubricants were found to be unsatisfactory).
The wide central neck of the 2-l. three-necked flask carries a
special stopper, provided at the top with two small rubber
stoppers through each of which passes a 3-mm. tungsten

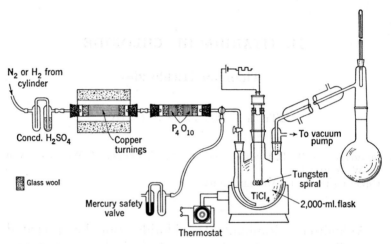

Fig. 7. Apparatus for the preparation of titanium(III) chloride.

rod.   (As an alternative, one may use, as in Sherfey's original preparation, a cylindrical flask with a separate four-hole
cover, joined to the flask with a flat grind.   Two of the
holes in the cover are then used for the tungsten wire leads.)
The ends of the rods are connected inside the flask by a
30-cm. length of 0.5-mm. tungsten wire, wound into a loose
spiral.   Some specimens of tungsten wire cannot be wound
into a spiral without heating because of their brittleness.
If this is the case, the wire can be wound around an
alumina tube of suitable diameter while it is heated with a
gentle gas-oxygen flame from a glass-blowing torch.   The
spacing of the turns should be regular, as otherwise the wire
will not be heated uniformly.   The spiral can be connected
to the lead rods by bending its ends into hooks and forcing

these into notches at the ends of the rods.   If the lead wires are not too thick, their ends can be bent into hooks (with heating, if necessary), and the spiral connected by simply hooking it to the lead wires.   It is then held in place by gravity and a slight tension of the spiral.

The reaction vessel is supported in an electric heating mantle.   The apparatus is freed from moist air and the film of moisture adhering to the glass walls is removed by evacuating the apparatus with an oil pump and carefully applying a small luminous flame to all its parts before dried nitrogen is admitted.   The lead-in tube for nitrogen (and, subsequently, hydrogen) should be fairly wide to prevent plugging with solid titanium(III) chloride during the reaction. The empty distillation flask is now quickly replaced by one containing about 1500 g. (7.9 mols) of pure titanium(IV) chloride,* which is then distilled into the reaction vessel.

During the distillation, a stream of dry nitrogen is passed into the reaction vessel, serving both to prevent the entrance of moist air in the event of sucking back and to drive out atmospheric oxygen, which must be absent during the subsequent reaction.   After the distillation, the nitrogen stream is temporarily increased and the distillation condenser is quickly replaced by an efficient reflux condenser, e.g., of the Dimroth type.   The inner surface of this condenser should also have been dried by evacuation, application of a flame, and admittance of dry nitrogen.   The reflux condenser is fitted at the top with a joint carrying a stopcock and connected by means of a long rubber tube to a wash bottle containing paraffin oil, so that the outflow of gases from the apparatus can be estimated.   When it may be assumed that all the air has been driven out by nitrogen, the nitrogen is replaced by purified hydrogen.

The purification is effected by passing the hydrogen through a porcelain tube containing copper turnings, which is heated in a tubular electric oven to about 800°, and next

* If the tetrachloride is discolored, it should be distilled from copper powder until colorless, several times if necessary.

through a tube containing an efficient drying agent, such as phosphorus(V) oxide. The reaction vessel is now heated, and as soon as reflux equilibrium is established a direct or alternating current is passed through the tungsten spiral. If alternating current is used, a particularly convenient procedure is to use two a.-c. transformers in series. This is desirable because 20 volts should be sufficient, and this is too easily exceeded when only one transformer is used. One of the two is set at 20 volts and the other is gradually raised from zero until copious formation of violet fumes of titanium(III) chloride is noted. The tungsten wire should then be a bright red color. The current will be about 15 amp.; so the connecting wires must be of adequate size to carry such a current.

At this stage the heating mantle may be switched off, because the heat emitted by the tungsten spiral (if the latter is suspended close above the surface of the liquid) is sufficient to maintain the titanium(IV) chloride at the reflux temperature. In view of the fact that the reduction is an equilibrium reaction, the stream of hydrogen should be fairly rapid. The titanium(III) chloride tends to deposit on the walls of the flask and on the lower parts of the condenser, and sometimes a small mound of the compound builds up towards the spiral. These deposits of the trichloride cannot easily be removed by tapping; so in order to remove them it is advisable temporarily to switch off the current and reflux the tetrachloride by switching on the electric heating mantle. The reaction should be stopped by switching off the current as soon as smooth refluxing ceases, i.e., when it starts to bump severely. The hydrogen is then replaced with nitrogen, which this time should be freed from possible traces of oxygen by passing it through the same apparatus that was used for purification of the hydrogen (except that the temperature of the copper turnings may be reduced to about 500°).

When all the hydrogen has been driven out by nitrogen, the reflux condenser is quickly replaced by a downward con-

denser to distill off the excess titanium(IV) chloride.   This
is connected to an oil pump via two liquid-air traps preceded
by an ice trap.

Of any tetrachloride that passes over, most will be condensed as a liquid in the ice trap, so that the possibility of
plugging the liquid-air traps with condensed solid is
reduced.   During the final stages of removal of the tetrachloride, when a good vacuum is needed, the ice trap can be
replaced with liquid air to prevent volatilization of the
tetrachloride from the trap.   The stream of nitrogen is discontinued and the excess of the tetrachloride is distilled off
in vacuo, the flask being heated again by the heating mantle.
If it is desired to avoid the switch of condensers, the reflux
and the downward condenser can be set up as a single unit
by simply connecting the latter to the top of the former.
The excess of tetrachloride can then be distilled after removing the water from the jacket of the reflux condenser.   During the distillation the temperature should be kept as low as
possible, as otherwise some of the product may dispropor-
tionate into the dichloride and tetrachloride, the former
remaining behind as an impurity.   To dislodge the tetrachloride from the surface of the trichloride, it is advantage-
ous from time to time to disconnect the vacuum, allow the
flask to fill up with nitrogen, shut off the latter, and sud-
denly reconnect the vacuum ("flash vacuum effect").
When all the tetrachloride has been removed, the flask is
allowed to cool and fill up with nitrogen.   The condenser is
replaced by a stopper, the stopcock of the lead-in tube is
closed, and the contents of the flask are transferred to storage vessels in an atmosphere of nitrogen.   This is done in a
dry-box.   A dry-box from which the air can be completely
removed by evacuation should be used.

During 8 to 10 hours' operation, 300 to 350 g. of titanium-
(III) chloride may be prepared.   The yield on the basis of
$TiCl_4$ not recovered is 80–85%.   On the basis of total
titanium(IV) chloride, the yield is 30 to 40% (Sherfey[1]
obtained 10%).

Properties

Titanium(III) chloride, as prepared according to the above method, is a violet crystalline powder, which is the alpha modification (a brown modification is also known). If oxygen and moisture have been painstakingly excluded, the product is substantially pure. The intensities of the lines in the x-ray powder diagram agree closely with those calculated by Klemm and Krose[2] for pure α-TiCl$_3$. The trichloride is soluble in oxygen-free water without decomposition. It is deliquescent and is slowly attacked by atmospheric oxygen. When heated *in vacuo* at about 450°, the trichloride disproportionates according to the equation: $2\text{TiCl}_3 \rightarrow \text{TiCl}_2 + \text{TiCl}_4$.

References

1. J. M. SHERFEY: *J. Research Natl. Bur. Standards*, **46**, 299 (1951); INORGANIC SYNTHESES, **6**, 57 (1960).
2. W. KLEMM and E. KROSE: *Z. anorg. Chem.*, **253**, 218 (1957).

12. BIS[TRIS(ACETYLACETONATO)TITANIUM(IV)] HEXACHLOROTITANATE(IV)

(Bis[tris(2,4-pentanedionato)titanium(IV)] Hexachlorotitanate(IV))

$$3\text{TiCl}_4 + 6\text{C}_5\text{H}_8\text{O}_2 \rightarrow [\text{Ti}(\text{C}_5\text{H}_7\text{O}_2)_3]_2\text{TiCl}_6 + 6\text{HCl}$$

SUBMITTED BY VERA DORON*
CHECKED BY DUWARD SHRIVER†

Bis[tris(acetylacetonato)titanium(IV)] hexachlorotitanate(IV) has been prepared by reaction of titanium(IV) chlo-

* Ford Motor Company, Scientific Laboratory, Dearborn, Mich.
† University of Michigan, Ann Arbor, Mich.

ride and acetylacetone (2,4-pentanedione) in acetic acid medium[1,2] and also by the interaction of the diketone with the etherate of the titanium halide.[3] The procedure outlined below, in which reaction between titanium(IV) chloride and acetylacetone is effected in benzene, is simpler than the methods described previously and gives substantially higher yields of product.

Procedure

A mixture of 20 g. (0.105 mol) of titanium(IV) chloride, 45 g. (0.45 mol) of acetylacetone, and 300 ml. of anhydrous benzene is refluxed for approximately 3 hours and then about two-thirds of the benzene is removed by distillation. The orange-red precipitate which forms is filtered, washed with petroleum ether, and vacuum-dried. The yield is 30.1 g. (90%). *Anal.* Calcd. for $[Ti(C_5H_7O_2)_3]_2TiCl_6$: Ti, 15.10; Cl, 22.37; C, 37.89; H, 4.45. Found: Ti, 14.90; Cl, 20.07; C, 38.17; H, 4.41.

Properties

Bis[tris(acetylacetonato)titanium(IV)] hexachlorotitanate(IV) is soluble in benzene and chloroform, slightly soluble in cold glacial acetic acid, and relatively insoluble in ether and petroleum ether. The compound undergoes hydrolysis on exposure to moist air, yielding acetylacetone, hydrous titanium(IV) oxide, and hydrochloric acid. When heated, the crystals change from a reddish orange to yellow and decompose at about 230°.

References

1. W. DILTHEY: *Ber.*, **37**, 589 (1904).
2. R. C. YOUNG and A. J. VANDER WEYDEN: INORGANIC SYNTHESES, **2**, 119 (1946).
3. A. ROSENHEIM, W. LOEWENSTEIN, and L. SINGER: *Ber.*, **36**, 1833 (1903).

13. ZIRCONIUM(IV) IODIDE

(Zirconium Tetraiodide)

$$Zr + 2I_2 \rightarrow ZrI_4$$

Submitted by Kenneth C. Eberly*
Checked by Bert Chamberland†

Zirconium and titanium halides have recently come into prominence as catalysts for the low-pressure synthesis of polyethylene (Ziegler reaction). The nature and amount of zirconium or titanium halide employed in the preparation of the Ziegler catalyst has a great influence upon the configuration of the resulting polymer.

A search of the literature does not reveal a synthesis of zirconium(IV) iodide from the elements. However, Blumenthal[1] mentions the fact that zirconium and iodine will react at temperatures as low as 340°, but no details are given. Bailey[2] and Dennis and Spencer[3] state that iodine vapor in a current of hydrogen does not attack heated zirconium.

Chaigneau[4] reported the preparation of zirconium(IV) iodide in high yield by heating zirconium(IV) oxide with anhydrous aluminum iodide. A check of this method gave a moderate yield of zirconium(IV) iodide (free from aluminum).

Procedure

In the rounded-off end of a dry 2.5-cm.-o.d. Pyrex bomb tube is placed 20.3072 g. (0.08 mol) of c.p. iodine. While the tube is laid horizontally, 3.6488 g. (0.04 mol) of fine

* Firestone Tire and Rubber Company, Akron 17, Ohio.
† E. I. du Pont de Nemours and Company, Wilmington, Del.

zirconium turnings is added in a pile 5 in. from the iodine. The iodine in the tube is cooled to $-80°$ with Dry Ice, and the tube is evacuated to 0.1-mm. pressure and sealed off 12 in. from the rounded end. The tube, still horizontal, is eased carefully into a 1-in. $\times$ 12-in. tube furnace until the zirconium but not the iodine is in the furnace. The furnace temperature is then quickly brought up to 450°.* As the iodine reacts with the zirconium, the tube is moved further and further into the furnace until completely housed (an operation consuming about 25 hours). After the completely housed tube is heated for another 15 hours in order to complete the reaction, the furnace is turned off.† When cool, the tube is cracked at both ends, and the crystals are transferred quickly and quantitatively to a dry tared weighing bottle (this operation is best performed in a dry-box). A trace of unreacted zirconium (about 0.0214 g.) remains in the middle of the tube at the end of the reaction. The yield of zirconium(IV) iodide is 23.725 g. (99.6% of theory based on the zirconium that had reacted).‡ *Anal.* Calcd. for ZrI_4: Zr, 15.23; I, 84.77. Found: Zr, 15.39, 15.25; I, 84.82, 84.71.

Analysis

About 0.5 g. of zirconium(IV) iodide is weighed analytically from a dry weighing bottle into a 250-ml. beaker. The

* As measured by a thermocouple in the middle of the furnace.

† The checker found it necessary to remove unreacted iodine at this point to obtain a pure product. This was done in the following manner. The reaction product, appearing at both ends of the tube (coolest parts of the furnace), was assembled at one end. This was accomplished by heating one end of the tube to 450° until all the zirconium(IV) iodide had collected at the cooler (room-temperature) end. The product was then centered in the furnace and heated to 150° for 24 hours to remove the unreacted iodine mixed with the product. The excess iodine was collected at the cooler end outside the furnace. When cool, the tube was cracked in a dry-box and the tetraiodide transferred rapidly to a weighing bottle.

‡ The yield obtained by the checker was 88% of theory based on the zirconium that had reacted.

weighed crystals are dissolved in 20 ml. of water containing
1 drop of nitric acid.   The solution is poured quantitatively
into a mixture of 10 ml. of concentrated ammonium hydroxide (28% NH_3) and 40 ml. of water.   A somewhat gelatinous precipitate of zirconium hydroxide is formed and is
filtered off, washed, and dried on the filter paper in an oven.
Ignition of the whole in a platinum crucible yields zirconium-
(IV) oxide, and it is weighed as such.   The filtrate from
above is just acidified with nitric acid, then treated with a
known excess of standardized 0.2 N silver nitrate solution.
The whole is then treated with 5 ml. of 10% iron(III) nitrate
solution and titrated with standardized 0.1 N potassium
thiocyanate solution to a faint red color.

Properties

Anhydrous zirconium(IV) iodide is an orange crystalline
solid which fumes heavily in air.   It dissolves completely in
water with the liberation of energy.   According to Blumenthal,[1] it has a heat of formation of 90 kcal./mol at 25°.   It
sublimes at 431° at atmospheric pressure and melts at 499°
at elevated pressures.   Its heat and entropy of sublimation
are 29.0 and 41.2 kcal./mol, respectively.   Its magnetic
susceptibility is -0.238×10^{-6} c.g.s. electromagnetic units.

References

1. W. BLUMENTHAL: "The Chemical Behavior of Zirconium," pp. 106, 115,
   D. Van Nostrand Company, Inc., Princeton, 1958.
2. G. H. BAILEY: Chem. News, **60**, 17, 32 (1889); Proc. Roy. Soc. (London),
   46, 74 (1889).
3. L. M. DENNIS and A. E. SPENCER, JR.: J. Am. Chem. Soc., **18**, 673 (1898).
4. M. CHAIGNEAU: Bull. soc. chim. France, **1957**, 886.

CHAPTER VA

See also: Phenylbiguanide-*p*-sulfonic acid complexes of copper(II), synthesis 2

Tetrakis[iodo(tri-*n*-butylphosphine)copper(I)] and iodo(2,2'-bipyridine)(tri-*n*-butylphosphine)copper(I), synthesis 3

Gallium(III) nitride, synthesis 5

Hydrides of germanium, tin, arsenic, and antimony, synthesis 10

Trichloro(tripyridine)chromium(III), synthesis 36

Trichloro(tripyridine)molybdenum(III), synthesis 39

Potassium octacyanotungstate(IV) 2-hydrate, synthesis 40

Chlorine(Cl^{36})-labeled thionyl chloride, silicon tetrachloride, boron chloride, germanium(IV) chloride, and phosphorus-(III) chloride, synthesis 44

Unipositive halogen complexes, synthesis 46

Monopyridineiodine(I) chloride, synthesis 47

Tris(3-nitroacetylacetonato)cobalt(III), synthesis 55

Inner complexes of cobalt(III) with diethylenetriamine, synthesis 56

Hydrated rhodium(III) chloride, chloroamminerhodium(III) salts, and a note on the recovery of rhodium wastes, synthesis 57

cis- and *trans*-Tetrachloro(dipyridine)iridium(IV), synthesis 58

cis- and *trans*-Pyridinium tetrachloro(dipyridine)iridate(III), synthesis 60

cis- and *trans*-Tetrachlorodiammineplatinum(IV), synthesis 62

cis- and *trans*-Dichlorodiammineplatinum(II), synthesis 63

cis- and *trans*-Dichlorobis(tri-*n*-butylphosphine)platinum(II), synthesis 64

cis- and *trans*-Dichloro(dipyridine)platinum(II), synthesis 65

14. BIGUANIDE SULFATE

(Guanylguanidinium Hydrogen Sulfate)

$$\underset{H_2N-\overset{\overset{\displaystyle NH}{\|}}{C}-NH-CN}{} + NH_4Cl \xrightarrow{\Delta} H_2N-\overset{\overset{\displaystyle NH}{\|}}{C}-NH-\overset{\overset{\displaystyle NH}{\|}}{C}-NH_2 \cdot HCl$$

$$2\,H_2N-\overset{\overset{\displaystyle NH}{\|}}{C}-NH-\overset{\overset{\displaystyle NH}{\|}}{C}-NH_2 \cdot HCl + [Cu(NH_3)_4]SO_4 \rightarrow$$

$$[Cu(C_2N_5H_7)_2]SO_4 + 2NH_4Cl + 2NH_3$$

$$[Cu(C_2N_5H_7)_2]SO_4 + 2H_2SO_4 + 4H_2O \rightarrow$$

$$2\,H_2N-\overset{\overset{\displaystyle NH}{\|}}{C}-NH-\overset{\overset{\displaystyle NH}{\|}}{C}-NH_2 \cdot H_2SO_4 \cdot 2H_2O + CuSO_4$$

$$H_2N-\overset{\overset{\displaystyle NH}{\|}}{C}-NH-\overset{\overset{\displaystyle NH}{\|}}{C}-NH_2 \cdot H_2SO_4 \cdot 2H_2O \xrightarrow{\Delta}$$

$$H_2N-\overset{\overset{\displaystyle NH}{\|}}{C}-NH-\overset{\overset{\displaystyle NH}{\|}}{C}-NH_2 \cdot H_2SO_4 + 2H_2O$$

SUBMITTED BY D. KARIPIDES* AND W. CONARD FERNELIUS*
CHECKED BY MELVIN D. JOESTON†

Biguanide is prepared by the ammoniation of dicyanodiamide (cyanoguanidine). The reaction is accomplished by ammonium salts in the molten condition[1,2] or by ammonia under pressure.[3,4] In the following preparation, which is essentially that of Bamberger and Dieckmann,[1] ammonium chloride is used as the ammoniating agent. The influence of reaction conditions on this type of reaction has been studied in some detail.[5,6]

* The Pennsylvania State University, University Park, Pa.
† University of Illinois, Urbana, Ill.

Procedure

Twenty-five and twenty-two hundredths grams (0.3 mol) of dicyanodiamide and 40.1 g. (0.75 mol) of ammonium chloride are separately ground to a fine state and then intimately mixed. This mixture, in a 250-ml. beaker, is gently heated with a Bunsen flame under constant stirring until a liquid melt is obtained (10 to 15 minutes). This melt is held at 160 to 165° for 10 minutes with constant stirring.

After the melt has cooled, the solid is crushed into small lumps and dissolved in 150 ml. of hot water (90 to 100°). The resulting mixture is filtered and the precipitate is washed with two 25-ml. portions of hot water. (The insoluble product is ammeline.[1]) The filtrate is next treated with a slight excess of ammoniacal copper(II) sulfate solution (the excess is noted by the appearance of a slight purple coloration). The precipitated rose-red copper biguanide sulfate is filtered, washed with water, and dissolved in 35 ml. of hot 10% sulfuric acid (the temperature should not exceed 90°). The resulting solution is then cooled by immersion in an ice bath. The crude crystals which form are separated and dissolved in 25 ml. of boiling water and the solution is cooled in ice. Again the crystals which form are dissolved in 25 ml. of boiling water and the solution is cooled in ice. The resulting colorless crystals of biguanide sulfate 2-hydrate are filtered, washed first with 10 ml. of cold water and then with 10 ml. of absolute ethanol, and dried at 110° for about 15 hours. The yield of anhydrous biguanide sulfate is 9.2 g. (15.4%); m.p. 231 to 232°. *Anal.* Calcd. for $C_2H_9N_5O_4S$: N, 35.16. Found: N, 35.28.

Properties

Pure anhydrous biguanide sulfate is a white amorphous solid that is not very soluble in cold water but is soluble in hot water, from which it crystallizes in colorless glistening rhombic crystals.[1] An aqueous solution of biguanide sulfate is acidic to litmus.   The compound does not dissolve in absolute ethanol to any appreciable extent and is insoluble in common organic solvents.

References

1. E. BAMBERGER and W. DIECKMANN: Ber., 25, 543 (1892).
2. A. OSTROGOVICH: Bul. Soc. Stunte Bucaresti, 19, 64 (1910); cf. Chem. Zentr. II, 1890 (1910).
3. A. SMOLKA and A. FREIDREICH: Monatsh., 9, 228 (1889); 10, 86 (1889).
4. K. RACHMANN: Ann., 376, 163 (1910).
5. T. L. DAVIS: J. Am. Chem. Soc., 43, 2234 (1921).
6. J. S. BLAIR and J. M. BRAHAM: ibid., 44, 2342 (1922).

15. BIGUANIDE

(Guanylguanidine; Amidino Guanidine)

$$
\underset{H_2N-\overset{\displaystyle\overset{NH}{\|}}{C}-NH-\overset{\displaystyle\overset{NH}{\|}}{C}-NH_2\cdot H_2SO_4}{} + 2NaOH \rightarrow
$$

$$
\underset{H_2N-\overset{\displaystyle\overset{NH}{\|}}{C}-NH-\overset{\displaystyle\overset{NH}{\|}}{C}-NH_2}{} + Na_2SO_4 + 2H_2O
$$

SUBMITTED BY SAMUEL N. HOLTER* AND W. CONARD FERNELIUS*
CHECKED BY DEVON MEEK†

From biguanide sulfate (synthesis 14) the free base can be obtained by treating a solution of the sulfate with barium hydroxide[1] or sodium hydroxide,[2] or by refluxing biguanide sulfate with alcoholic sodium ethoxide.[3]   The procedure using sodium hydroxide is simple and cheap and produces a satisfactory product.

* The Pennsylvania State University, University Park, Pa.
† The Ohio State University, Columbus, Ohio

Procedure

To a solution of 16 g. (0.4 mol) of sodium hydroxide in
350 ml. of dry methanol, 19.9 g. (0.1 mol) of anhydrous
biguanide sulfate is added. The mixture is stirred for
2 hours at room temperature and then for 45 min. at the
reflux temperature. The hot solution is filtered and the
sodium sulfate cake is washed with 40 ml. of hot methanol.
The filtrate and wash are concentrated under reduced pressure (solution temperature below 45°) until a heavy crop of
crystals separates. Precipitation is completed by the addition of 150 ml. of dry ethyl ether. The product is filtered,
washed with dry ether, and dried in a vacuum desiccator.
Yield 9.0 g. (89%); m.p. 133 to 134° (decomp. 137 to 139°).
The product is stored in a desiccator since it turns yellow on
exposure to the atmosphere.

Properties

Pure biguanide crystallizes from absolute ethanol in
colorless prisms. Biguanide is soluble in cold water. Its
aqueous solution is alkaline. Biguanide is a stronger base
($pK_1 = 11.52$; $pK_2 = 2.93$)[4] than ammonia ($pK = 9.61$).
It is soluble in absolute ethanol and insoluble in ethyl ether,
chloroform, and benzene. It gradually decomposes on
heating or on long standing in aqueous solution.[1] The
melting point is given as 130°[1] (decomp. 142°[3]).

References

1. K. RACHMANN: *Ann.*, **376**, 163 (1910).
2. D. W. JAYNE, JR.: U.S. patent 2,311,295 (1943); cf. *C.A.*, **37**, 4408 (1943).
3. K. H. SLOTTA and R. TSCHESCHE: *Ber.*, **62**, 1390 (1929).
4. B. DAS SARMA: *J. Ind. Chem. Soc.*, **29**, 217 (1952).

16. BLACK PHOSPHORUS

SUBMITTED BY H. KREBS*
CHECKED BY H. MAJEWSKI†

Black phosphorus was prepared for the first time by Bridgman[1] by heating white phosphorus to 200° under a pressure of 12,000 atmospheres. This modification of phosphorus can also be prepared without the application of pressure by heating an intimate mixture of white phosphorus and metallic mercury at temperatures between 200 and 400°.[2] Above 400° red phosphorus is formed; below 360° the rate of conversion is very slow.

Procedure

White phosphorus of commercial grade is first freed from oxygen-containing contaminants by melting and agitating it in dilute aqueous potassium dichromate solution weakly acidified with sulfuric acid. After decanting and washing the phosphorus with cold water, the melting in the oxidizing solution is repeated until the phosphorus appears transparent. It is washed with cold water and cut into pieces, most suitably under ice water.

The preparation of black phosphorus is carried out in a glass ampul A (see Fig. 8) of 7-cm. length and 2-cm. i.d. Inside the ampul are five steel balls, like the ones used in ball bearings. Twenty grams of mercury and about 50 mg. of black phosphorus (seed crystals) in pieces, not pulverized, are placed in the ampul. About 20 g. of purified white phosphorus is then transferred under an inert atmosphere to B and the apparatus sealed at C.

* Chemical Institute, University of Bonn, Bonn, West Germany.
† Victor Chemical Works, Division of Stauffer Chemical Company, Chicago Heights, Ill.

A connection to a high-vacuum pump is made via the ground-glass joint at D, and the white phosphorus is distilled into the glass tube A until the latter is about two-thirds full. The ampul is then sealed off at the constriction E.

By means of a sealed-on glass rod F, the ampul is brought to the center of a horizontally positioned tubular furnace in such a way that it can be rotated rapidly by a motor.

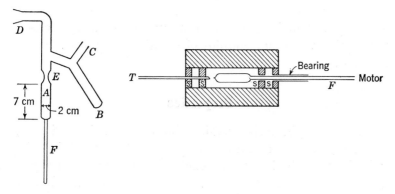

Fig. 8. Apparatus for the preparation of black phosphorus.

Several asbestos plugs (S) serve as heat insulators. The temperature is measured by a thermocouple (T).

The polymerization of the white phosphorus to the initially still reactive light red phosphorus takes place at 280° under rapid rotation of the ampul, so that the seed crystals are dispersed in the molten white phosphorus and an intimate mixture of red phosphorus, seed crystals, and metallic mercury results. After 3 days, the temperature is raised to 360° for one day and then maintained at 380° for 3 days. The rate of the rotation of the tube may now be reduced since its contents have become solid. After cooling, the tube can be opened. A fine film of impure red phosphorus which is observed occasionally on the surface of the black phosphorus can be blown off easily. The black phosphorus is soft, like graphite, and can be cut with a knife.   The yield, if seed crystals are used, is quantitative.*

Most of the mercury adhering to the reaction product can be removed by amalgamation with lead.   The pulverized black phosphorus is placed in one half and lead in the other half of an ampul which is constricted in the middle.   The free gas space is to be kept as small as possible since the vapor phase consists of P_4 molecules.   The ampul is heated for several days at a temperature between 300 and 450°. By repeating this procedure, a mercury content of less than 1 atom per cent is reached.   Finally, by replacing the lead with gold, a mercury content of about 0.5 atom per cent is reached.

Properties

Black phosphorus is a semiconductor.[3,4]   It has a density of 2.70 g./sq. cm. and a hardness of 2.   The crystal lattice is built up of double layers, each layer consisting of zigzag chains of phosphorus atoms.   In these chains the P–P–P bond angle is 99° and the phosphorus–phosphorus distance 2.17 A.   Black phosphorus is stable in air.

References

1. P. W. BRIDGMAN: *Phys. Rev.*, **3**, 187 (1914); *J. Am. Chem. Soc.*, **36**, 1344 (1914).
2. H. KREBS, H. WEITZ, and K. H. WORMS, *Z. anorg. u. allgem. Chem.*, **280**, 119 (1955).
3. H. KREBS, *Angew. Chem.*, **70**, 615 (1958); *Acta Cryst.*, **9**, 95 (1956).
4. R. W. KEYES: *Phys. Rev.*, **92**, 580 (1953).

* If seed crystals are not available, they can be obtained readily in the following manner.   A weighed amount of mercury and from the same to twice the volume of white phosphorus are placed in a glass ampul of approximately 0.8-mm. o.d. and 6-cm. length.   The ampul in an iron shield is placed in an oven which has been preheated from 300 to 320°, and the ampul is maintained at this temperature for 3 days.   The ampul is then heated for 2 days at 340° and finally for 2 additional days at 360°.   Generally, in a sample so treated, about one-half of the phosphorus is converted to the black form, which is mixed with the mercury.

17. PENTACALCIUM MONOHYDROXYORTHOPHOSPHATE

(Hydroxylapatite)

$$5Ca(NO_3)_2 + 3(NH_4)_3PO_4 + NH_4OH \rightarrow$$
$$Ca_5(OH)(PO_4)_3 + 10NH_4NO_3$$

Submitted by Erich Hayek* and Heinrich Newesely*
Checked by Max L. Rumpel†

Hydroxylapatite is the stable orthophosphate of calcium in neutral and alkaline media. Its preparation in pure form is difficult, since with the customary precipitation reaction the monohydrogen phosphate ion always forms according to the reaction:

$$5Ca^{++} + 4PO_4^{3-} + H_2O \leftrightarrows Ca_5(OH)(PO_4)_3 + HPO_4^{--}$$

Therefore, tetracalcium monohydrogen triphosphate ("octaphosphate"), $Ca_4H(PO_4)_3 \cdot 2H_2O$, which displays a structure similar to apatite, readily forms, solely or at least partially, in the place of hydroxylapatite.[1] Such precipitates change to the β-tricalcium phosphate upon ca'cination. In the preparation of a uniformly crystalline product one must perform a tedious boiling-out process[2] or the hydrothermal synthesis;[3] either of these methods, however, accommodates only a small lot (*ca.* 70 mg., crystal size 0.3 mm.) or else the preparation has a small sodium content[4] (0.5% from 2 g. of material and up to 2-mm. crystal size). In either case, considerable apparatus and expenditure of time are required.

These difficulties can be overcome, for example, by carrying out the precipitation at normal temperature in a medium of sufficiently high pH so that the PO_4^{3-} concentration is not exceeded by that of HPO_4^{--} and, moreover, by

* Institute for Inorganic and Analytical Chemistry, Innsbruck University, Innsbruck, Austria.
† University of Kansas, Lawrence, Kan.

employing the easily volatilized ammonia in the precipitation.[5] It is necessary both to bring the reaction medium to a high pH value and to allow the phosphate solution to flow into that of the calcium salt to obtain a homogeneous product. Furthermore, it is important to employ a nitrate solution instead of a chloride; otherwise, during calcination of the voluminous precipitate, some ammonium chloride and chlorapatite may be formed through metathesis.

Procedure

Seventy-eight and seven-tenths grams (0.33 mol) of $Ca(NO_3)_2 \cdot 4H_2O$ is dissolved in 300 ml. of water in a 2-l. flask. The solution is adjusted to a pH of 12 by the addition of concentrated ammonia (CO_2-free) and is then diluted to 600 ml. Into this solution is dropped slowly, with vigorous stirring, a solution of 26.4 g. (0.2 mol) of diammonium hydrogen phosphate in 500 ml. water, which similarly has been brought to pH 12 with ammonia and thereafter diluted to 800 ml. A voluminous precipitate forms. The filtering properties of the reaction mixture may be improved by gently boiling it for 10 minutes. The precipitate is allowed to settle and the supernatant solution is separated from the precipitate by decantation and by use of a suction filter, with application of a weak vacuum.

The filter cake is washed with 100 ml. of hot water, dried at 150°, and heated for an hour at 240° to remove the ammonium nitrate. By strong heating at 800° for an hour, the product becomes largely anhydrous and considerably hardened. This hardening is of importance when the solid is to be ground to a predetermined particle size.

The yield, theoretically 33.5 g., amounts to 30 to 32 g. because of mechanical losses which are difficult to avoid.

Properties

The hydroxylapatite obtained by this method is in the form of white fragments which appear highly porous.

Under the electron microscope the material shows a structure corresponding to hexagonal prisms which terminate in pyramids, length about 30 to 60 mμ, width 10 to 20 mμ. By the use of analytically pure starting materials in the indicated proportions, the atomic ratio Ca/P corresponds within a deviation of less than 1% of the theoretical value 1.67. Even by using less pure starting materials important amounts of the impurities iron, aluminum, and manganese, as well as in part magnesium, are removed by filtration of the ammoniacal solution. Owing to the great surface area, a little water content ($<1\%$) is retained even after heating at red heat according to the above procedure; it can be removed only by long heating at 900°. Hydroxylapatite begins to decompose above 1100°.

References

1. E. HAYEK, H. NEWESELY, W. HASSENTEUFEL, and B. KRISMER: *Monatsh.*, **91**, 249 (1960).
2. E. HAYEK, F. MULLNER, and K. KOLLER: *ibid.*, **82**, 959 (1951).
3. A. PERLOFF and A. S. POSNER: *Science*, **124**, 583 (1956); INORGANIC SYNTHESES, **6**, 16 (1960).
4. E. HAYEK, W. BOHLER, J. LECHLEITNER, and H. PETTER: *Z. anorg. u. allgem. Chem.*, **295**, 241 (1958).
5. E. HAYEK and W. STADLMANN: *Angew. Chem.*, **67**, 327 (1955).

18. TETRAAMMONIUM PYROPHOSPHATE

$$H_4P_2O_7 + 4NH_3 \rightarrow (NH_4)_4P_2O_7$$

SUBMITTED BY C. SWANSON* AND F. McCOLLOUGH*
CHECKED BY RALPH K. BIRDWHISTELL†

Tetraammonium pyrophosphate has been prepared by bubbling ammonia into an ice-water solution of pyrophos-

* Victor Chemical Works, Division of Stauffer Chemical Company, Chicago Heights, Ill.
† Butler University, Indianapolis, Ind.

phoric acid and then precipitating the salt with ethanol.[1]
The procedure given be'ow, in which ammoniation of pyrophosphoric acid is carried out in ethanol solution, is rapid
and convenient and gives high yields of the product.

Procedure

Fifty grams (0.28 mol) of solid pyrophosphoric acid[2] is
dissolved, with stirring, in 2 l. of 95% ethanol maintained
at 5° in a 3-l. beaker. A small quantity of decolorizing
charcoal is added and the solution is filtered by suction into
another 3-l. beaker which is kept in a salt-ice-water bath.
The pyrophosphoric acid solution is agitated vigorously
while ammonia is bubbled through a gas inlet tube of 1 cm.
i.d. into the solution.   The ammonia is added at a rate such
that the temperature of the solution does not rise above
10°.* Almost immediately, diammonium dihydrogen pyrophosphate precipitates from solution; however, continued
ammoniation converts this substance to the tetraammonium
salt.

Ammoniation is complete when a 1% solution of a portion
of the solid product (which has been washed thoroughly
with fresh ethanol) has a pH of approximately 8.2.   (For
complete reaction, ammonia must be added for 2 to 4 hours.)
When conversion to the tetraammonium salt has been completed, passage of ammonia is discontinued, but stirring is
maintained until the temperature of the reaction mixture
reaches 20°.   The product is then filtered under suction
onto a Büchner funnel and air is pulled through the filter
cake for one hour.   The product is placed on a large dish
and vacuum-dried at 25°.   Yields of 90 to 95% are obtained.
Anal. Calcd. for $(NH_4)_4P_2O_7$: P, 25.2; N, 22.8.   Found: P,
25.6; N, 22.8.

---

* If the reaction mixture becomes too warm, the pyrophosphoric acid
reacts with the ethanol to form ethyl dihydrogen orthophosphate and
orthophosphoric acid.

Properties

Tetraammonium pyrophosphate is a colorless, water-soluble crystalline compound which loses ammonia very slowly when exposed to the atmosphere.

References

1. J. R. VAN WAZER: "Phosphorus and Its Compounds," Vol. 1, p. 626, Interscience Publishers, Inc., New York, 1958.
2. J. E. MALOWAN: INORGANIC SYNTHESES, **3**, 96 (1950).

19. (TRIPHENYL)AMINOPHOSPHONIUM CHLORIDE

$$(C_6H_5)_3P + NH_2Cl \rightarrow [(C_6H_5)_3PNH_2]Cl$$

SUBMITTED BY HARRY H. SISLER* AND NATHAN L. SMITH*
CHECKED BY PETER BARNA†

The chloramidation of tertiary amines by introducing gaseous chloramide (chloramine) into the anhydrous amine or a solution of the amine in an inert solvent results in the formation of 1,1,1-trisubstituted hydrazonium chlorides.[1] It has been found that a similar chloramidation reaction with tertiary phosphines can be made to yield analogous compounds of the general formula $[R_3PNH_2]Cl$, i.e., P,P,P-trisubstituted aminophosphonium chlorides.[2] The following aminophosphonium chlorides were prepared by this reaction: P,P,P-triphenyl; P,P,P-tri-n-butyl; P-phenyl-P,P-(cyclotetramethylene); and P-phenyl-P,P-(cyclopentamethylene). The method for the preparation of (triphenyl)-aminophosphonium chloride is given as representative of the procedure.

* The University of Florida, Gainesville, Florida.
† University of California, Berkeley, Calif.

Procedure

The apparatus used for the generation of chloramide is the same as described previously.[1] The gaseous effluent of the chloramide generator (at a flow rate of *ca.* 0.1 mol of chloramide per hour) is passed into a solution of 5.0 g. (0.19 mol) of triphenylphosphine in 35 ml. of dry benzene* maintained at 15 to 25°. Crystallization of (triphenyl)-aminophosphonium chloride begins to occur as the chloramide is passed through the solution. The reaction is continued for 10 to 15 minutes. The reaction mixture is filtered and the residue washed thoroughly with ethyl ether and dried. The washed residue (4.8 to 5.2 g.) consists of (triphenyl)aminophosphonium chloride contaminated with 2 to 4% of ammonium chloride. The yield of aminophosphonium salt is better than 95%. The product, which melts at 224 to 227°, is sufficiently pure for most synthetic work.

It may be purified by the following procedure. The crude aminophosphonium chloride is dissolved in a conveniently small volume (*ca.* 25 ml.) of chloroform, leaving most of the ammonium chloride undissolved. After filtration, aminophosphonium crystals of high purity (m.p. 238 to 240° uncor.) are obtained by the addition of cyclohexane to the chloroform solution. The identity of these crystals was checked by elementary analysis. *Anal.* Calcd. for $[(C_6H_5)_3PNH_2]Cl$: C, 68.90; H, 5.42; N, 4.46; P, 9.89; Cl, 11.32. Found: C, 68.50; H, 5.75; N, 4.40; P, 9.78; Cl, 11.18.

Properties

The trisubstituted aminophosphonium chlorides are colorless crystalline compounds which are generally highly hygroscopic. They are readily and quantitatively hydro-

* The reaction may also be conducted in dry ethyl ether or dichloromethane.

lyzed to the trisubstituted phosphine oxides in neutral, acidic, or basic aqueous solutions. They may be conveniently converted to a variety of different aminophosphonium salts by metatheses involving the corresponding sodium or potassium salts. (Triphenyl)aminophosphonium salts prepared in this way include the hexafluorophosphate, the perchlorate, the nitroprusside, the periodate, and the hexachloroplatinate(IV). Such metatheses must be carried out rapidly to avoid hydrolysis of the aminophosphonium ion.

References

1. H. H. Sisler and G. Omietanske: Inorganic Syntheses, **5**, 91 (1957).
2. H. H. Sisler, A. Sarkis, H. S. Ahuja, R. J. Drago, and N. L. Smith: *J. Am. Chem. Soc.*, **81**, 2982 (1959).

20. (DIMETHYLAMIDO)PHOSPHORYL DICHLORIDE

(Dimethylphosphoramidic Dichloride)

$$POCl_3 + 2(CH_3)_2NH \rightarrow (CH_3)_2NPOCl_2 + (CH_3)_2NH \cdot HCl$$
$$POCl_3 + (CH_3)_2NH \cdot HCl \rightarrow (CH_3)_2NPOCl_2 + 2HCl$$

Submitted by E. N. Walsh* and A. D. F. Toy*
Checked by M. L. Nielsen† and T. J. Morrow†

(Dimethylamido)phosphoryl dichloride has been prepared by the action of dimethylamine on an excess of phosphorus(V) oxychloride.[1] This procedure combines the reactions shown above. If dimethylammonium chloride is available as the raw material, the compound may be pre-

* Victor Chemical Works, Division of Stauffer Chemical Company, Chicago Heights, Ill.
† Monsanto Chemical Company, Dayton, Ohio.

pared by the reaction shown in the second equation.[2] This reaction may be carried out easily by heating the mixture of dimethylammonium chloride with an excess of phosphorus(V) oxychloride as described in the second half of the following procedure.

Procedure

In a 3-l. three-necked flask equipped with a stirrer, a thermometer, a gas-inlet tube having a $\frac{1}{2}$-in. bottom opening and a reflux condenser protected with a soda-lime drying tube is placed 1675 g. (10.9 mols) of phosphorus(V) oxychloride. In a distilling flask containing a boiling chip, there is condensed 118 g. (2.62 mols) of dimethylamine by cooling in an ice-salt bath. This distilling flask is then connected to a safety bottle which in turn is connected to the gas-inlet tube of the reaction flask, and the dimethylamine is distilled into the phosphorus(V) oxychloride under the liquid surface. The temperature of the reaction mixture is kept below 50° by means of an ice-salt bath. Dimethylammonium chloride precipitates immediately. The addition of dimethylamine is completed within one hour. The distillation flask is removed and the opening is sealed with a rubber stopper. The reaction mixture is heated to reflux (110 to 115°) and held at reflux with stirring until the evolution of hydrogen chloride almost ceases (12 to 18 hours). At this point only few, if any, crystals of dimethylammonium chloride remain. The reaction mixture is cooled and transferred to a 2-l. flask connected to a distillation apparatus provided for fractionation. Most of the excess phosphorus(V) oxychloride is removed by distillation to a liquid temperature of 140° at atmospheric pressure. Ice water is then circulated through the condenser and the remaining phosphorus(V) oxychloride is removed by gradually reducing the pressure to 20 mm. and heating the still pot residue to 80°. The product is then collected by distilling at 1 mm. of pressure. The fraction boiling at 43 to 46° at 1 mm. is collected as product. This fraction weighs 403 g., 96% of theory based on the dimethylamine used. Redistillation through an 18-in. Vigreux column yields the pure product (b.p. 45° at 1 mm.) in 88 to 95% yield. *Anal.* Calcd. for $(CH_3)_2NPOCl_2$: P, 19.1; N, 8.7; Cl, 43.7. Found: P, 19.1; N, 8.7; Cl, 43.5.

Properties

(Dimethylamido)phosphoryl dichloride is a water-white liquid with the following physical constants: b.p. 45° at 1 mm.; 88° at 18 mm.; 90 to 91° at 22 mm.; 194 to 195° at 760 mm.; sp. gr., 1.369 $\dfrac{15.5}{15.5}$; n_D^{25}, 1.4610. It is very reactive toward water, alcohol, and amines. On long standing, some precipitation of dimethylammonium chloride is noted.

References

1. T. Götz: German patent 855,248 (1952); cf. *C.A.*, **48**, 11481 (1954).
2. A. Michaelis: *Ann.*, **326**, 179 (1903).

21. BIS(DIMETHYLAMIDO)PHOSPHORYL CHLORIDE

(Tetramethylphosphorodiamidic Chloride)

$$(CH_3)_2NPOCl_2 + 2(CH_3)_2NH \rightarrow$$
$$[(CH_3)_2N]_2POCl + (CH_3)_2NH \cdot HCl$$

Submitted by E. N. Walsh[*] and A. D. F. Toy[*]
Checked by M. L. Nielsen[†] and T. J. Morrow[†]

Bis(dimethylamido)phosphoryl chloride has been prepared by the reaction of phosphorus(V) oxychloride with

[*] Victor Chemical Works, Division of Stauffer Chemical Company, Chicago Heights, Ill.
[†] Monsanto Chemical Company, Dayton, Ohio.

the calculated quantity of dimethylamine,[1] by the reaction
of hexamethylphosphoramide with phosphorus(V) oxychloride,[2] and by the action of dimethylamine on (dimethylamido)phosphoryl dichloride.[3] The procedure described
here is a modification of the preparation using (dimethylamido)phosphoryl dichloride as the starting material.

Procedure

In a 3-l. three-necked flask equipped with a stirrer, thermometer, gas-inlet tube with a $\frac{1}{2}$-in. bottom opening, and a
reflux condenser equipped with a soda-lime drying tube at
the top, are put 400 g. (2.47 mols) of (dimethylamido)phos-
phoryl dichloride (synthesis 20) and 1250 ml. of carbon
tetrachloride.   Dimethylamine, 222.3 g. (4.94 mols), is condensed in a 500-ml. distilling flask containing a boiling chip.
This distillation flask is then attached to a safety bottle,
which is connected to the gas-inlet tube of the reactor.
With stirring, the dimethylamine is distilled into the reactor
under the surface of the liquid.   The temperature of the
reaction is maintained below 45° by means of an ice-salt
bath.   Dimethylammonium chloride separates immediately.   When the addition of dimethylamine is complete
(in about 4 hours), the reaction mixture, a thick suspension
of dimethylammonium chloride in the carbon tetrachloride
solution of the desired product, is held at 45° for one more
hour.   It is then cooled and filtered through a sintered-glass
funnel.   The dimethylammonium chloride is washed free of
product with a total of 500 ml. of carbon tetrachloride.
The filter cake may be freed of solvent under reduced pressure and used as a reagent for the preparation of (dimethylamido)phosphoryl dichloride.   The filtrate is placed in a
distillation apparatus equipped for fractionation and distillation under reduced pressure.   An 18-in. Vigreux column
is inserted in the still, and ice-cooled water is circulated
through the condenser.   The major portion of the carbon
tetrachloride is removed by distillation at atmospheric pres-

sure to a liquid temperature of 80°. The pressure is then reduced gradually to 40 mm. to remove the last trace of solvent. The pressure is reduced further to 1 mm., and after removal of a small forerun (10–20 g.) consisting primarily of (dimethylamido)phosphoryl dichloride, the fraction boiling at 64 to 67° at 1 to 2 mm. is collected as product. This weighs about 400 g. (95% yield). Redistillation through an 18-in. Vigreux column results in a yield of 377 g. (86%) of pure product. *Anal.* Calcd. for $[(CH_3)_2N]_2POCl$: P, 18.2; N, 16.4; Cl, 20.8. Found: P, 18.2; N, 16.2; Cl, 20.8.

Properties

Bis(dimethylamido)phosphoryl chloride is a water-white liquid having the following physical constants: b.p., 63° at 1 mm.; 97 to 98° at 4 mm.; 102° at 6 mm.; n_D^{25}, 1.4642; sp. gr., $1.177 \frac{15.5}{15.5}$.

References

1. H. G. Cook, J. D. Ilett, B. C. Saunders, G. J. Stacey, H. G. Watson, I. G. E. Wilding, and S. J. Woodcock: *J. Chem. Soc.*, **1949**, 2921.
2. P. Lester: U.S. patent 2,678,335 (1954); cf. *C.A.*, **49**, 6300 (1954).
3. J. E. Gardiner and B. A. Kilby: *J. Chem. Soc.*, **1950**, 1769.

22. OCTAMETHYLPYROPHOSPHORAMIDE

$$2[(CH_3)_2N]_2POCl + H_2O + 2(C_2H_5)_3N \rightarrow$$
$$[(CH_3)_2N]_2OPOPO[N(CH_3)_2]_2 + 2(C_2H_5)_3N \cdot HCl$$

Submitted by A. D. F. Toy* and E. N. Walsh*
Checked by M. L. Nielsen† and T. J. Morrow†

Octamethylpyrophosphoramide has been prepared by the action of $[(CH_3)_2N]_2POCl$ on $[(CH_3)_2N]_2OPOC_2H_5$ or

* Victor Chemical Works, Division of the Stauffer Chemical Company, Chicago Heights, Ill.
† Monsanto Chemical Company, Dayton, Ohio.

[(CH₃)₂N]₂OPONa,[1] and by the treatment of [(CH₃)₂N]₂-POCl with inorganic alkali,[2,3,4] or with water and tertiary amine.[5,6] It is also reported to have been prepared by the reaction of pyrophosphoryl chloride with dimethylamine,[7] and from the reaction of [(CH₃)₂N]₂OPOCH₃ with acetic anhydride.[8] The procedure described here is a modification of the reaction of [(CH₃)₂N]₂POCl with water in the presence of triethylamine.[6]

Procedure

Caution! Octamethylpyrophosphoramide is very toxic (see Properties) and must be handled with great care. All work should be conducted in a vented hood; rubber gloves and plastic aprons should be worn by all personnel. Typical symptoms of intoxication from this compound are abdominal cramps and diarrhea. A common symptom of acute intoxication is constriction of the pupils of the eyes. In case of accident leading to possible intoxication, get immediate medical attention. Atropine sulfate is a specific antidote. The checkers make it a practice to soak glassware that has been used for octamethylphosphoramide in a 20 per cent sodium hydroxide solution for 24 hours to destroy residues.

In a 1-l. three-necked round-bottomed flask equipped with a 50-ml. buret, a 500-ml. graduated dropping funnel, a thermometer, a stirrer, and an exhaust vent protected with a soda-lime drying tube, is placed 378.4 g. (2.22 mols) of bis(dimethylamido)phosphoryl chloride (synthesis 21). In the buret there is placed 20 ml. (1.11 mols) of water, in the graduated dropping funnel is added 232.0 g. (2.30 mols) of triethylamine, and the volume (approximately 320 ml.) is recorded. The contents of the reaction flask are heated to 45 to 50° and then the heater is removed. One milliliter of water is added, followed by one-twentieth (approximately 16 ml.) of the triethylamine. The reaction mixture is stirred until the mildly exothermic reaction subsides (*ca.* 5 minutes), and the addition of 1 ml. of water followed by the approximately 16-ml. increment of triethylamine is repeated. Again, the reaction mixture is stirred until no further evolution of heat is noted. This alternate addition of water and triethylamine is repeated eighteen times, the 1 ml. of water always being added before the triethylamine. The reaction temperature is maintained at 45 to 50° throughout this addition period by alternate heating or cooling as required. The total addition time required is approximately 100 minutes. When the addition is complete, 20 ml. of water is placed in the buret. This water is added to the reaction mixture dropwise at 45 to 50° with stirring. The reaction becomes much more vigorous during this addition, which is complete in 30 minutes. The reaction mixture, a thick but stirrable paste, is held at 45 to 50° for 4 more hours. After the first hour, the reaction is no longer noticeably exothermic and external heating must be applied. The reaction mixture is then cooled to 25° and 400 ml. of chloroform is added to dissolve the product. Water (300 ml.) is added to dissolve the triethylammonium chloride. The solutions are then transferred to a separatory funnel and the chloroform phase (lower) is separated and washed first with 200 ml. and then with 100 ml. of water. The aqueous phase and the two wash waters are each extracted separately and in turn with two 400-ml. portions of chloroform. The three chloroform solutions are combined and placed in a distillation flask connected to a distillation apparatus equipped for fractionation and distillation under reduced pressure. The chloroform is removed by distillation under reduced pressure with ice-cooled water circulating through the condenser. The bulk of the chloroform is distilled at 200-mm. pressure to a still-pot temperature of 60°. The pressure is then gradually reduced to 2 mm. and the residue is heated to 60° at 2 mm. The residue thus collected weighs 300 g. (94.5% yield). *Anal.* Calcd. for $[(CH_3)_2N]_2OPOPO[N(CH_3)_2]_2$: P, 21.6; N, 19.6; Cl, 0.0. Found: P, 21.5; N, 19.5; Cl, 0.0.

The crude product has an assay of 99.0% by paper chromatographic analysis.

Properties

Octamethylpyrophosphoramide, when very pure, is a colorless somewhat viscous oil with the following physical constants: b.p. 120 to 122° at 0.5 mm.; 154° at 2 mm.; sp. gr., 1.09_4^{25}. Normally the color is yellow to amber. The compound is miscible with water, soluble in most organic solvents, and insoluble in higher aliphatic hydrocarbons.[9] It is a very toxic substance with a MLD_{50} to white mice of 17 mg./kg. by intraperitoneal injection.

References

1. G. SCHRADER: *B.I.O.S. Report* 1808 (1947).
2. M. PIANKA: *J. Appl. Chem.,* **5,** 109 (1955).
3. A. D. F. TOY and J. R. COSTELLO: U.S. patent 2,706,738 (1955); cf. *C.A.,* **50,** 2653 (1956).
4. W. M. LANHAM and P. L. SMITH, U.S. patent 2,810,757 (1957); cf. *C.A.,* **52,** 3850 (1958).
5. G. S. HARTLEY and D. W. POUND: British patent 652,981 (1951); cf. *C.A.,* **46,** 1025 (1952).
6. A. D. F. TOY and J. R. COSTELLO: U.S. patent 2,717,249 (1955); cf. *C.A.,* **50,** 8747 (1956).
7. M. GOEHRING and K. NIEDENZU: *Angew. Chem.,* **68,** 704 (1956).
8. H. W. COOVER, JR.: U.S. patent 2,756,250 (1956); cf. *C.A.,* **51,** 1275 (1951).
9. W. E. RIPPER, R. M. GREENSLADE, and L. A. LICKERISH: *Nature,* **163,** 787 (1949).

23. TRIMERIC AND TETRAMERIC PHOSPHONITRILE BROMIDES

$$n\text{PBr}_3 + n\text{Br}_2 + n\text{NH}_4\text{Br} \rightarrow (\text{PNBr}_2)_n + 4n\text{HBr}$$
$$(n = 3 \text{ or } 4)$$

SUBMITTED BY KARL JOHN* AND THERALD MOELLER*
CHECKED BY RAYMOND E. McGLOTHLIN† AND R. A. ZINGARO†

The phosphonitrile bromides were first obtained by the ammonolysis of phosphorus(V) bromide.[1] Reported prepa-

* University of Illinois, Urbana, Ill.
† Agricultural and Mechanical College of Texas, College Station, Tex.

rations based upon reaction of phosphorus(V) bromide with ammonium bromide in *sym*-tetrachloroethane[2-4] give comparatively small yields. A comparable reaction involving phosphorus(III) bromide, bromine, and ammonium bromide in the same solvent gives somewhat better yields of trimer and tetramer.[5]

Procedure

Three hundred grams (3.06 mols) of dry, finely ground ammonium bromide and 300 g. (1.1 mols) of phosphorus-(III) bromide in 600 ml. of dry *sym*-tetrachloroethane are placed in a 1-l. round-bottomed flask equipped with a dropping funnel* containing 350 g. (2.19 mols) of bromine and an efficient condenser connected to a drying tube containing phosphorus(V) oxide.† To start the reaction, approximately one-half of the bromine is added, and the mixture is shaken thoroughly. The flask is then immersed up to its neck in an oil bath, the temperature of which is raised gradually over a period of 5 days to 142°. The bath is maintained at this temperature for an additional 5 days.‡ Evolution of hydrogen bromide, together with some bromine, begins at *ca.* 100°. To compensate for losses, the remaining bromine is added in small quantities as the reaction proceeds. At the end of the reaction period, the hot suspension is filtered by means of an exposed, coarse, sintered-glass funnel, to remove unreacted ammonium bromide. The dark brown filtrate is evaporated under a pressure of 2 mm. with the water-bath temperature beginning at 40°.§ The resulting residue is then digested with

* Concentrated sulfuric acid may be used as a stopcock lubricant.

† If smaller quantities of product are desired, the synthesis can be carried out on any fraction of the recommended scale. Periodic replacement of the drying agent is essential.

‡ The appearance of dark-brown solid $PNBr_2 \cdot PBr_n$ indicates that either the temperature was too low or the period of heating too short. A corresponding reduction in yield then results.

§ Bromine and hydrogen bromide are evolved at this temperature. It is necessary to raise the temperature finally to 80 to 90° for complete removal of the solvent.

800 ml. of anhydrous benzene for 12 hours by heating in an oil bath at 90°. The benzene layer is decanted from any remaining solid, and the extraction is repeated with a fresh 500-ml. portion of anhydrous benzene. The combined benzene extracts are evaporated to a dark semicrystalline mass which contains the trimer, the tetramer, and the oily higher polymeric homologs. The mixture is then heated in a sublimation apparatus at 160 to 180° and 0.25 to 0.50 mm. The trimer and tetramer sublime almost completely, but the higher homologs polymerize to a rubber.* The sublimate, which is commonly colored as a result of splashing, is resublimed to a white crystalline product containing about 8% of the tetramer. The yield is 119 to 132 g. (52.5 to 58.0%).

The trimer and tetramer are best separated by fractional crystallization from anhydrous† *n*-heptane or petroleum ether (b.p., 90 to 100°).‡ The mixture is dissolved in sufficient hot solvent to yield a nearly saturated solution. The solution is cooled slowly as long as the characteristic flat prismatic crystals of the trimer continue to form but not until the needle-like crystals of the tetramer form. The remaining mother liquor is then removed by decantation, and the procedure is repeated with the decantate until about 70 to 75% of the trimer is recovered. Further crystallization from more dilute solutions then yields the tetramer. Both trimer and tetramer are purified by recrystallization from the same solvent, using activated charcoal to remove traces of color. The total recovery of separated trimer and tetramer depends upon how far the fractionation is carried but should amount to 90 to 95% of the original trimer-tetramer mixture. *Anal.* Calcd. for $(PNBr_2)_3$ or $(PNBr_2)_4$: N, 6.84. Found: N, 6.87.

* Small but varying quantities of trimer and tetramer are occluded by the rubber. These can be removed by finely dividing the rubber and subliming *in vacuo* at 220°.

† Dried over sodium.

‡ These solvents dissolve only small quantities of the trimer and tetramer at room temperature and exhibit the largest differences in solvent power for trimer and tetramer of any solvents studied.

Properties

Pure trimeric and tetrameric phosphonitrile bromides melt at 192° and 202°, respectively. Both compounds dissolve in a variety of organic solvents, but the trimer is the more soluble. Thus, solubilities in anhydrous *n*-heptane and petroleum ether (b.p., 90 to 110°) at 25° are, respectively, trimer, 1.45 g. and 2.30 g., and tetramer, 0.15 g. and 0.27 g., each per 100 g. of solvent. The pure compounds hydrolyze slowly in contact with water or moist air. The infrared spectra are characterized by P–N stretching frequencies of 1175 cm.⁻¹ for the trimer and 1272 cm.⁻¹ for the tetramer.

References

1. A. BESSON: *Compt. rend.*, **114**, 1479 (1892).
2. W. GRIMME: dissertation, Münster (1926).
3. H. BODE: *Z. anorg. u. allgem. Chem.*, **252**, 113 (1943).
4. N. E. BEAN and R. A. SHAW: *Chem. and Ind. (London)*, **1960**, 1189.
5. K. JOHN and T. MOELLER: *J. Am. Chem. Soc.*, **82**, 2647 (1960).

24. PHOSPHORUS(V) CHLORIDE–BORON CHLORIDE COMPLEX

$$PCl_5 + BCl_3 \rightarrow PCl_5 \cdot BCl_3$$

SUBMITTED BY R. R. HOLMES*
CHECKED BY H. MAJEWSKI†

The phosphorus(V) chloride–boron chloride complex has been prepared by the chlorination of the phosphorus(III) bromide–boron bromide complex at room temperature,[1] by chlorinating an equimolar mixture of phosphorus(III)

* Carnegie Institute of Technology, Pittsburgh 13, Penn.
† Victor Chemical Works, Division of Stauffer Chemical Company, Chicago Heights, Ill.

chloride and boron chloride at $-78°$,[2] and by the reaction of phosphorus(V) chloride and boron chloride in the vapor phase or in carbon tetrachloride solution.[2] The last is the most convenient method, simply involving bubbling tank boron chloride through a carbon tetrachloride solution of phosphorus(V) chloride. It also has an advantage in that almost any desired amount of material may easily be prepared.

Procedure

A 250-ml. Erlenmeyer flask is fitted with a two-hole stopper containing an inlet tube extending nearly to the bottom. The other hole is fitted with a drying tube filled with Drierite to protect the contents from moisture and to allow excess boron chloride to escape. Freshly sublimed phosphorus(V) chloride (4.5 g.; 0.022 mol) in carbon tetrachloride (125 ml., dried with calcium hydride) is placed in the flask and boron chloride from a tank is bubbled through the solution. A white precipitate forms. The boron chloride bubbling is continued until the solution is saturated with the gas, as noted by the hydrolysis of excess boron chloride emerging through the drying tube. After most of the solvent is decanted, the white precipitate is filtered through a sintered-glass crucible in a filtering flask, the operation being carried out in a nitrogen-filled dry-box. Suction may be applied by means of a rubber bulb aspirator. The product is then washed with small portions of dry carbon tetrachloride, transferred to weighed ampuls, and dried by pumping off the remaining liquid which is caught in a liquid-nitrogen trap. The ampuls containing the powdery product are sealed under vacuum, reweighed, and stored until needed. The yield of product is 4.3 g. (62% of theory).

Alternatively, the filtering operation may be carried out in a nitrogen-flushed filtration apparatus, a positive nitrogen pressure being maintained above the sintered-glass filter.

Properties

The compound $PCl_5 \cdot BCl_3$ is a white solid, easily hydrolyzed by water, and insoluble in nonpolar solvents such as carbon tetrachloride and chloroform. It sublimes completely in a sealed tube at about 340°, the temperature of sublimation varying somewhat with the pressure developed in the tube. The vapor at 340° is yellow-green, indicating dissociation into chlorine, boron chloride, and phosphorus-(III) chloride. Conductance in liquid phosphorus(V) oxychloride[3] indicates an ionic structure, postulated to be $[PCl_4]^+[BCl_4]^-$.

References

1. J. TARIBLE: *Compt. rend.*, **116**, 1521 (1893).
2. R. R. HOLMES: *J. Inorg. & Nuclear Chem.*, **14**, 179 (1960).
3. W. L. GROENEVELD and A. P. ZUUR: *Rec. trav. chim.*, **72**, 617 (1953).

25. PHOSPHORUS(V) CHLORIDE–GALLIUM(III) CHLORIDE COMPLEX

$$2PCl_5 + Ga_2Cl_6 \rightarrow 2PCl_5 \cdot GaCl_3$$

SUBMITTED BY R. R. HOLMES*
CHECKED BY R. N. RAMSEY† AND JOHN D. CORBETT†

The phosphorus(V) chloride–gallium(III) chloride complex has been prepared[1] by a method analogous to that used for the preparation of the corresponding phosphorus(V) chloride–boron chloride complex (synthesis 24).

Procedure

Solutions of freshly sublimed phosphorus(V) chloride (1.44 g.; 0.00692 mol) in carbon tetrachloride (40 ml.) and

* Carnegie Institute of Technology, Pittsburgh, Pa.
† Iowa State University, Ames, Iowa.

gallium(III) chloride (1.22 g.; 0.00692 mol based on the formula $GaCl_3$) in carbon tetrachloride (35 ml.) are made up inside a nitrogen-flushed dry-box. The two solutions are then mixed slowly. A white crystalline precipitate forms. This is filtered (in the dry-box) through a sintered-glass crucible, washed with dry carbon tetrachloride, and transferred to ampuls. The ampuls are removed from the dry-box, the remaining solvent is pumped off, and the product is sealed under vacuum. The yield of product is about 2.5 g. (94% of theory).

Properties

Phosphorus(V) chloride–gallium(III) chloride is a moisture-sensitive white crystalline solid melting at 368 to 371°. It is insoluble in carbon tetrachloride and chloroform, reacts with acetone, and is immediately hydrolyzed by water. In comparison with the corresponding phosphorus(V) chloride–boron chloride complex, it is much more difficult to sublime. Indications[1] are that the structure is ionic, $[PCl_4]^+[GaCl_4]^-$.

Reference

1. R. R. Holmes: *J. Inorg. & Nuclear Chem.*, **14**, 179 (1960).

26. METHYLBROMOARSINES

$$3CH_3Br + 2As \xrightarrow{Cu} (CH_3)_2AsBr + CH_3AsBr_2$$

Submitted by Ludwig Maier*
Checked by William Jensen†

Dimethylbromoarsine, one of the first known organoarsenic compounds, may be prepared by distilling cacodyl

* Monsanto Research, S. A., Zurich, Switzerland.
† State University of Iowa, Iowa City, Iowa.

oxide–mercury(II) chloride with fum'ng hydrogen bromide[1] or by reducing cacodylic acid with sodium hypophosphite and hydrogen bromide.[2] Other methods may also be used.[3] Methyldibromoarsine is not described in the literature, but probably the same methods can be applied for its preparation as described for the preparation of methyldichloroarsine.[3] The recommended method for the preparation of methylbromoarsines involves the direct reaction of methyl bromide with arsenic at 370° in the presence of copper as a catalyst.[4]

Procedure

Caution! Both of the methylbromoarsines must be handled with the greatest care, and use of a very efficient hood is necessary. Contact must be avoided with either the liquid or the vapor. The vapor irritates the mucous membranes very severely.

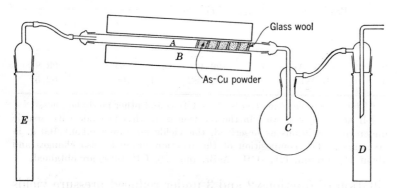

FIG. 9. Apparatus for the preparation of methylbromoarsines.

One hundred grams (1.334 mols) of commercial arsenic (crushed to pass a DIN 40 sieve) is mixed with 20 g. of copper powder.* The ground powders are packed loosely with glass wool into a Pyrex tube (A) (Fig. 9) 2.5 cm. in diameter and 70 cm. long; this tube has ground joints on

* Cuprum per electrolysem pulv., F. Merck A. G. Darmstadt.

both ends.   The reaction tube is heated in a combustion furnace (B) to 370° while a slow stream of hydrogen is passed through the charge for one hour.   Then one end of the tube is connected to a receiver (C) and a trap (D) kept at $-80°$, while the outlet tube leads to the hood.   The other end bears a short inlet tube which is connected to the methyl bromide container (E).

The methyl bromide vaporizes fast enough at room temperature to give a stream of about 45 to 48 g. per hour in the arrangement shown in the figure.   Over an interval of 10 hours the total yield is about 230 g. or 23 g./hour.   Altogether, 480 g. (5.05 mols) of methyl bromide is introduced, 100 g. of which is recovered in the trap D.   The reaction products are distilled through a column, yielding fractions in approximately the proportions shown in Table I.   Redis-

TABLE I

Products		B.p. at 717 mm., °C.	Weight	
			g.	Percentage†
1	forerun*	64–120	5.5	3.3
2	$(CH_3)_2AsBr$	126–131	54.5	33.8
3	CH_3AsBr_2	176–182	100	62.5

* The forerun contains traces of $As(CH_3)_3$ and other methylarsines.

† If no catalyst is used in the reaction of methyl bromide with arsenic under the conditions as described, the yields are lower (about 100 g. in 10 hours).   The composition of the reaction products also changes and about 1% forerun, 42% $(CH_3)_2AsBr$, and 57% CH_3AsBr_2 are obtained.

tillation of fractions 2 and 3 under reduced pressure yields the pure compounds $(CH_3)_2AsBr$, b.p. 51° at 42 mm., and CH_3AsBr_2, b.p. 89° at 41 mm.

Properties

Dimethylbromoarsine is a nearly colorless liquid which boils at 51° at 42 mm. or 128 to 130° at 720 mm.; d_4^{23} 1.9053; n_D^{20} 1.5713.   Methyldibromoarsine is an oily pale yellow liquid which boils at 89° at 41 mm. or 179 to 181° at 720 mm.; d_4^{23} 2.6588; n_D^{20} 1.6808. The compounds hydrolyze slowly in cold water and react with halogenated hydrocarbons to form the arsonium salts.

Notes

Other alkyl halo compounds of the group V elements may be prepared similarly:

1) The action of methyl chloride on powdered arsenic at 350 to 370° with copper as a catalyst gives a mixture of 80% CH_3AsCl_2 and 20% $(CH_3)_2AsCl$; methyl iodide reacts at 280° to produce the corresponding methyliodoarsines, and ethyl chloride gives a low yield of ethylchloroarsines.[4] Halides of unsaturated hydrocarbons, such as vinyl bromide and vinyl chloride, react at 400 to 440° with a mixture of arsenic, copper, and zinc to give vinyldihaloarsines, divinylhaloarsines, and arsenic trihalides.[4] At 500° bromobenzene reacts with arsenic in the presence of silver as a catalyst to yield phenyldibromoarsine.[4] 2) Methyl chloride reacts with red phosphorus in the presence of copper as a catalyst at 340 to 360° to give good yields of CH_3PCl_2, $(CH_3)_2PCl$, and $(CH_3)_3P$; other methylphosphines are formed in small quantities. Methyl bromide gives (at 350°) excellent yields of CH_3PBr_2 (97%) in this reaction; $(CH_3)_2PBr$ (2%) is also produced. Ethyl bromide yields about 95% $C_2H_5PBr_2$ and 4% $(C_2H_5)_2PBr$.[5] 3) Antimony reacts with methyl chloride at 360° in the presence of copper to form 10% $(CH_3)_2$-SbCl, 58% CH_3SbCl_2, and 32% $SbCl_3$, and with methyl bromide at 350° to yield 38% $(CH_3)_2SbBr$, 40% CH_3SbBr_2, and 22% $SbBr_3$.[4] 4) In the reaction of bismuth with methyl chloride, no methylbismuth chloride (methylchlorobismuthine) has been isolated. However, it is possible to isolate methylbismuth dibromide (methyldibromobismuthine) in low yield in the reaction of methyl bromide with bismuth at 250°.[4]

References

1. R. Bunsen: *Ann.*, **37**, 38 (1841).
2. W. Steinkopf and G. Schwen: *Ber.*, **54**, 1454 (1921).
3. E. Krause and A. von Grosse: "Die Chemie der metallorganischen Verbindungen," pp. 464–475, Bontraeger Berlin, 1937; photolithographed by Edwards Bros., Inc., Ann Arbor, Mich., 1943.
4. L. Maier, E. G. Rochow, and W. C. Fernelius: *J. Inorg. & Nuclear Chem.*, **16**, 213 (1961).
5. L. Maier: *Angew. Chem.*, **71**, 574 (1959).

CHAPTER VB

See also: Anhydrous metal chlorides, synthesis 45

27. VANADIUM(III) FLUORIDE

(Vanadium Trifluoride)

$$6NH_4HF_2 + V_2O_3 \xrightarrow{250°} 2(NH_4)_3VF_6 + 3H_2O$$
$$(NH_4)_3VF_6 \xrightarrow{500°} VF_3 + 3NH_3 + 3HF$$

SUBMITTED BY B. J. STURM* AND C. W. SHERIDAN*
CHECKED BY P. H. CRAYTON† AND R. N. VANCE, JR.‡

The product resulting from the evaporation of a hydro-fluoric acid solution of vanadium(III) oxide is the hydrate $VF_3 \cdot 3H_2O$.[1-3] It can be dehydrated by treatment with anhydrous hydrogen fluoride gas at 300°.[3,4] Anhydrous hydrogen fluoride similarly converts vanadium(III) oxide into anhydrous vanadium(III) fluoride by forming $VF_3 \cdot 3H_2O$ as an intermediate.[3,5-8] The procedure is regarded as a very difficult and mechanically complex operation,[4] as agitation is required to ensure complete reaction.[5] Hydrofluorination of vanadium(III) chloride[9-11] at 600° or of vanadium(II) chloride[11] at 700° gives vanadium(III) fluoride. Conversion of the chlorides entails a procedure involving many steps for the preparation and purification

* Oak Ridge National Laboratory, Oak Ridge, Tenn.
† Research and Development Division, The Carborundum Company, Niagara Falls, N.Y.
‡ Research Center, Hooker Chemical Company, Niagara Falls, N.Y.

of the starting material.[11]   Vanadium(III) fluoride, contaminated with tin, is produced by the reaction of vanadium metal with molten tin(II) fluoride.[11a]

Pure anhydrous vanadium(III) fluoride is more conveniently prepared by the thermal decomposition, in an inert atmosphere, of ammonium hexafluorovanadate(III), the latter being formed by the fusion of ammonium hydrogen fluoride with vanadium(III) oxide.   Long and Wilhelm[3] were unsuccessful in their efforts to prepare vanadium(III) fluoride by these reactions; their product became oxidized since it was not protected by an inert atmosphere.   Also, there is evidence that these investigators started with impure vanadium(III) oxide.   The procedure described below employs an inert atmosphere for the decomposition of the hexafluorovanadate.

A. PREPARATION OF
AMMONIUM HEXAFLUOROVANADATE(III)

Previously, ammonium hexafluorovanadate(III) has been obtained only from aqueous solution.[2,12,13]   Its preparation in molten ammonium hydrogen fluoride has the advantage that it yields a product which is anhydrous.   Aqueous preparations of ammonium hexafluorovanadate(III) tend to have sorbed moisture, which, during the decomposition, could through hydrolysis contaminate the vanadium(III) fluoride with oxide.

Procedure

One hundred and fifty grams (1 mol) of vanadium(III) oxide, either the commercial powder or that prepared by hydrogen reduction of vanadium(V) oxide,[3,14] is mixed with 684 g. (12 mols) of ammonium hydrogen fluoride.   The excess ammonium hydrogen fluoride serves to ensure complete reaction of the vanadium(III) oxide.   The mixture is heated in a graphite crucible of the approximate dimensions 5-in. o.d. × 6-in. height × ¼-in. thickness.   After it has become fluid at 100°, the material is stirred with a graphite rod (approx. $\frac{3}{8}$-in. o.d. × 10-in. length) which has a well drilled into it to accommodate a thermocouple.* (During the stirring process, gloves should be used for protection of the hands from the irritating fumes.) The temperature is slowly raised to 250° to hasten the evolution of water and excess ammonium hydrogen fluoride. This treatment leaves a green solid residue. This residue has the crystallographic properties reported for ammonium hexafluorovanadate(III).[13,15—18]

B. DECOMPOSITION OF AMMONIUM HEXAFLUOROVANADATE(III)

Procedure

The ammonium hexafluorovanadate(III) is thermally decomposed in a gas-tight cylindrical nickel container† made by welding a plate to close one end of a 6-in. length of standard 4-in. pipe. A gas-inlet tube of $\frac{1}{4}$-in. or slightly larger nickel tubing extends through the lid nearly to the bottom of the container. The lid also has an outlet of standard $\frac{1}{2}$-in. nickel pipe which is electrically heated to prevent condensation of the volatile decomposition products. During the decomposition an inert gas, nitrogen or helium, is passed through the reactor to drive off the vapors. A temperature of 500 to 600° is maintained until white fumes are no longer observed. The flow of inert gas is continued while cooling the product to room temperature. If the ammonium hexafluorovanadate(III) is not protected from

---

* During the fusion of ammonium hydrogen fluoride with pure vanadium(III) oxide the yellow fumes reported by Long and Wilhelm[3] were not observed. However, yellow fumes were obtained on heating the acid fluoride with vanadium(V) oxide. This indicates that their vanadium(III) oxide was contaminated with pentoxide. Vanadium(V) oxide probably is converted to the pentafluoride, which is reported to react with moist air to form yellow oxyfluorides.[10]

† The checkers found a graphite crucible to be a satisfactory container for the thermal decomposition of ammonium hexafluorovanadate(III).

air during the decomposition, it is oxidized to vanadium(V) oxide, presumably by the reaction:

$$4(NH_4)_3VF_6 + 11O_2 \rightarrow 2V_2O_5 + 6N_2 + 12H_2O + 24HF$$

When pure reactants are employed, the yield of vanadium-(III) fluoride is quantitative, as this procedure does not involve the formation of volatile vanadium compounds.

Analysis

The product is a fine gray-green powder which has the crystallographic properties reported for the trifluoride.[19,20] *Anal.* Calcd. for VF_3: V, 47.0; F, 53.0. Found: V, 47.0; F, 52.1. Fluorine is determined by a pyrohydrolytic procedure.[21] Vanadium is determined by permanganate titration of a sample dissolved in sulfuric acid.[22] Contamination of the product by nickel from the container is less than 0.05%, the limit of detection by spectroscopy.

Properties

Vanadium(III) fluoride is a yellow-green solid which is practically insoluble in all ordinary solvents.[10]

Melting Point. Previously reported to be above 800°,[10] the melting point of vanadium(III) fluoride proved to be even too high for measurement by thermal analysis in equipment useful to 1250°. When heated to 1250°, it did not even sinter, but remained a free-flowing powder. No allotropic modifications were indicated up to this temperature. The melting point was found by heating the compound to various higher temperatures with a Baker High-Temperature Furnace. To prevent oxidation or volatilization during heating the compound was sealed in platinum capsules ($\frac{1}{8}$-in. o.d. × 0.010-in. thickness × $1\frac{3}{4}$-in. length) with a helium atmosphere. Examination of the cooled product showed that melting had occurred in capsules heated to $1419 \pm 5°$, but not in those heated to $1392 \pm 5°$.

Accordingly, the melting point is represented as $1406 \pm 15°$. No decomposition took place during melting, as shown by analysis of the cooled material.

Optical Crystallographic Properties. As prepared by the thermal decomposition of ammonium hexafluorovanadate-(III), vanadium(III) fluoride has too fine a crystal size for the determination of optical properties with a polarizing microscope. Heating to 1350° in a platinum tube forms twinned crystals that are easily studied. According to Weaver,[23] these crystals are biaxial ($\nleftrightarrow$) with optic angle (2V) of 5 to 10°. The α- and γ-refractive indexes are, respectively, 1.536 and 1.544.

Chemical Properties. Vanadium(III) fluoride was found not to attack vanadium or nickel metal at temperatures up to 1250°. Published free-energy values[24] had indicated reduction to a hypothetical vanadium(II) fluoride under these conditions.

References

1. E. PETERSEN: *Chem. News*, **60**, 210 (1889).
2. E. PETERSEN: *J. prakt. Chem.*, [2], **40**, 44 (1889).
3. J. R. LONG and H. A. WILHELM: *A.E.C. Report* No. ISC-244, pp. 32–35 (1951).
4. B. WEAVER: "Electromagnetically Enriched Isotopes and Mass Spectrometry," pp. 82–83, Academic Press, New York, 1956.
5. T. S. MACKEY and K. O. JOHNSSON: *A.E.C. Report* No. Y-575 (1950): Unclassified version No. AECD-3171 (1950).
6. D. E. CARPENTER, C. P. JOHNSTON, H. P. HOUSE, and K. O. JOHNSSON: U.S. patent 2,743,171 (1956); cf. *C.A.*, **50**, 12416h (1956).
7. J. R. Long: *Iowa State College J. Sci.*, **27**, 213 (1953).
8. O. E. MYERS: *Wright Air Development Center Technical Report* 56-4, Part II, pp. 22–23 (1956); *ASTIA Document* No. AD131097 (1957).
9. G. BRAUER: "Handbuch der präparativen anorganischen Chemie," Vol. I, 2d ed., pp. 233, Ferdinand Enke Verlag, Stuttgart, Germany, 1960.
10. O. RUFF and H. LICKFETT: *Ber.*, **44**, 2539 (1911).
11. H. J. EMELÉUS and V. GUTMANN: *J. Chem. Soc.*, **1949**, 2979.
11a. B. J. STURM: "Preparation of Inorganic Fluorides," *Reactor Chemistry Division Annual Progress Report for Period Ending January 31, 1960*, *A.E.C. Report* No. ORNL-2931, pp. 186–187.
12. E. PETERSEN: *Ber.*, **21**, 3257 (1888).

13. L. Passerini and R. Pirani: *Gazz. chim. ital.*, **62**, 279 (1932).
14. F. E. Brown and F. A. Griffitts: Inorganic Syntheses, **4**, 80 (1953).
15. American Society for Testing Materials, *X-Ray Diffraction Data Card* No. 2-1136.
16. R. W. G. Wyckoff: "Crystal Structures," Vol. III, p. 23, Interscience Publishers, Inc., New York, 1953.
17. C. Hermann, O. Lohrmann, and H. Philipp, "Strukturbericht," Vol. II, p. 491, Akademische Verlagsgesellschaft, Leipzig, 1937.
18. H. Bode and E. Voss: *Z. anorg. u. allgem. Chem.*, **290**, 1 (1957).
19. K. H. Jack and V. Gutmann: *Acta Cryst.* **4**, 246 (1951).
20. American Society for Testing Materials, *X-Ray Diffraction Data Card* No. 6-0209.
21. C. D. Susano, J. C. White, and J. E. Lee: *A.E.C. Report* No. ORNL-1744 (1954).
22. W. W. Scott and N. H. Furman: "Standard Methods of Chemical Analysis," 5th ed., Vol. I, pp. 1037–1038, D. Van Nostrand and Co., Inc., Princeton, N.J., 1939.
23. C. F. Weaver: Oak Ridge National Laboratory, private communication, 1960.
24. A. Glassner: *A.E.C. Report* No. ANL-5750 (1957).

28. VANADIUM(III) SULFATE

$$V_2O_5 + 3H_2SO_4 + S \rightarrow V_2(SO_4)_3 + 3H_2O + SO_2$$

Submitted by Robert T. Claunch* and Mark M. Jones*
Checked by Wayne C. Wolsey†

Pure anhydrous vanadium(III) sulfate can be prepared by the reduction of vanadium(V) oxide dissolved in sulfuric acid with elemental sulfur as the reducing agent.[1,2] The procedure given below is an adaptation of this method.

Procedure

A 500-ml. three-necked, round-bottomed Pyrex flask is used as the reaction vessel. A glass or Teflon stirrer is inserted in the central opening and a water or air condenser

* Vanderbilt University, Nashville, Tenn.
† University of Kansas, Lawrence, Kan.

and a thermometer are inserted in the side openings. Thirty-six and four-tenths grams (0.2 mol) of pure vanadium(V) oxide is added to 9.6 g. (0.3 mol) of sulfur. Four hundred and fifty grams of concentrated sulfuric acid (95 to 98%) is then added and the mixture is stirred. The mixture is heated with a heating mantle to 170 to 200° and kept there with continuous stirring for 16 hours. The initial brown color of the slurry changes first to light blue and finally to yellow. This yellow powder is collected on a fritted-glass Büchner funnel and washed with 100 ml. of water. The unreacted sulfur is removed by suspending the material in 100 ml. of 50% ethanol, pouring 100 ml. of carbon disulfide into this, and stirring at room temperature for half an hour. If a large excess of sulfur is used in the reduction process, the excess collects in spheres which can be easily separated from the vanadium(III) sulfate. The yield is 75 g. (96%).

If the length of reaction time is extended from 16 to 30 hours, larger particles of vanadium(III) sulfate are obtained which are much easier to handle. If the length of reaction time is decreased to 12 hours, a very fine powder is obtained which is very difficult to use.

Analysis

Vanadium is determined by ignition of the sulfate in air to vanadium(V) oxide. Sulfate is determined by dissolving a sample of the vanadium(III) sulfate in hot 3 N HNO_3, adding about 1 ml. of 65% hydrazine hydrate to reduce any vanadates which may have formed, and precipitating the sulfate as barium sulfate. *Anal.* Calcd. for $V_2(SO_4)_3$: V, 26.12; SO_4^{--}, 73.88. Found: V, 26.13; SO_4^{--}, 74.16.

Properties

Vanadium(III) sulfate is a lemon-yellow powder, which is quite stable in air in contrast to most vanadium(III) compounds. However, upon exposure to moist air over a period of several weeks a green hydrate forms. Vanadium-(III) sulfate dissolves slowly in boiling water and very slowly in water at room temperature. It dissolves more readily in dilute and concentrated nitric acid. The compound is essentially insoluble in concentrated sulfuric acid. When heated in a vacuum at or slightly below 410°, it decomposes into vanadium(IV) oxide sulfate, $VOSO_4$, and sulfur dioxide.[2]

References

1. V. AUGER: *Compt. rend.*, **173**, 306 (1921).
2. F. RIVENG: *Bull. soc. chim. France*, **4**, 1697 (1937).

29. VANADIUM(II) SULFATE

$$V_2O_5 + SO_2 + H_2SO_4 \rightarrow 2VOSO_4 + H_2O$$
$$VOSO_4 + 2H^+ + 2e^- \rightarrow VSO_4 + H_2O$$

SUBMITTED BY MAKSYMILIAN KRANZ*
CHECKED BY DAVID E. GOLDBERG† AND AARON RIBNER†

Vanadium(II) sulfate can be prepared by reduction of vanadium(V) oxide in sulfuric acid solution either electrolytically or with sodium amalgam or with zinc, followed by evaporation of the solution *in vacuo* over phosphorus(V) oxide.[1-6] It also may be prepared by the electrolytic reduction of vanadium(IV) oxide sulfate, $VOSO_4$, which is the basis of this procedure.

Procedure

Eighteen grams (0.099 mol) of vanadium(V) oxide, 30 ml. of concentrated H_2SO_4, and 40 ml. of water are stirred and

* Institute of Applied Chemistry, A. Mickiewicz University, Poznan, Poland.
† Brooklyn College, Brooklyn, N.Y.

heated on a water bath for 20 minutes. Distilled water is added to dilute the solution to 375 ml. and sulfur dioxide is bubbled through the solution to reduce the vanadium(V) to vanadium(IV). The muddy suspension is changed into a deep blue solution of vanadium(IV) oxide sulfate, which must be further reduced electrolytically.

The sulfate solution is evaporated to one-fifth its original volume; then carbon dioxide is bubbled through to ensure

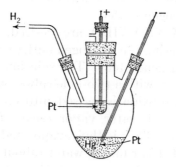

FIG. 10. Apparatus for the preparation of vanadium(II) sulfate solution.

complete removal of sulfur dioxide. Before reduction, the solution is diluted to one liter with boiled water saturated with carbon dioxide. Ten milliliters of this solution contains about 0.1 g. of vanadium(IV). The solution is titrated with potassium permanganate to determine the exact titer:

$$5VO^{++} + MnO_4^- + 8H^+ \rightarrow 5VO^{3+} + Mn^{++} + 4H_2O$$

A 100-ml. three-necked flask (Fig. 10) is used for the reduction. This arrangement, based on the work of Piccini,[1,2] ensures air-free conditions and gives a good yield. The solution is conveniently discharged from the vessel by the hydrogen generated in the cell after the reduction of the vanadium is complete. The anolyte (about 3 ml. of 2 N H_2SO_4) is placed in a vertical tube with a sintered-glass bottom. The anode is a 1-sq.-cm. sheet of platinum, and the cathode is mercury.

One hundred milliliters of vanadium oxide sulfate solution is placed in the flask, and the level of the solution is marked. The level must be maintained by the continual addition of distilled water saturated with carbon dioxide. A current of 2–2.5 amp. is applied with a voltage of 9 volts for approximately 3 hours. During electrolysis, the flask is cooled by water. The yield is equivalent to about 1 g. of vanadium in the form of a solution of $VSO_4·7H_2O$. The solution may be stored for several hours without oxidation by tightly closing the hydrogen outlet.

If crystals of $VSO_4·7H_2O$ are desired, the solution is removed by lowering the hydrogen outlet tube while hydrogen is still being generated. The solution is passed into a 200-ml. flask fitted with a two-hole rubber stopper with two tubes. Carbon dioxide is passed into one tube, and the carbon dioxide and water vapor escape from the other. The solution in the flask is thus evaporated to about 20 ml. The flask is cooled in running water (about 12°) for 5 days. After crystallization has occurred, the product is removed under a carbon dioxide funnel, washed with ethanol which has been distilled in a nitrogen atmosphere, and dried on filter paper. The product must be stored away from contact with air.

Properties

$VSO_4·7H_2O$ is a violet salt which it is extremely easy to oxidize. It forms mixed crystals with other salts of the type $MSO_4·7H_2O$ and is isomorphous with such salts.

References

1. A. Piccini: *Z. anorg. Chem.*, **19**, 204 (1899).
2. A. Piccini and L. Marino: *ibid.*, **32**, 55 (1902).
3. L. Marino: *ibid.*, **50**, 49 (1906).
4. T. F. Rutter: *ibid.*, **52**, 368 (1907).
5. T. F. Rutter: *Z. Elektrochem.*, **12**, 230 (1906).
6. J. Meyer and M. Aulich: *Z. anorg. u. allgem. Chem.*, **194**, 278 (1930).

30. VANADIUM(II) HYDROXIDE

$$VSO_4 + 2OH^- \rightarrow V(OH)_2 + SO_4^{--}$$

SUBMITTED BY MAKSYMILIAN KRANZ*
CHECKED BY DAVID E. GOLDBERG† AND AARON RIBNER†

Vanadium(II) hydroxide is among the most powerful reducing agents known in inorganic chemistry.[1] It is very unstable and extremely sensitive to atmospheric oxidation. In aqueous solution it is oxidized by water, unless some stabilizing substance such as thiocyanate or tellurate(IV) ion is present.[2] In this procedure the hydroxide is made from the corresponding sulfate (synthesis 29).

FIG. 11. Apparatus for the preparation of vanadium(II) hydroxide.

Procedure

Thirty milliliters of sodium hydroxide solution (0.02 g./ml.), 10 to 15 ml. of potassium thiocyanate‡ or potassium tellurate(IV),‡ and 70 ml. of distilled water are placed in a 500-ml. reaction flask (Fig. 11). The pH of this solution is about 10. The mixture is boiled for 30 minutes with the stopcock open to remove dissolved air. The heating is stopped and the stopcock closed simultaneously. When the temperature drops to 20°, 10 ml. of freshly reduced vanadium(II) sulfate solution, containing about 0.1 g. of vanadium(II), is added directly from the electrolytic cell

---

* Institute of Applied Chemistry, A. Mickiewicz University, Poznan, Poland.

† Brooklyn College, Brooklyn, N.Y.

‡ One mg./ml. of anion, i.e., 0.1674 g. of KSCN or 0.1442 g. of K_2TeO_3 per 100 ml. of distilled water, is required.

(synthesis 29). The precipitated vanadium(II) hydroxide is filtered and washed with freshly boiled distilled water or with water saturated with carbon dioxide under the CO_2-funnel shown in Fig. 12. The product is then dried in a vacuum desiccator. Analysis* is performed by permanganate titration. The conversion is essentially quantitative.

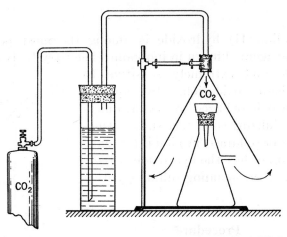

FIG. 12. Apparatus for filtration and washing of vanadium(II) hydroxide.

Immediate analysis of a product prepared under similar conditions but with no added thiocyanate or tellurate(IV) ion shows only about 80% vanadium(II), and analysis after 17 hours shows only 62% vanadium(II).

The quantity of stabilizing substance may be increased to provide greater protection from atmospheric oxidation. For example, with the use of 30 to 40 ml. of potassium thiocyanate or tellurate(IV) (or a mixture of the two) it is possible to obtain the hydroxide in a form which may be filtered in air and dried for 17 hours on the filter funnel without oxidation. The stabilized hydroxide will return to its original unstable form by treatment with oxidation-accelerating substances such as tetrachloroauric(III) acid [hydrogen tetrachloroaurate(III)], copper(II) sulfate, or palla-

* Before analysis, the stabilizing ions must be removed.

dium(II) chloride in quantities equal to those of the stabilizing ions.*

Properties

Vanadium(II) hydroxide is a grayish violet gelatinous substance. It absorbs oxygen from the air, even when dry, to form a greenish hydroxide of vanadium(III).

References

1. J. W. MELLOR: "A Comprehensive Treatise on Inorganic and Theoretical Chemistry," Vol. IX, p. 740, Longmans, Green & Co., London, 1929; Gmelin-Kraut, "Handbuch der anorganischen Chemie," Vol. III, Part 2, p. 74, Carl Winter's Universitätsbuchhandlung, Heidelberg, 1908.
2. M. KRANZ: *Przemysl Chem.*, **39**, 18 (1960).

31. CYCLOPENTADIENYL METAL CARBONYLS AND SOME DERIVATIVES

SUBMITTED BY R. B. KING†‡ AND F. G. A. STONE†
CHECKED BY WILLIAM L. JOLLY,§ GORDON AUSTIN,§ WILLIAM COVEY,§ DAVID RABINOVICH,§ HENRY STEINBERG,§ AND ROY TSUGAWA§

Cyclopentadienyl carbonyls of several transition metals have been reported during the last decade, and these compounds have been shown to undergo a variety of interesting reactions.[1] Two general methods have been used to prepare these materials: treatment of metal carbonyls with cyclopentadiene or cyclopentadienylsodium, and the reac-

* One mg./ml. of $AuCl_4^-$, Cu^{++}, or Pd^{++}, i.e., 0.1215 g. of $HAuCl_4·4H_2O$, 0.3928 g. of $CuSO_4·5H_2O$, or 0.2004 g. of $PdCl_2·2H_2O$ in 100 ml. of distilled water.

† Harvard University, Cambridge, Mass.

‡ Present address: Explosives Department, Experimental Station, E. I. du Pont de Nemours & Company, Wilmington, Del.

§ University of California, Berkeley, Calif.

tion between cyclopentadienyl metal derivatives and carbon monoxide under pressure. Procedures are described below for the preparation of cyclopentadienyl carbonyls of vanadium, chromium, molybdenum, iron, and cobalt. Syntheses of certain derivatives of some of the cyclopentadienyl metal carbonyls are also given. The preparations of cyclopentadienylvanadium tetracarbonyl, $C_5H_5V(CO)_4$, and cyclopentadienylcobalt dicarbonyl, $C_5H_5Co(CO)_2$, illustrate the reaction of the bis(cyclopentadienyl) metal derivatives with carbon monoxide. Cyclopentadienylmanganese tricarbonyl, $C_5H_5Mn(CO)_3$, can also be synthesized by an analogous procedure. The preparations of compounds containing the cyclopentadienylchromium tricarbonyl, cyclopentadienylmolybdenum tricarbonyl, and cyclopentadienyliron dicarbonyl groups illustrate preparations involving treatment of metal carbonyls with cyclopentadiene.

A. CYCLOPENTADIENYLVANADIUM TETRACARBONYL
[Tetracarbonyl(cyclopentadienyl)vanadium]

The only known syntheses of cyclopentadienylvanadium tetracarbonyl, $C_5H_5V(CO)_4$, are based on the reaction of bis(cyclopentadienyl)vanadium with carbon monoxide under pressure.[1] The procedure given below is based on this reaction but avoids isolation of pyrophoric bis-(cyclopentadienyl)vanadium by direct carbonylation of the solution obtained from vanadium(III) chloride and cyclopentadienylsodium.

For this synthesis anhydrous vanadium(III) chloride is required. This may be purchased,* or prepared either from vanadium(V) oxide via vanadium(IV) chloride[2] or by refluxing vanadium(V) oxide with excess hexachloropropene for several days and filtering the purple solid produced.

Procedure

A 1-l. three-necked flask is fitted with a nitrogen inlet, reflux condenser, and stirrer. After flushing the apparatus

* Anderson Chemical Co., Weston, Mich.

with nitrogen, 100 ml. of xylene (previously dried over sodium) and 11.5 g. (0.5 mol) of sodium metal are placed in the flask and the mixture is heated to the boiling point of the xylene. The molten sodium is stirred at the boiling point to produce sodium sand. After stopping the stirring, the sodium is allowed to cool to room temperature and the xylene is removed with a syringe. The sodium sand* thus obtained is washed once with about 100 ml. of tetrahydrofuran, freshly distilled from lithium aluminum hydride (lithium tetrahydroaluminate) to remove water and peroxides. After removing tetrahydrofuran with a syringe, a further 150 ml. of redistilled tetrahydrofuran is added to the sodium.

Meanwhile, cyclopentadiene is prepared from commercial dicyclopentadiene ($3a$,4,7,$7a$-tetrahydro-4,7-methanoindene) by heating it at the boiling point in a flask fitted with a Vigreux column with a distillation head and condenser. Monomeric cyclopentadiene distills over at about 42° as a colorless liquid, which should be used within one hour or kept at −78° until use.

A dropping funnel is attached to the flask containing the sodium and tetrahydrofuran, and 50 ml. (40 g.; 0.6 mol) of the freshly cracked cyclopentadiene in 150 ml. of tetrahydrofuran is placed in the funnel. This cyclopentadiene solution is added to the sodium sand over a period of about 30 minutes to 1 hour with stirring, and the stirring continued for about 1 to 2 hours until all of the sodium dissolves, giving a red solution of cyclopentadienylsodium. If some of the sodium fails to dissolve after a reasonable amount of time, more of the cyclopentadiene may be added and the stirring continued. If the tetrahydrofuran used as solvent has not been carefully purified, the cyclopentadienylsodium solution may be brown.†

* If commercial sodium dispersions are used in this preparation, the mineral oil in which they are shipped contaminates the final product.

† All manipulations are carried out under nitrogen. Cyclopentadienylsodium solutions are quite air-sensitive and the solids obtained on evaporating such solutions are pyrophoric.

The cyclopentadienyl sodium solution, obtained as just described, is treated with 25 g. (0.16 mol) of anhydrous vanadium(III) chloride.* An exothermic reaction occurs and the solution becomes a dark purple.

The next step of the synthesis, carbonylation of the resulting solution of bis(cyclopentadienyl)vanadium, is carried out in an autoclave capable of withstanding at least 5000 p.s.i., and preferably 10,000 p.s.i., and equipped with devices for heating and rocking, and preferably with attached temperature and pressure recorders. For the quantities of reactants given above, an autoclave equipped with a stainless-steel liner of 1-l. capacity is suitable.

After stirring the solution of bis(cyclopentadienyl)vanadium for 1 to 2 hours, it is loaded into the liner of the autoclave. In order to prevent oxidation of the solution during the transfer, both the flask containing the solution and the liner of the autoclave are kept under rapid streams of pre-purified nitrogen. When the vanadium solution has been added, the liner is closed, placed in the autoclave, and the latter closed and connected to the high-pressure system. The high-pressure apparatus is then flushed out once with 500 p.s.i. of c.p. carbon monoxide,† and then pressurized to 800 to 1000 p.s.i. of carbon monoxide. The apparatus is heated with rocking at 120 to 140° for 6 to 12 hours. After cooling to room temperature and venting the gases, the autoclave is opened and the dark solution transferred to a flask. Solvent is removed at 15 to 40 mm. (water aspirator). If the residue is still sticky, it may be dried at about 1-mm. pressure.

The resulting residue is then transferred to a sublimation apparatus (Fig. 13) and the product sublimed from the

---

* Vanadium(IV) chloride may be substituted here, but a correspondingly larger quantity of cyclopentadienylsodium must be used and the halide must be diluted with benzene to avoid too vigorous a reaction. For an autoclave of the size specified, however, no more than 400 ml. of solvent should be used. Vanadium(IV) chloride has the disadvantage of being very corrosive and unstable.

† *Caution!* Extremely poisonous gas.

residue at 80 to 100° at 0.1 mm. onto a water-cooled probe. The sublimation will probably have to be done in several portions and it will probably take 1.5 to 3 hours to sublime the product from each portion. The product appears (on

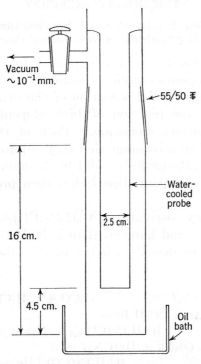

FIG. 13. Apparatus for the sublimation of $C_5H_5V(CO)_4$.

the probe) as bright orange crystals in yields of 15 to 25% (5.4 to 9.0 g.). The residues from the sublimations are very pyrophoric.

Properties

Cyclopentadienylvanadium tetracarbonyl is an orange crystalline solid. On prolonged exposure to air, especially when slightly impure, it darkens in color, finally becoming black. It is therefore best stored under a nitrogen atmos-

phere. It has been used to prepare many novel organo-
vanadium compounds.

B. CYCLOPENTADIENYLCHROMIUM TRICARBONYL DIMER AND BIS(CYCLOPENTADIENYLCHROMIUM TRICARBONYL)MERCURY

{Tricarbonyl(cyclopentadienyl)chromium Dimer and
Mercuribis[tricarbonyl(cyclopentadienyl)chromium]}

Two methods have been reported for the preparation of cyclopentadienylchromium tricarbonyl dimer,
$[C_5H_5Cr(CO)_3]_2$: partial oxidation of the hydride C_5H_5Cr-
$(CO)_3H$,[3] and the reaction of bis(cyclopentadienyl)chro-
mium with carbon monoxide.[4] Both of these methods
suffer from the disadvantage that they require the handling
of pyrophoric intermediates, and furthermore, the method
involving bis(cyclopentadienyl)chromium proceeds in low
yield.

The mercury derivative, $[C_5H_5Cr(CO)_3]_2Hg$, is more
easily prepared and handled than is $[C_5H_5Cr(CO)_3]_2$.

The syntheses described below involve the sequence of
reactions:

$$NaC_5H_5 + Cr(CO)_6 \xrightarrow{\text{``diglyme''}} 3CO + C_5H_5Cr(CO)_3Na \quad (1)$$
$$2C_5H_5Cr(CO)_3Na + 2C_7H_7Br \rightarrow$$
$$[C_5H_5Cr(CO)_3]_2 + 2NaBr + C_{14}H_{14} \quad (2a)$$
$$\text{or} \quad 2C_5H_5Cr(CO)_3Na + Hg(CN)_2 \rightarrow$$
$$[C_5H_5Cr(CO)_3]_2Hg + 2NaCN \quad (2b)$$

Procedure

Although the chromium hexacarbonyl necessary for this
preparation may be obtained by the method described in an
earlier synthesis,[5] several improved procedures have been
developed recently.[1c] Of these, the carbonylation of a mixture of chromium(III) acetylacetonate [2,4-pentanedionato-
chromium(III)], magnesium, and pyridine in the presence
of catalytic quantities of iodine,[6] or the carbonylation of a
mixture of chromium(III) chloride, aluminum chloride,

aluminum powder, and benzene,[7] are the most convenient and economical.

Tropylium bromide (cycloheptatrienocarbonium bromide), C_7H_7Br, required for reaction (2a) above may be prepared by bromination of cycloheptatriene* in carbon tetrachloride, followed by removal of the carbon tetrachloride and heating the residue *in vacuo* (60° at 20 mm.) for several days.[8] The product so obtained is washed with tetrahydrofuran. Recrystallization is unnecessary. Tropylium bromide is deliquescent and must be stored in a dry atmosphere. Allyl chloride or bromide may be substituted for tropylium bromide in reaction (2a).

A 500-ml. three-necked flask is fitted with a nitrogen inlet, reflux condenser, and stirrer. Unless otherwise indicated, the reactions are carried out under nitrogen. After flushing out the apparatus with nitrogen, 1.4 g. (0.06 mol) of sodium metal and 50 ml. of the dimethyl ether of diethylene glycol ("diglyme," Ansul Ether 141)† are placed in the flask, and the sodium is converted to sodium sand by the procedure described above for the preparation of cyclopentadienylvanadium tetracarbonyl. It will be noted, however, that the use of xylene is unnecessary since diglyme has a boiling point considerably above the melting point of sodium. Commercial 50% sodium dispersion in mineral oil may also be used in this preparation.

The sodium sand is treated with excess of freshly cracked cyclopentadiene (see preparation of cyclopentadienylvanadium tetracarbonyl for details) to prepare a red solution of cyclopentadienylsodium. To the resulting solution is added 8.8 g. (0.04 mol) of solid chromium hexacarbonyl, and the mixture is then refluxed with stirring until no unreacted chromium hexacarbonyl, or very little, remains in the reflux condenser (3 to 6 hours). The resulting yellow solution of

* Available from the Shell Chemical Co.

† The commercial product should be redistilled over lithium aluminum hydride. Tetrahydrofuran cannot be used here because its boiling point is too low.

the sodium compound, $C_5H_5Cr(CO)_3Na$, is allowed to cool to room temperature.

If cyclopentadienylchromium tricarbonyl dimer is desired [reaction (2*a*)], the resulting solution is treated with 10.2 g. (0.06 mol) of tropylium bromide or an equivalent quantity of an allyl halide. The reaction is exothermic, and the mixture becomes dark brown. When the solution has cooled to room temperature (about 30 minutes), 10 ml. of methanol followed by 200 ml. of water is added, precipitating out cyclopentadienylchromium tricarbonyl dimer, ditropyl (bicycloheptatrienyl), and some brown decomposition products. After filtration, the ditropyl is washed out with 250 ml. of pentane in several portions and may be recovered by evaporation of the pentane washings followed by sublimation (50° at 0.1 mm.). The residue from the pentane washings is sublimed at 100 to 120° at 0.1 mm. (Fig. 13) to give the product, a deep green sublimate. The residue from the sublimation is very pyrophoric and care must be taken that absolutely none of this residue is transferred mechanically to the sublimation probe. If this occurs, the product will be pyrophoric and will inflame spontaneously upon exposure of the probe to air. Although cyclopentadienylchromium tricarbonyl dimer is not especially air-sensitive, the product from this preparation is best handled under nitrogen because of its potentially pyrophoric character. In a typical experiment 3.0 g. (37% yield) of cyclopentadienylchromium tricarbonyl dimer and a corresponding amount of ditropyl are obtained.

If the mercury derivative, $[C_5H_5Cr(CO)_3]_2Hg$, is desired [reaction (2*b*)], the diglyme solution of $C_5H_5Cr(CO)_3Na$ is poured into 200 ml. of an aqueous solution of 20 g. (0.08 mol) of mercury(II) cyanide, a voluminous yellow precipitate of the mercury derivative forming. After about 30 minutes, the precipitate is filtered by suction, washed with two 300-ml. portions of water, and sucked dry. The yield of crude material is nearly quantitative.

In order to obtain a more nearly pure, more crystalline product, the crude material is dissolved in about 500 ml. of boiling acetone.   The deep yellow solutions of the mercury compound seem to be fairly stable to air oxidation and an inert atmosphere is not necessary at this point.   The mixture is filtered and the product crystallized by addition of pentane and by evaporation with the use of a water aspirator.   The stable yellow crystalline solid is obtained in about 40% yield.

Properties

Cyclopentadienylchromium tricarbonyl dimer is a deep green crystalline solid, sparingly soluble in organic solvents to give yellow or green solutions, depending on the concentration.   The solid sublimes at 100 to 120° at 0.1 mm.   The mercury derivative, $[C_5H_5Cr(CO)_3]_2Hg$, is a yellow crystalline solid, which is fairly so'uble in organic solvents.   For a compound which must contain a mercury-chromium bond, it is remarkably stable thermally.   It sublimes at 130° at 0.1 mm. with only slight decomposition.   Unlike many metal-metal bonds, such as that in manganese carbonyl, the mercury-chromium bond is even stable to 1% sodium amalgam in tetrahydrofuran at 25°, none of the sodium salt, $C_5H_5Cr(CO)_3Na$, being formed.   The mercury compound is considerably more stable to oxidation than cyclopentadienylchromium tricarbonyl dimer.

C. CYCLOPENTADIENYLMOLYBDENUM TRICARBONYL DIMER AND CYCLOPENTADIENYLMOLYBDENUM TRICARBONYL HYDRIDE

{Tricarbonyl(cyclopentadienyl)molybdenum Dimer and Hydrogen tricarbonyl(cyclopentadienyl)molybdate(-I)}

$$NaC_5H_5 + Mo(CO)_6 \xrightarrow{\text{tetrahydrofuran}} C_5H_5Mo(CO)_3Na + 3CO$$

$$C_5H_5Mo(CO)_3Na + CH_3COOH \rightarrow$$
$$CH_3COONa + C_5H_5Mo(CO)_3H$$

$$4C_5H_5Mo(CO)_3H + O_2 \xrightarrow{\text{tetrahydrofuran}} 2[C_5H_5Mo(CO)_3]_2 + 2H_2O$$

Cyclopentadienylmolybdenum tricarbonyl dimer has been prepared by oxidation of the hydride $C_5H_5Mo(CO)_3H$

by air in ethereal solution.[9]   The procedure given below is based on this reaction but avoids the isolation of the intermediate hydride.   The preparation of this hydride is also described.

Procedure*

The synthesis is carried out in a 500-ml. three-necked flask equipped with a nitrogen inlet, reflux condenser, and stirrer.   A solution of cyclopentadienylsodium is prepared under nitrogen, as described under Procedure A, from 2.8 g. (0.12 mol) of sodium sand (or an equivalent quantity of commercial sodium dispersion in mineral oil) in about 125 ml. of redistilled tetrahydrofuran and about 13 ml. (about 0.16 mol) of freshly cracked cyclopentadiene.   This solution is treated with 26.4 g. (0.1 mol) of molybdenum hexacarbonyl and the mixture is refluxed at the boiling point for 10 to 16 hours with stirring, producing a yellow to yellow-brown   solution of the sodium compound, $C_5H_5Mo(CO)_3Na$.   Heating should be kept to the minimum necessary to maintain the mixture at the boiling point and at the same time prevent excessive loss of solvent. However, the salt $C_5H_5Mo(CO)_3Na$ is sufficiently stable so that even if complete loss of solvent should occur during this heating period, some product would still be obtained.

After cooling the $C_5H_5Mo(CO)_3Na$ solution to room temperature and replacing any solvent lost by evaporation, excess (2 to 4 times the stoichiometric amount) of glacial acetic acid is added.   If the pure hydride is desired, the solvent is removed in the vacuum of a water aspirator after about an hour of stirring and a residue colored purple-red from traces of cyclopentadienylmolybdenum tricarbonyl remains.   Nitrogen is admitted to the evacuated flask and the residue is transferred to a sublimation apparatus (Fig. 13) under nitrogen.   The sublimation onto an ice-cooled

---

* The molybdenum hexacarbonyl required for this preparation may be purchased from Climax Molybdenum Co.

probe is carried out at 50 to 70° at 0.1 mm., yielding air-sensitive yellow crystals of the hydride, $C_5H_5Mo(CO)_3H$,* which may be removed and stored under nitrogen. The residues from such sublimations may be pyrophoric.

If the dimeric cyclopentadienylmolybdenum tricarbonyl is desired, the tetrahydrofuran solution of $C_5H_5Mo(CO)_3H$, obtained from the sodium compound and glacial acetic acid, is treated with a rapid stream of air for about 5 hours. The mixture becomes dark red immediately, and considerable solvent loss occurs during this process. After the aeration treatment is complete, the remaining solvent is removed with a water aspirator and the product extracted from the residue with several hundred milliliters of hot benzene. The product is not especially air-sensitive, and the extractions with hot benzene may be carried out in air. As long as the extracts are dark red, worth-while product is being obtained. The combined benzene extracts are filtered, and the filtrate is evaporated at aspirator pressure, leaving about 12 g. (50% yield) of red-violet crystals of the dimer, $[C_5H_5Mo(CO)_3]_2$. Although this material is sufficiently pure for preparative purposes, further purification may be carried out if desired, but with considerable loss, by sublimation at 150 to 160° at 0.1 mm. or by recrystallization from mixtures of pentane and dichloromethane.

Properties

Cyclopentadienylmolybdenum tricarbonyl hydride is a yellow crystalline solid subliming easily at 50° at 0.1 mm. It is quite air-sensitive, darkening noticeably immediately on exposure to air, and therefore it should always be handled and stored under nitrogen.

Cyclopentadienylmolybdenum tricarbonyl dimer is a red-violet crystalline solid subliming with difficulty at 150° at 0.1 mm. with fairly extensive decomposition. It is spar-

* See also synthesis 38 for details for the preparation of this compound.

ingly soluble in pentane but more soluble in polar organic solvents. Unlike the hydride, it is not particularly air-sensitive and may, if pure, be stored in air. However, solutions or impure material are oxidized gradually in air.

D. CYCLOPENTADIENYLIRON DICARBONYL DIMER AND CYCLOPENTADIENYLIRON DICARBONYL IODIDE

{Dicarbonyl(cyclopentadienyl)iron Dimer and
Dicarbonyl(cyclopentadienyl)iron Iodide}

$$2Fe(CO)_5 + 2C_5H_6 \rightarrow 2[H] + [C_5H_5Fe(CO)_2]_2 + 6CO$$
$$[C_5H_5Fe(CO)_2]_2 + I_2 \rightarrow 2C_5H_5Fe(CO)_2I$$

The only practical preparations of cyclopentadienyliron dicarbonyl dimer involve reactions of iron pentacarbonyl with either cyclopentadiene[10] or its dimer[11] at elevated temperatures. Although the use of monomeric cyclopentadiene is reported to give a higher yield and possibly a purer product, use of an autoclave is required because of the low boiling point of cyclopentadiene if a reasonable amount of product is to be prepared. For this reason the reaction between iron pentacarbonyl and dicyclopentadiene may well be more convenient since it can be carried out in an open system. The preparation described below involves dicyclopentadiene.

Procedure

The synthesis of the dimer is carried out in a 2-l. three-necked flask equipped with a nitrogen inlet, reflux condenser, and thermometer well. The reaction is conducted under nitrogen. During the heating period the temperature should never be allowed to exceed 140°. If this occurs, extensive decomposition will result and little or no product will be obtained.

The flask is charged with a mixture of 1 kg. of technical dicyclopentadiene and 150 ml. (*ca.* 215 g.; 1.1 mols) of iron

pentacarbonyl.* The mixture is heated at 130 to 140°†
until yellow vapors of iron pentacarbonyl are no longer
observed. This process takes about 8 hours. The deep
red mixture is allowed to cool to room temperature, preferably over a period of several hours, during which time red-
purple crystals of the product separate. The crystals are
filtered by suction and washed with several portions of
pentane to remove excess dicyclopentadiene. In this manner about 76 g. (38% yield) of red-violet crystals are
obtained. The product will still contain traces of dicyclopentadiene, as evidenced by its odor. Although the product is now satisfactory for preparative purposes, it may, if
desired, be purified either by recrystallization from a
pentane-dichloromethane mixture or by sublimation in
small portions at 110° at 0.1 mm. Significant loss of compound, however, occurs during purification.

If several preparations of cyclopentadienyliron dicarbonyl dimer are contemplated, it is desirable to retain the
dicyclopentadiene filtrate (but not the pentane washings);
the filtrate should be kept under nitrogen, and about 50 or
100 ml. of fresh dicyclopentadiene should be added for the
next preparation. Besides being more economical in terms
of dicyclopentadiene consumed, this technique may raise
the yield of product from 40 to 60–70%.

In order to convert cyclopentadienyliron dicarbonyl
dimer to cyclopentadienyliron dicarbonyl iodide, it is
treated with iodine in chloroform.[9]

A mixture of 50 g. (0.141 mol) of cyclopentadienyliron
dicarbonyl dimer, 50 g. (0.197 mol) of iodine, and 250 ml. of
chloroform is refluxed in a 500-ml. flask for about 30 minutes, an inert atmosphere being unnecessary. After cooling
to room temperature, the mixture is washed in several portions in a separatory funnel with a solution of 100 g. of

---

* Iron pentacarbonyl is commercially available (Antara Chemicals) and
inexpensive. It is quite toxic and should be handled in a hood.

† The checkers found it necessary to employ a temperature of 140 to
150°; no product was obtained at 130 to 140°.

sodium thiosulfate 5-hydrate in 400 ml. of water. The black chloroform layer is separated from the aqueous layer and filtered, and the filtrate is evaporated to dryness with the use of a water aspirator, to give black crystals of $C_5H_5Fe(CO)_2I$. The crystals are washed on a filter with 150 ml. of pentane in several portions and are sucked dry, giving 61 g. (65% yield) of the product.

Properties

Cyclopentadienyliron dicarbonyl dimer is a red-violet crystalline solid, sparingly soluble in pentane, but more soluble in polar organic solvents. It is fairly air-stable in the solid state, although solutions are slowly oxidized to iron(III) oxide. It may be sublimed at 110° at 0.1 mm., but extensive decomposition usually occurs. It reacts with dilute sodium amalgam to produce the sodium derivative, $C_5H_5Fe(CO)_2Na$, which may be used to prepare a variety of derivatives.

Cyclopentadienyliron dicarbonyl iodide is a black crystalline solid, which resembles cyclopentadienyliron dicarbonyl dimer in its solubility and air stability. It sublimes at about 90° at 0.1 mm. It may be used to prepare a variety of organoiron compounds.[1]

E. CYCLOPENTADIENYLCOBALT DICARBONYL

[Dicarbonyl(cyclopentadienyl)cobalt]

Two general methods have been used for the preparation of cyclopentadienylcobalt dicarbonyl: the reaction between dicobalt octacarbonyl and cyclopentadiene[12] and the reaction of bis(cyclopentadienyl)cobalt with carbon monoxide at elevated temperatures and pressures.[13] The method given here is a modification of the second method, and as in the preparation of cyclopentadienylvanadium tetracarbonyl described above, avoids isolation of the intermediate pyrophoric bis(cyclopentadienyl)metal derivative.

Procedure

The anhydrous cobalt(II) chloride required for this preparation is conveniently prepared by heating reagent-grade cobalt(II) chloride 6-hydrate at 160° or above at a pressure of 5 mm. or less until the pink salt has turned blue. The water may be collected in a trap cooled in a −78° bath in order to protect the pump. To prevent clogging of the system, it may be necessary to remove the water from time to time.

Preparation of the solution of bis(cyclopentadienyl)cobalt is best carried out in a 2-l. three-necked flask equipped with a nitrogen inlet, reflux condenser, stirrer, and dropping funnel. A solution of cyclopentadienylsodium in 1 l. of redistilled tetrahydrofuran is prepared from 40 g. (1.74 mols) of sodium metal* and about 200 ml. (160 g.; 2.4 mols) of freshly cracked cyclopentadiene. This solution is then treated with 110 g. (0.85 mol) of anhydrous cobalt(II) chloride, and the mixture is stirred for at least 2 hours at room temperature.

The stirrer is replaced with a stopper in order to prevent possible oxidation of the bis(cyclopentadienyl)cobalt, and solvent is removed by means of an aspirator, leaving a sticky black residue. To avoid oxidation, nitrogen is admitted to the flask.

Meanwhile, approximately 300 ml. of thiophene-free benzene is deaerated by bubbling prepurified nitrogen vigorously through the solvent for several minutes. The bis(cyclopentadienyl)cobalt is extracted with this benzene and the deep purple extracts are poured under nitrogen into the liner of the 1-l. autoclave, the techniques being similar to those described for the preparation of cyclopentadienylvanadium tetracarbonyl. The liner is c'osed immediately and placed in the autoclave, and the autoclave is closed and connected to the high-pressure system. After being flushed

* Commercially available 50% dispersion in mineral oil, or sodium sand prepared as described in earlier procedures.

out once with hydrogen, nitrogen, or carbon monoxide under at least 800 p.s.i., or several times with gas under a lower pressure, the autoclave is pressurized with at least 2250 p.s.i. of carbon monoxide. The autoclave is heated with rocking at 130° for about 10 hours; considerable carbon monoxide absorption occurs initially. After the reaction is over, the autoclave is cooled below 50°, the excess carbon monoxide is vented and the autoclave is opened, preferably after being flushed with an inert gas.

The dark solution in the autoclave is removed and filtered with suction. The autoclave is rinsed and the residues are washed with at least an additional 200 ml. of benzene. The filtrate is then distilled through a Vigreux column at reduced pressure. Benzene is removed first at such a pressure as to give a pot temperature of 35 to 45°. The benzene distills over slightly red in color due to the presence of traces of the product. The product is then distilled at 37 to 38.5° at 2 mm. to give 39 g. (25% yield) of cyclopentadienylcobalt dicarbonyl as a deep red liquid. The product is best stored under nitrogen in a refrigerator.

Properties

Cyclopentadienylcobalt dicarbonyl is a deep red liquid, easily miscible with the usual organic solvents. It is somewhat air-sensitive and is best stored under nitrogen. It undergoes a variety of interesting reactions.[1,14]

References

1. For recent review articles see (a) E. O. FISCHER and H. P. FRITZ, "Advances in Inorganic Chemistry and Radiochemistry," H. J. Emeléus and A. G. Sharpe (eds.), Vol. 1, p. 55, Academic Press Inc., New York, 1959; (b) G. WILKINSON and F. A. COTTON, "Progress in Inorganic Chemistry," F. A. Cotton (ed.), Vol. 1, p. 1., Interscience Publishers, Inc., New York, 1959; (c) J. CHATT, P. L. PAUSON, and L. M. VENANZI, "Organometallic Chemistry," H. Zeiss (ed.), Am. Chem. Soc. Monograph, p. 468, Reinhold Publishing Corporation, New York, 1960; (d) P. L. PAUSON, *ibid.*, p. 346.

2. R. C. Young and M. E. Smith: Inorganic Syntheses, **4**, 128 (1953).
3. E. O. Fischer, W. Hafner, and H. O. Stahl: *Z. anorg. Chem.*, **282**, 47 (1955).
4. E. O. Fischer and W. Hafner: *Z. Naturforsch.*, **10b**, 140 (1955).
5. B. B. Owen, J. English, Jr., H. G. Cassidy, and C. V. Dundon: Inorganic Syntheses, **3**, 156 (1950).
6. G. Natta, R. Ercoli, F. Calderazzo, and A. Rabizzoni: *J. Am. Chem. Soc.*, **79**, 3611 (1957).
7. E. O. Fischer, W. Hafner, and K. Öfele: *Ber.*, **92**, 3050 (1959).
8. W. von E. Doering and L. H. Knox: *J. Am. Chem. Soc.*, **79**, 352 (1957).
9. T. S. Piper and G. Wilkinson: *J. Inorg. & Nuclear Chem.*, **3**, 104 (1956).
10. B. F. Hallam and P. L. Pauson: *J. Chem. Soc.*, **1956**, 3030.
11. B. F. Hallam, O. S. Mills, and P. L. Pauson: *J. Inorg. & Nuclear Chem.*, **1**, 313 (1955).
12. T. S. Piper, F. A. Cotton, and G. Wilkinson: *ibid.*, **1**, 165 (1955).
13. E. O. Fischer and R. Jira: *Z. Naturforsch.*, **10b**, 354 (1955).
14. R. B. King, P. M. Treichel, and F. G. A. Stone: *J. Am. Chem. Soc.*, **83**, 3600 (1961).

CHAPTER VIA

32. SULFUR(S^{35})

SUBMITTED BY C. BRISKE,* N. H. HARTSHORNE,* AND D. R. STRANKS†
CHECKED BY FLOYD B. BAKER‡

Sulfur-35 is the only long-lived radioactive isotope of
sulfur and it may be produced by the direct neutron irradiation of elemental sulfur: $S^{34}(n,\gamma)S^{35}$. However, the specific activity attained is quite low even in high-neutron
fluxes. It is preferable to irradiate potassium chloride and
take advantage of the reaction: $Cl^{35}(n,p)S^{35}$. Four weeks'
irradiation of ten grams of potassium chloride in a thermal-
neutron flux of 10^{12} neutrons cm.$^{-2}$ sec.$^{-1}$ yields about
5 millicuries of S^{35}, which when dissolved in water is isolable
as "carrier-free" sulfate ion. Nevertheless, the isotopes
Cl^{38}, P^{32}, K^{42}, and Na^{24} are concurrently produced in the
neutron irradiation of potassium chloride, and a chemical

* School of Chemistry, University of Leeds, Leeds, England.
† University of Melbourne, Victoria, Australia.
‡ Los Alamos Scientific Laboratory, Los Alamos, N.M.

separation, based on the precipitation of $MgNH_4PO_4$ in the presence of a "hold-back" sulfate carrier, is necessary. This separation has been performed on the "carrier-free" sodium sulfate(S^{35}) solutions* available commercially at relatively low cost. The following preparation employs such a solution, since for the S^{35} activities normally required (e.g., millicuries) an individual chemical separation of an irradiated potassium chloride sample is uneconomic.

Procedure

A. SODIUM SULFIDE(S^{35})

$$Na_2S^{35}O_4 + 4H_2 \rightarrow Na_2S^{35} + 4H_2O$$

This preparation should be conducted in a well-ventilated fume hood. Analytical reagent-grade anhydrous sodium sulfate (0.500 g.; 0.0035 mol) is heated to constant weight in a platinum combustion boat whose surface area should be as large as possible. The desired quantity of sodium sulfate(S^{35}) "carrier-free" solution is added dropwise to the solid sodium sulfate and the contents of the boat are dried slowly under an infrared lamp. The boat is placed in a silica tube through which is passed a stream of oxygen-free hydrogen previously dried by passage through a calcium chloride tube. The hydrogen gas is led out through a sintered-glass bubbler charged with dilute potassium hydroxide solution (to trap sulfur compounds) and then through a small aluminum jet. The hydrogen is passed for about five minutes to displace air in the apparatus, the hydrogen is then ignited at the exit jet, and the platinum boat is slowly heated to a dull red heat by means of an efficient fish-tail Bunsen burner. For best results all the sodium sulfate sample should be molten during the reduction process. (In the final stages a slight darkening of the contents of the boat

* These solutions usually contain about 10 micrograms of sodium sulfate per millicurie of S^{35}.

may be observed.)   After two and a half hours, the heating is stopped, and after cooling in a desiccator, the boat is weighed.   The mass of the residue should correspond to within 3% of the theoretical yield of sodium sulfide (0.258 g.). If necessary, an additional heating period of thirty minutes is permissible but prolonged heating is inadvisable as losses of product may result.

B. SULFUR(S^{35})

$$Na_2S^{35} + I_2 \rightarrow S^{35} + 2NaI$$

The sodium sulfide(S^{35}) is quantitatively transferred with the minimum of cold distilled water to a 15-ml. centrifuge tube.   The tube is placed in a rack within a hot-water bath and a saturated solution of iodine in 10% potassium iodide is added dropwise.   After a yellow suspension forms, the iodine is cautiously added until one drop causes the yellow suspension to turn white.   The white solid is coagulated by standing for five minutes in the hot water bath and is then centrifuged.*   The sulfur precipitate is washed first with 0.01 M potassium iodide solution (three times) and then with distilled water (normally at least six times) until the washings are completely free from iodide.   After the washed sulfur is nearly dry in the boiling water bath, it is transferred to a vacuum desiccator and dried for 24 hours.†

The chemical and isotopic yields, based on the conversion of sodium sulfate to sulfur, are 92%.   Usually 2 to 3% of unreduced sulfate is recoverable.   The remaining losses of about 5% are mainly due to losses of colloidal sulfur and of hydrogen sulfide from the solid sodium sulfide.

The synthesis may be conducted with larger or smaller amounts of sodium sulfate provided a relatively large surface of molten sulfate is presented to the hydrogen stream.

---

* The supernatant liquid will contain any unreduced sulfate, which may be recovered as barium sulfate.

† If the active sulfur is to be employed in different allotropic forms, it should be first annealed in an oven at 90 to 95° for two days.

The synthesis is not limited by the amount of S^{35} employed. With an initial activity of 10 millicuries of $S^{35}O_4^{--}$, the final specific activity of sulfur will be about 100 millicuries per gram for the quantities specified above.

Properties

Isotopic. Sulfur-35 emits β-particles of 0.167 M.e.v. maximum energy and has a half-life of 87.1 days. It is readily assayed as a solid with a thin-mica-end-window Geiger counter.

Chemical. In addition to its intrinsic interest, sulfur serves as a starting point for the synthesis of many labeled molecules. Digestion of sulfur in aqueous sulfites yields thiosulfates, which when heated with iodine lead to tetrathionates and trithionates. Digestion of sulfur in alcoholic cyanide solutions yields thiocyanates, thence thiocyanogen and thiourea with its derivatives and coordination complexes. Oxidation of sulfur to sulfur dioxide is a potential route to labeled sulfamic acid and its derivatives and to labeled sulfuryl chloride. The intermediate sodium sulfide readily yields hydrogen sulfide and metallic sulfides.

33. SULFUR(IV) FLUORIDE

(Sulfur Tetrafluoride)

$$3SCl_2 + 4NaF \rightarrow SF_4 + S_2Cl_2 + 4NaCl$$

Submitted by F. S. Fawcett* and C. W. Tullock*
Checked by Claude I. Merrill†

Sulfur(IV) fluoride has been prepared by fluorination of elemental sulfur with cobalt(III) fluoride[1] or with elemental

* E. I. du Pont de Nemours & Company, Wilmington, Del. Contribution No. 578 from the Central Research Department, Experimental Station.

† University of Washington, Seattle, Wash.

fluorine[2] and by the reaction of iodine(V) fluoride with sulfur(I) bromide.[3] The present procedure is based on a synthesis recently reported by Tullock.[4]

Procedure

Caution. *Sulfur(IV) fluoride, sulfur chlorides, and sodium fluoride are toxic chemicals. This procedure should be carried out in a well-ventilated hood with allowance for the fact that vapors heavier than air are involved.*

A 2-l. four-necked glass flask with ground-glass joints is provided with a thermometer, a 500-ml. dropping funnel equipped with a pressure-equalizing side tube, a Tru-bore stirrer with a paddle of Teflon polytetrafluoroethylene, a heater, and an efficient reflux condenser cooled with water at a temperature below 10°. Ground-glass connections are lubricated with silicone or with Halocarbon stopcock grease. The top of the reflux condenser is connected by means of Tygon polyvinyl chloride tubing to a receiver cooled in a mixture of solid carbon dioxide and acetone. The apparatus is thoroughly dried before use and is protected from moisture during the preparation. Four hundred and twenty grams (10 mols) of finely divided sodium fluoride* and 1 l. of dry acetonitrile† are put in the flask, and 520 g. (325 ml.; 5 mols) of distilled sulfur(II) chloride (b.p. 20 to 25° at 115 mm.)‡ is placed in the funnel. The dichloride is

---

* Sodium fluoride of small particle size is essential for good results. Mallinckrodt Analytical Reagent powder has generally been satisfactory. Estimation of particle sizes by examination with an optical microscope has indicated that samples having a major portion of the particles below 8μ in diameter are suitable. Bulk density of the powdered material measured after tapping in a graduated cylinder to constant level gives some indication of reactivity. Bulk densities for very good samples of sodium fluoride have been in the range 0.85 to 0.90 g./ml., whereas some samples with bulk densities of 1.35 to 1.67 g./ml. have given poorer results.

† Anhydrous grade, Carbide and Carbon Co.

‡ Technical-grade sulfur(II) chloride obtained from Matheson, Coleman & Bell (SCl₂, b.p. 76°) commonly contains 25 to 30% sulfur(I) chloride (S₂Cl₂, b.p. 138°) and some free chlorine (b.p. −35°). The S₂Cl₂ has no

added during half an hour to the stirred slurry initially at 25°.* During the addition the temperature rises spontaneously to about 40° and, near the end, refluxing occurs at a low rate and a small amount of product collects in the cooled receiver. After the addition is completed the mixture is stirred and heated to 50° over a one-hour period, to 70° over an additional one-hour period, and then maintained at 65 to 70° for another half-hour while the crude liquid sulfur(IV) fluoride is collected in the receiver. After the preparation is completed, the cooled reaction residue is disposed of by pouring it slowly into a stirred mixture of aqueous sodium hydroxide and ice. All connections are disassembled and cleaned promptly in order to prevent freezing. Rinsing with acetone is effective in cleaning vessels containing small amounts of sulfur halides. (Caution. *Vigorous reaction if on a large scale.*)

The crude sulfur(IV) fluoride that collects in the receiver is distilled into the pot of a dry low-temperature glass fractionating column, for example, one having a rectifying section 12 mm. in diameter and 280 mm. in length packed with $\frac{3}{32}$-in.-i.d. glass helixes and cooled with solid carbon dioxide

---

deleterious effect on the reaction. The presence of free chlorine, however, is undesirable because it is not readily separated from SF_4 by distillation. The preparation is preferably carried out with distilled SCl_2 by using the portion boiling at 20 to 25° at 115 mm. Good results have also been obtained with technical sulfur(II) chloride from which the chlorine has been stripped by distillation at 115 mm.; distillation is stopped when about 10 to 15% of the charge has collected in a receiver cooled in a mixture of acetone and solid carbon dioxide. Density data for binary mixtures of SCl_2 and S_2Cl_2 have been reported.[5]

* This method of adding the dichloride provides a product that, after moderately efficient distillation, is essentially water-white. For larger-scale operation this procedure is not recommended, but rather the sodium fluoride-acetonitrile slurry is preheated to 65 to 70°, the sulfur(II) chloride is added gradually to the mixture, and the sulfur(IV) fluoride is collected as it is formed. On the scale shown, the gradual addition of SCl_2 at 65 to 70° during 2 hours followed by an additional 1 hour at this temperature gives a yield of sulfur(IV) fluoride equal to that shown, but more careful fractionation is required to separate the low-boiling colored impurities. The preparation has been conducted by gradual addition of dichloride at 65 to 70° on a scale six times that shown with equally good results.

and acetone refrigerant.*   During this transfer there is left behind a residue of 5 to 10 ml. of a less volatile red liquid, which is discarded. On distillation at atmospheric pressure, a yellow-colored forerun of about 5 ml. (liquid at −78°) is rejected and then 120 to 160 g. (60 to 80%) of sulfur(IV) fluoride is collected at −38° to −35° (uncor.) as a water-white to very pale yellow liquid containing 5 to 10% thionyl fluoride as determined by infrared absorption data (see Properties). It may be stored temporarily in glass vessels at −78° or indefinitely in metal cylinders at room temperature.

If the product contains free chlorine and is accordingly yellow or greenish yellow in color (as may occur, for example, if chlorine is not removed completely from the sulfur chloride or if sodium fluoride of insufficient reactivity is used and sulfur(II) chloride is decomposed *in situ*), the chlorine may be removed as follows. The crude tetrafluoride is condensed into an evacuated metal vessel that contains powdered sulfur. It is stored overnight at room temperature and is redistilled to separate it from the higher-boiling sulfur chloride that is formed.

The sulfur(IV) fluoride may be transferred to a stainless-steel cylinder for storage as follows. The distilled product is collected in a trap that can be agitated or swirled while the liquid is frozen with liquid nitrogen. A stainless-steel cylinder equipped with a safety rupture disk assembly and of sufficient volume to provide at least 1 ml./g. of the tetrafluoride is dried and evacuated before use. The trap containing the tetrafluoride is connected by means of glass and heavy-wall tubing (Tygon polyvinyl fluoride, Butyl rubber, or neoprene) to the cylinder via a T-connection, the third arm of which is connected via another T-connection to a 1-m. mercury-filled open-end manometer and a stopcock leading to a vacuum pump. With cautious swirling to avoid breaking of the trap during freezing, the tetrafluoride

* Podbielniak columns with stainless-steel Heli-grid packing may also be used.

is cooled in liquid nitrogen, the trap and lines are evacuated to *ca.* 1 mm., and the connection to the pump is closed. The stainless-steel (18–8 type 304) cylinder is cooled in liquid nitrogen, and the tetrafluoride is distilled into it *in vacuo* without the application of heat. (Caution. *Use of ordinary steel cylinders in liquid-nitrogen baths may result in serious failure due to low-temperature embrittlement of the metal.*[8])

Properties

Sulfur(IV) fluoride has b.p. −38° and m.p. −121°.[3] Its vapor pressure at 25° is about 12 atmospheres and the critical temperature is approximately 90°. Although sulfur(IV) fluoride is very reactive with water, it can be handled in dry Pyrex-brand glass equipment without etching. The adverse effect of moisture on the preparation and handling of the tetrafluoride is increased in glass apparatus since hydrogen fluoride is formed along with thionyl fluoride. The former may cause etching of the glass with formation of silicon tetrafluoride and water, with the possibility of further etching. Any thionyl fluoride (b.p. −44°) so formed is not easily removed from the tetrafluoride, but it generally does not interfere with the reactions of the latter.

The purity of sulfur(IV) fluoride may be estimated from infrared absorption data. Characteristic absorption bands are as follows, the *italicized* values being those most useful for this analysis: for SF_4,[6] moderately intense sharp band at *1744* cm.$^{-1}$ (*5.74μ*), moderately intense band at 1281 cm.$^{-1}$ (7.80μ), strong triplet bands centered at *889* cm.$^{-1}$ (*11.25μ*) and *867* cm.$^{-1}$ (*11.55μ*), and a strong band at 728 cm.$^{-1}$ (13.75μ); for SOF_2,[7] strong bands at 1546 cm.$^{-1}$ (6.47μ) and 1480 cm.$^{-1}$ (6.76μ), strong doublet at *1333* cm.$^{-1}$ (*7.50μ*), and strong bands at *806* cm.$^{-1}$ (*12.40μ*) and *748* cm.$^{-1}$ (*13.35μ*). Sulfur(IV) fluoride prepared by this procedure has typically contained 5 to 10 mol % SOF_2 as determined by infrared or mass spectrometry.

References

1. J. FISCHER and W. JAENCKNER: *Z. angew. Chem.*, **42**, 810 (1929).
2. F. BROWN and P. L. ROBINSON: *J. Chem. Soc.*, **1955**, 3147.
3. W. SCHMIDT: *Monatsh.*, **85**, 452 (1954).
4. C. W. TULLOCK, F. S. FAWCETT, W. C. SMITH, and D. D. COFFMAN: *J. Am. Chem. Soc.*, **82**, 539 (1960).
5. G. H. WHITING: *J. Appl. Chem. (London)*, **2**, 381 (1952). (d^{15} SCl$_2$, 1.6291 g./ml.; S$_2$Cl$_2$, 1.6860 g./ml.).
6. R. E. DODD, L. A. WOODWARD, and H. L. ROBERTS: *Trans. Faraday Soc.*, **52**, 1052 (1956).
7. J. K. O'LOANE and M. K. WILSON: *J. Chem. Phys.*, **23**, 1313 (1955).
8. E. R. PARKER: "Brittle Behavior of Engineering Structures," John Wiley & Sons, Inc., New York, 1957.

34. PEROXYDISULFURYL DIFLUORIDE

$$2SO_3 + F_2 \xrightarrow{AgF_2} S_2O_6F_2$$

SUBMITTED BY JEAN'NE M. SHREEVE* AND GEORGE H. CADY*
CHECKED BY CHARLES CLEAVER† AND E. L. MUETTERTIES†

Peroxydisulfuryl difluoride can be prepared by reaction of fluorine with an excess of sulfur trioxide at about 250° and by the combination of fluorine fluorosulfate with sulfur trioxide. The catalytic fluorination of sulfur trioxide vapor by fluorine in the presence of a heated catalyst of copper ribbon coated with silver(II) fluoride provides a good method for the preparation of a product which can be purified easily.

Procedure

A 1-l. flask is equipped with a 24/40 standard taper outer joint and an exit tube attached at the neck. An inlet tube

* University of Washington, Seattle 5, Wash.
† E. I. du Pont de Nemours & Company, Wilmington, Del.

sealed through a ring seal to a 24/40 inner joint is extended nearly to the bottom of the flask.   It is convenient to fit the inlet and exit tubes with 2-mm. stopcocks to prevent the entrance of moist air when the generator is not in use. When used in the process, this flask contains about 500 g. of "Sulfan B."* At first this material is a liquid (γ-SO_3).   As it is used it becomes largely a solid (β-SO_3).

A copper tube about 90 cm. long and 7.6 cm. in diameter, packed with copper turnings which are plated with silver, is used as the reaction vessel.   The reactor is closed at the ends by disks of copper fastened on by silver solder.   An inlet tube of $\frac{1}{4}$-in. copper tubing is silver-soldered to the vessel at one end and an outlet tube is attached in the same manner at the other end.   In the preparation of the catalyst about 4.5 kg. of annealed thin copper ribbon (in the form of "chore balls" of the type normally used for cleaning dishes)† is plated with 50 to 100 g. of silver by displacement from a solution containing $Ag(CN)_2^-$ ion.[1]   The plated ribbon is washed, dried, and packed firmly into the reactor to which one end-plate is attached.‡   The second end-plate is then attached and the reactor is insulated with a layer of asbestos paper and wound with Nichrome ribbon to permit electrical heating.   Before use, the reactor is heated to 200° and treated with fluorine until the gas appears to be absorbed no longer.   About 40 g. of fluorine is required.

Apparatus is assembled so that dry nitrogen flowing at a rate of about 8 l. per hour through a calibrated flowmeter (made with 1-mm. capillary tubing as the orifice) passes through the sulfur trioxide in its flask at about 25° and thence into the reactor.§   A stream of fluorine also enters

* Commercially available from the Allied Chemical Co.

† Available from the Metal Textile Corp., Roselle, N.J.

‡ The checkers were able to pack only 2.2 kg. of catalyst into their reactor.   They did not anneal the copper ribbon.

§ Checkers' comment: "Dry helium which flows at a rate of about 8 l. per hour through a calibrated Fisher and Porter Flowrator (size 08 bore) passes through the sulfur trioxide in its flask at about 30–35°.   We found very little product when the SO_3 was held at 25°."

the reactor, the two streams of gas coming together just before entering the reactor. The reactor is held at about 150° and the residence time of the reactants is about 15 minutes. Gases coming from the reactor are passed through: (1) a glass trap at about $-78°$ where most of the crude $S_2O_6F_2$ condenses and (2) a glass trap cooled to $-183°$ by liquid oxygen. Volatile by-products and some $S_2O_6F_2$ collect in the second trap. Use of oxygen as the coolant precludes the possibility of condensing liquid fluorine which is run in in slight excess.* The rate of flow of fluorine from a commercial cylinder of the gas is adjusted (to about 1.1 l. per hour) with a nickel diaphragm valve (Hoke No. 413K) and the gas is passed through a calibrated flowmeter (made by using a pin hole in a thin platinum sheet as the orifice), so that some unreacted fluorine passes through the system. This is detected by darkening of potassium iodide paper held in the stream of gas issuing from the trap at $-183°$.†

After the flow rates have become established, all material which has condensed in the trap at $-78°$ is allowed to evaporate, by warming the trap to room temperature, and the trap is again cooled to $-78°$. The product which now collects is free from sulfur trioxide. The only reason for continuing to use the trap at $-183°$ is to provide a means of testing for excess fluorine in the exit gases. Substantially all the peroxydisulfuryl difluoride condenses in the trap at $-78°$.

Purification of the product is accomplished by holding the trap at $-78°$ and pumping away the volatile materials

---

* Checkers' comment: "(2) a glass trap cooled to $-196°C$ by liquid nitrogen, and (3) an exit bubbler containing a low liquid level of 'Halocarbon oil.' The exit bubbler is a convenient way of roughly checking gas flow rates and gives an immediate visual check as to whether air or liquid oxygen is condensing in the liquid nitrogen trap."

† The checkers used as a flowmeter a flowrator composed of a 08 Fisher and Porter tube connected at each end with $\frac{1}{4}$-in. Teflon tubing, the stainless ball being stopped at each end of the glass tube by a sliver of platinum. A ball reading of 1 to 2 was used. Fluorine was used from a cylinder containing 100 g. of sodium fluoride pellets to remove hydrogen fluoride and thereby reduce the rate of attack upon the flowrator tube.

through a condenser trap cooled by liquid nitrogen or oxygen. Pumping is continued until the observed molecular weight of the remaining material is 198 to 200. The vapor density may be measured from time to time by allowing the material to warm temporarily to room temperature so that a sample of its vapor can be collected at about 100-mm. pressure in a 250-ml. gas density bulb equipped with a Kern stopcock lightly lubricated with Kel-F grease. When the correct vapor density is reached, the product is substantially pure $S_2O_6F_2$. This situation probably would not be true if an excess of fluorine were not used in the reactor so that sulfur trioxide would be totally consumed.*

The above conditions produce about 6 g. of $S_2O_6F_2$ per hour after flow conditions are established and the reactor has become filled with reactants. The yield based upon the consumption of SO_3 may exceed 90% of theoretical.

Properties

Peroxydisulfuryl difluoride is a colorless liquid having an extremely unpleasant odor and a vapor pressure of 146.4 mm. at 25.8°. It has a melting point of −55.4° and a boiling point of 67.1°, and its density is given by the equation $\sigma = 2.3959 - 2.434 \times 10^{-3}$ T°K for the temperature range of 35.5 to 45.0°.[2] It hydrolyzes in water, giving oxygen and fluorosulfuric acid; the latter continues to hydrolyze slowly to give sulfuric and hydrofluoric acids. Peroxydisulfuryl difluoride reacts readily with potassium iodide solution, liberating iodine. It ignites organic materials immediately upon contact. In many of its reactions the gas becomes brown, presumably because of the presence of fluorosulfate free radicals. Purity may be determined from

---

* The checkers purified their product by distillation in a 1-ft. glass spinning band column containing a platinum band, Teflon platinum take-off regulators, and lubricated where necessary with Halocarbon stopcock grease. From 26 g. of crude product they obtained 5.2 g. of a foreshort boiling at 48 to 65°, composed mainly of SO_3, and 16 g. of $S_2O_6F_2$ boiling at 65 to 67°.

vapor-density and infrared measurements. Elementary analysis may be performed after a 24-hour basic hydrolysis at 100°.

References

1. K. B. KELLOGG and G. H. CADY: *J. Am. Chem. Soc.*, **70**, 3986 (1948).
2. F. B. DUDLEY and G. H. CADY: *ibid.*, **79**, 513 (1957).

35. SODIUM HYDROGEN SULFIDE

$$C_2H_5ONa + H_2S \rightarrow NaHS + C_2H_5OH$$

SUBMITTED BY RICHARD E. EIBECK*
CHECKED BY RALPH A. ZINGARO† AND RAYMOND E. McGLOTHLIN†

Anhydrous sodium hydrogen sulfide was first obtained by the action of hydrogen sulfide on sodium.[1] The anhydrous material was again reported by Sabatier,[2] who obtained it by saturating sodium sulfide 9-hydrate with hydrogen sulfide and then evaporating the water in an atmosphere of hydrogen sulfide. A novel synthesis, upon which the following procedure is based, was reported by Rule in 1911.[3] Rule prepared sodium hydrogen sulfide from sodium ethoxide and hydrogen sulfide, using ethanol as a solvent. The anhydrous material may also be prepared by adding sodium to liquid hydrogen sulfide[4] or by passing hydrogen sulfide into a solution of sodium in liquid ammonia until the blue color is discharged.[5]

Procedure

An oven-dried 1-l. three-necked flask is fitted with a stirrer (all glass or glass shaft with Teflon paddle) and a

* General Chemical Division, Allied Chemical Corp., Morristown, N.J.
† Agricultural and Mechanical College of Texas, College Station, Tex.

reflux condenser with a calcium chloride drying tube attached to its other end. The other opening of the flask is closed with a solid stopper.*

The flask is placed in a 1-l. heating mantle so that it may be heated when necessary to speed up the reaction between sodium and ethanol.

The flask is flushed with dry nitrogen, and 200 ml. (3.40 mols) of anhydrous ethanol is added. Twelve grams (0.522 mol) of clean sodium metal, cut into small pieces, is then rapidly added to the ethanol. Reaction occurs immediately. The flask is closed and the reaction allowed to continue. The reaction mixture is stirred and heated so that the ethanol refluxes. This serves to speed up the reaction and to increase the solubility of the product, sodium ethoxide. The excess ethanol is necessary to keep the sodium ethoxide in solution.

After the sodium has dissolved, the flask is fitted with a gas-delivery tube (5-mm. i.d.) in the unused neck. (See footnote below.) The delivery tube is arranged so that the end is below the surface of the sodium ethoxide solution. Care is taken that the stirrer blade does not hit the delivery tube. It is advisable to have the hydrogen sulfide passing through the tube before it is inserted into the flask so as to prevent clogging by sodium hydrogen sulfide.

Hydrogen sulfide, dried over phosphorus(V) oxide, is then passed through the stirred solution, at a rate of five to ten bubbles per second, for two hours. As the resulting solution cools, some sodium hydrogen sulfide is deposited. When the solution has cooled to room temperature, 750 ml. of anhydrous ethyl ether is added as rapidly as possible to precipitate completely the sodium hydrogen sulfide.

* The checkers have suggested that a gas-delivery tube be inserted initially instead of a solid stopper. The delivery tube is attached, through a stopcock, to a phosphorus(V) oxide drying tube, which in turn is attached to a Y-tube leading directly to the nitrogen or hydrogen sulfide source. The flow of these gases may be controlled individually with stopcocks. This arrangement avoids the necessity of removing the stopper during the actual operation.

The following operations are performed as rapidly as possible to prevent the absorption of water by the sodium hydrogen sulfide. The precipitate is quickly separated from the ether-ethanol solution by vacuum filtration on a coarse fritted-glass filtering funnel and is washed three times with anhydrous ethyl ether. After the last washing, nearly all of the ether is allowed to evaporate and the product is rapidly transferred to a container which is then placed in a vacuum desiccator over calcium chloride. The desiccator is connected to a vacuum line for several hours to free the product of residual ethyl ether.

The pure white sodium hydrogen sulfide is very hygroscopic and may be exposed to the atmosphere for only very short periods. From 10 g. of sodium it is possible to prepare approximately 24.5 g. of sodium hydrogen sulfide which is over 98% pure. The yield is practically quantitative, except for mechanical losses.

Analysis

The method of analysis involves oxidation of the sulfide to sulfur by means of iodine. A sample of approximately 60 mg. is added from a weighing bottle to 25 ml. of 0.100 N iodine in potassium iodide solution. After the sample has reacted, 70 ml. of water and 5 ml. of 1:1 hydrochloric acid are added. The excess iodine is then back-titrated with 0.100 N sodium thiosulfate solution to a starch end point.

Properties

Anhydrous sodium hydrogen sulfide, as prepared by the foregoing method, is a fine white hygroscopic powder. The melting point of the substance is 350°. It is soluble in water, ethanol, and probably other hydroxylic solvents with slow decomposition. Anhydrous sodium hydrogen sulfide also dissolves in dry N,N-dimethylformamide to give a blue-green solution. Two hydrates, $NaHS \cdot 2H_2O$ and

NaHS·3H$_2$O, are known.[6] Below 90°, sodium hydrogen sulfide has a rhombohedral structure, whereas above 90° its structure is cubic.[7]

The anhydrous material is readily hydrolyzed in moist air to sodium hydroxide and hydrogen sulfide.

References

1. J. L. GAY-LUSSAC and L. J. THENARD: *Recherches physicochimiques*, Paris, **1**, 200 (1811).
2. P. SABATIER: *Ann. chim. phys.*, [V], **22**, 21 (1881).
3. A. J. RULE: *J. Chem. Soc.*, **99**, 558 (1911).
4. A. F. WELLS: "Structural Inorganic Chemistry," 2d ed., p. 347, Clarendon Press, Oxford, 1950.
5. R. J. A. OTTO: WADC Technical Report, 58-51, ASTIA Document No. 151177, p. 118, April, 1958.
6. W. P. BLOXAM: *J. Chem. Soc.*, **77**, 764 (1900).
7. C. D. WEST: *Z. Krist.*, **88**, 97 (1934).

CHAPTER VIB

See also: Cyclopentadienyl metal carbonyls and some derivatives, synthesis 31

Anhydrous metal chlorides, synthesis 45

36. TRICHLORO(TRIPYRIDINE)CHROMIUM(III)

$$CrCl_3 + 3C_5H_5N \rightarrow [Cr(C_5H_5N)_3Cl_3]$$

SUBMITTED BY JAMES C. TAFT* AND MARK M. JONES*

CHECKED BY RONALD S. SCHREIBER† AND HENRY F. HOLTZCLAW, JR.†

Pfeiffer prepared trichloro(tripyridine)chromium(III) from anhydrous chromium(III) chloride[1] and from dichlorotetraaquochromium(III) chloride 2-hydrate[2] (the common hydrated chromic chloride of commerce), but neither details of the preparations nor yields were reported. The reaction of $[Cr(H_2O)_4Cl_2]Cl \cdot 2H_2O$ with pyridine gives $[Cr(C_5H_5N)_3Cl_3]$ with a yield of about 4%. In the procedure described here, the complex can be prepared in about 90% yield when anhydrous chromium(III) chloride is used as the starting material.

Procedure

Caution. This reaction should be carried out in a well-ventilated hood.

Twenty-six and four-tenths grams (0.16 mol) of anhydrous chromium(III) chloride‡ and 79.1 g (1 mol) of anhydrous pyridine and a stirring magnet are placed in a 1-l. round-bottomed flask which has a standard taper opening.

* Vanderbilt University, Nashville, Tenn.

† University of Nebraska, Lincoln 8, Neb.

‡ See INORGANIC SYNTHESES, **2**, 193 (1946); **5**, 154 (1957); the compound is also available from Diamond Alkali Co., Cleveland, Ohio.

A water condenser (65 cm. in length) is connected to this opening and a Vigreux column (25 cm. in length) is inserted in the top of the condenser. The slurry is stirred with a magnetic stirrer and heated slowly with a heating mantle until the pyridine boils gently.* In 10 to 15 minutes a vigorous reaction occurs and most of the chromium(III) chloride reacts. A considerable amount of heat is evolved and the Vigreux column serves to prevent the loss of pyridine at this point. After this stage the mixture is stirred and heated at reflux for 5 hours. The contents of the flask should be swirled around the sides occasionally to remove any solid above the liquid level. The solution is then allowed to cool (pyridine vapors are toxic) and 500 ml. of ice-cold water is poured into the flask. The dark green crystals which result are collected on a Büchner funnel and washed with cold water until the filtrate is clear. The solid is dried thoroughly on a porous clay plate and is then extracted with chloroform in a Soxhlet extractor. The compound has a limited solubility in chloroform (3.4 g./ 100 ml. at 29°), and the solvent in the extractor should be renewed when enough solid collects in the bottom flask to cause bumping. Extraction is complete when the chloroform returning to the distilling flask is colorless or nearly so. If the solid in the extraction thimble lumps up in the process, these lumps should be pulverized and reextracted. The complex can then be obtained by evaporating the chloroform in the extract. The final yield is 60 g. (91% of theory). *Anal.* Calcd. for $[Cr(C_5H_5N)_3Cl_3]$: Cr, 13.14; C, 45.53; H, 3.82; N, 10.62. Found: Cr, 13.15; C, 44.96; H, 3.77 (the checkers found C, 45.46; H, 3.75; N, 10.85).

Properties

Trichloro(tripyridine)chromium(III) is a light green solid when finely pulverized. The compound does not

---

* The initial heating should be very gentle; otherwise, the Vigreux column may not contain the reaction once it begins.

melt, but loses pyridine rapidly at 255 to 260°. It is slightly soluble in pyridine, chloroform, ethanol, and methanol. The solubility in nitric acid has been described by Pfeiffer.[1] The compound is extremely soluble in concentrated nitric acid and can be reprecipitated from this medium by the addition of water if the minimum amount of acid is used to dissolve it. It is insoluble in concentrated hydrochloric acid but dissolves in concentrated sulfuric acid with decomposition and the evolution of hydrochloric acid.

References

1. P. PFEIFFER: *Z. anorg. Chem.*, **24**, 283 (1900).
2. P. PFEIFFER: *ibid.*, **55**, 99 (1907).

37. TRIS(3-BROMOACETYLACETONATO)-CHROMIUM(III)

Tris(3-bromo-2,4-pentanedionato)chromium(III)]

$$[(CH_3CO)_2CH]_3Cr + 3C_4H_4O_2NBr \rightarrow$$
$$[(CH_3CO)_2CBr]_3Cr + 3C_4H_5O_2N$$

SUBMITTED BY JAMES P. COLLMAN*
CHECKED BY GEORGE B. KAUFFMAN† AND STANLEY E. GORDON†

The direct substitution of bromine into the chelate rings of metal acetylacetonates is an example of the reaction of a coordinated ligand. Tris(3-bromoacetylacetonato)chromium(III) has been prepared by the action of elementary bromine on chromium(III) acetylacetonate [2,4-pentane-dionatochromium(III)].[1] The procedure given here is

* The University of North Carolina, Chapel Hill, N.C.
† Fresno State College, Fresno 26, Calif.

general, and iodine and chlorine can also be introduced into the chelate rings of several metal acetylacetonates by this method.[2]

Procedure

To a solution of 5.0 g. (0.014 mol) of chromium(III) acetylacetonate* in 75 ml. of chloroform is added 8.0 g. (0.044 mol) of N-bromosuccinimide,† and the mixture is heated to boiling for 5 minutes in a hood. During this period, mechanical agitation is necessary to prevent bumping. The initially violet solution becomes deep green and a brown precipitate forms. The mixture is transferred to an evaporating dish and the solvent is removed under a stream of air in a hood.

The brown solid is collected on a suction filter and washed successively with 15 ml. of 95% ethanol, two 15-ml. portions of 5% aqueous sodium hydrogen sulfite solution, 20 ml. of water, and two 20-ml. portions of hot 95% ethanol. Although the ethanol washings are green, little product is lost in this step.

The air-dried brown powder is dissolved in 50 ml. of boiling benzene; the solution is filtered through a fluted filter and combined with 100 ml. of boiling heptane. The mixture is allowed to cool to room temperature over at least a 4-hour period, then chilled in an ice bath and filtered. The brown crystals are washed with two 10-ml. portions of 95% ethanol and air-dried. The yield is 5.8 to 6.2 g. (70 to 75%). The melting point is 227 to 229°.

Anal. Calcd. for $Cr(C_5H_6O_2Br)_3$: C, 30.74; H, 3.09; Br, 40.91. Found: C, 30.95; H, 3.35; Br, 40.72.

* Prepared according to the directions of W. C. Fernelius and J. E. Blanch, INORGANIC SYNTHESES, **5**, 130 (1957).

† The N-bromosuccinimide was purified by dissolving the crude material in a minimum amount of boiling water, rapidly filtering the mixture into a cooled beaker, collecting the white crystals on a suction filter, and drying the solid in a vacuum desiccator. Use of unrecrystallized N-bromosuccinimide results in a lower yield.

Properties

Tris(3-bromoacetylacetonato)chromium(III) is a dark red-brown crystalline material, which dissolves in benzene to form a green solution. The infrared spectrum of this chelate exhibits a characteristic strong singlet at 1540 cm.$^{-1}$, whereas chromium(III) acetylacetonate exhibits two peaks in this region, at 1560 and 1520 cm.$^{-1}$. The ultraviolet spectrum of the brominated chromium chelate in chloroform exhibits a λ_{max} at 358 mμ(ϵ = 13,070).[2] The brominated chelate is reported to form a stable clathrate complex with chloroform (m.p. 240 to 241°).[3]

References

1. H. REIHLEN, R. ILLIG, and R. WITTIG: *Ber.*, **58B**, 12 (1925).
2. J. P. COLLMAN, R. A. MOSS, H. MALTZ, and C. C. HEINDEL: *J. Am. Chem. Soc.*, **83**, 531 (1961).
3. R. W. KLUIBER: *ibid.*, **82**, 4839 (1960).

38. CYCLOPENTADIENYL TRICARBONYL HYDRIDES OF CHROMIUM, MOLYBDENUM, AND TUNGSTEN

{Hydrogen tricarbonyl(cyclopentadienyl)chromate(0), -molybdate(0), and -tungstate(0)}

$$M(CO)_6 + M'C_5H_5 \rightarrow M'[C_5H_5M(CO)_3] + 3CO$$
$$M'[C_5H_5M(CO)_3] + HC_2H_3O_2 \rightarrow C_5H_5M(CO)_3H + M'C_2H_3O_2$$
$$(M = Cr,Mo,W; \; M' = \text{alkali metal})$$

SUBMITTED BY E. O. FISCHER[*]
CHECKED BY ROY L. PRUETT[†]

Cyclopentadienyl tricarbonyl hydrides of chromium, molybdenum, and tungsten can be prepared by reaction of

* Institute for Inorganic Chemistry, The University, Munich, Germany.
† Union Carbide Chemicals Company, South Charleston, W.Va.

the hexacarbonyls of these metals with alkali metal derivatives of cyclopentadiene in polar solvents such as N,N-dimethylformamide, followed by acidification of the reaction mixture.[1] The cyclopentadienyl tricarbonyl hydride of chromium can also be prepared by reaction of bis(cyclopentadienyl)chromium, $Cr(C_5H_5)_2$, with hydrogen (50 atm.) and carbon monoxide (150 atm.) for 12 hours at 70° in an autoclave.[2]

Procedure

A 250-ml. three-necked flask, equipped with reflux condenser, nitrogen-inlet tube, and stirrer, is charged with equimolar quantities (e.g., 0.02 mol) of metal carbonyl [4.4 g. of $Cr(CO)_6$; 5.3 g. of $Mo(CO)_6$; 7.0 g. of $W(CO)_6$] and an alkali metal derivative of cyclopentadiene (1.4 g. of LiC_5H_5; 1.8 g. of NaC_5H_5; 2.1 g. of KC_5H_5) in about 70 ml. of carefully dried N,N-dimethylformamide as solvent, and the system is well swept out with nitrogen. A mercury valve is placed on the reflux condenser. (It is necessary to make all joints secure to accommodate the pressure which is built up during reaction.) The nitrogen stream is discontinued and the reaction mixture warmed slowly with vigorous stirring to about 130° over the course of 30 minutes. It is maintained at this temperature for 2 hours. The beginning of carbon monoxide cleavage ($Cr(CO)_6 \sim 110°$; $Mo(CO)_6 \sim 75°$; $W(CO)_6 \sim 110°$), as well as its completion, can be observed by means of the mercury valve.

After carbon monoxide evolution is complete, the light brown solution is cooled, the stirrer and reflux condenser are removed under nitrogen, and the solvent is distilled in a vacuum at about 100°. The dark brown oily residue is dissolved in about 25 ml. of 0.5 N nitrogen-saturated sodium hydroxide solution and filtered under nitrogen through a sintered-glass filter of average pore diameter in the range 15 to 40μ. For the removal of organic impurities, the solution is extracted twice with ether. The solution is then transferred to the apparatus shown in Fig. 14 where, under the careful exclusion of air and with cooling by means of an ice bath, it is acidified with 2 N acetic acid saturated with

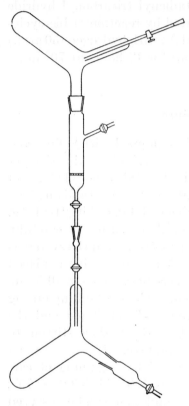

nitrogen. The voluminous precipitate of free hydride which forms immediately is filtered with suction through the sintered-glass filter (Fig. 14) of average pore diameter in the range 3 to 15μ. The precipitate is washed under nitrogen with 10 ml. of water saturated with nitrogen.

Better yields can often be obtained, if, instead of filtering, the free hydride is dissolved in ether and the solvent is removed *in vacuo.*

After careful drying in a high vacuum, the crude product is transferred under nitrogen into a suitable sublimation apparatus and is subjected to sublimation at 45° in a high vacuum. Difficultly volatile by-products are thereby left behind. The cyclopentadienyl carbonyl hydrides are separated as yellow crystals in 30 to 60% yield. *Anal.* Calcd.

Fig. 14. Apparatus for the acidification of the alkali metal derivatives of the cyclopentadienyl carbonyl hydrides of chromium, molybdenum, and tungsten.

for $C_5H_5Cr(CO)_3H$: Cr, 25.73; C, 47.53; H, 2.99. Found: Cr, 25.84; C, 47.42; H, 2.99. Calcd. for $C_5H_5Mo(CO)_3H$: Mo, 39.02; C, 39.02; H, 2.46. Found: Mo, 39.29; C, 38.97; H, 2.20. Calcd. for $C_5H_5W(CO)_3H$: W, 55.09; C, 28.81; H, 1.81. Found: W, 55.22; C, 29.08; H, 1.79.

Properties

The three hydrides are readily volatile, oxidation-sensitive, diamagnetic compounds, which are very soluble in such organic media as benzene, ether, and petroleum ether. In conformity with their character as weak acids, they dissolve in solutions of alkali to form anions which are considerably more stable in air than the parent compounds. The hydrides are bright in color, ranging from golden-yellow for $C_5H_5Cr(CO)_3H$ to bright yellow for $C_5H_5Mo(CO)_3H$ to pale yellow for $C_5H_5W(CO)_3H$. The chromium and molybdenum compounds evolve the hydrogen very slowly at room temperature but rapidly at the respective melting points of 57 to 58° and 50 to 52°, with the formation, respectively, of the dimeric green $[C_5H_5Cr(CO)_3]_2$ and the red $[C_5H_5Mo(CO)_3]_2$. The former dimer is converted to the original hydride by the action of hydrogen (150 atm.) at 70°. The cyclopentadienyl tricarbonyl hydride of tungsten remains as a stable pale yellow liquid far above its melting point of 66 to 67°. With oxygen, the tungsten compound, like the other hydrides, reacts to form a dimeric compound of the type $[C_5H_5M(CO)_3]_2$ (synthesis 31). With all three cyclopentadienyl tricarbonyl hydrides the hydrogen is replaceable by alkyl and aryl groups. Thus, $C_5H_5W(CO)_3H$ reacts with diazomethane to yield the readily volatile orange $C_5H_5W(CO)_3CH_3$.[3]

Structures for the compounds have been proposed which involve bonding between hydrogen and the metals.[3,4]

References

1. E. O. FISCHER, W. HAFNER, and H. O. STAHL: *Z. anorg. u. allgem. Chem.*, **282**, 47 (1955).
2. E. O. FISCHER and W. HAFNER: *Z. Naturforsch.*, **10b**, 140 (1954).
3. T. S. PIPER and G. WILKINSON: *J. Inorg. & Nuclear Chem.*, **3**, 104 (1956).
4. A. D. LIEHR: *Naturwissenschaften*, **44**, 61 (1957).

39. TRICHLORO(TRIPYRIDINE)MOLYBDENUM(III)

$$K_3MoCl_6 + 3C_5H_5N \rightarrow Mo(C_5H_5N)_3Cl_3 + 3KCl$$

SUBMITTED BY HANS B. JONASSEN* AND LIONEL J. BAILIN*
CHECKED BY GEORGE SLUSARCZUK† AND STANLEY KIRSCHNER†

Trichloro(tripyridine)molybdenum(III) has been prepared by the reaction of molybdenum(III) chloride with pyridine at 270° for 5 hours in a sealed tube.[1] The preparation described below using potassium hexachloromolybdate-(III) as starting material is carried out at a lower temperature, requires less time, and involves no special apparatus.

Procedure

To 50 ml. (about 0.6 mol) of reagent-grade pyridine in a 125-ml. round-bottomed flask there is added 8.5 g. (0.02 mol) of potassium hexachloromolybdate(III).[2] The mixture is heated with a Glas Col mantle, or microburner, and refluxed at 115 to 117° for 3 hours using a conventional water-cooled reflux column. At the end of the reaction time, upon cooling, a yellow precipitate suspended in a dark brown solution is observed.

The entire contents of the reaction vessel are now poured into about 300 ml. of distilled water. A color change from dark brown to yellow-green occurs. The mixture is stirred thoroughly for 2 hours and the color changes to yellow-brown. The suspension is filtered by suction through a 90-mm. No. 40 Whatman filter paper in a Büchner funnel. The yellow precipitate is washed with 1 l. of distilled water, air-dried on the filter paper, and then dried at 100 to 110° under nitrogen in a conventional tube furnace or a drying pistol containing Drierite. The yield is approximately 6 g. (about 70%) based on the weight of the potassium hexachloromolybdate(III).

* Tulane University, New Orleans, La.
† Wayne State University, Detroit, Mich.

Purification for purposes of elemental analyses is carried out by redissolving the precipitate in 40 ml. of pyridine and refluxing for 2 hours and then precipitating, washing, and drying as above. Removal of traces of water and pyridine is carried out by pistol drying under 10-mm. pressure at the reflux temperature of acetone, 57°.

Analysis

Molybdenum: About 0.3 g. of the product in a porcelain crucible is treated with 5 ml. of 60 to 62% perchloric acid to destroy the organic part of the molecule and to oxidize the molybdenum to the +6 state. The mixture is evaporated slowly to near dryness, allowed to cool, and diluted with distilled water. It is then made basic with 2 N sodium hydroxide, neutralized with 2 N sulfuric acid, and buffered with 2 N ammonium acetate to a pH of 5 to 6. To this solution in a 400-ml. flask there is added 10 ml. of a 5% solution of 8-quinolinol. The 8-quinolinolate is filtered onto a tared sintered-glass crucible, washed, dried in the usual manner, and then weighed. **Chloride:** To about 0.10 to 0.15 g. of sample in a porcelain crucible there is added 3 ml. of 16 N nitric acid, and the mixture is diluted to 10 ml. with distilled water. The sample is transferred to a 125-ml. Erlenmeyer flask and digested on a steam bath for 20 minutes. After cooling, titration in the acid solution is carried out with a standard solution of mercury(II) nitrate. **Carbon and hydrogen** are determined by combustion techniques, and **nitrogen** by difference. *Anal.* Calcd. for $Mo(C_5H_5N)_3Cl_3$: Mo, 21.83; Cl, 24.19; C, 40.98; H, 3.44; N, 9.56. Found: Mo, 21.47; Cl, 23.49; C, 40.85; H, 3.52; N, 10.05.

Properties

Trichloro(tripyridine)molybdenum(III) is a deep yellow solid, which decomposes at 172 to 182°, yielding free pyridine.   It does not melt, but turns black and then yellow on ignition in air, forming molybdenum(VI) oxide.

The compound is almost completely insoluble in hot or cold water, slightly soluble in 95% ethanol, benzene, and acetone, and soluble in methanol and glacial acetic acid. No solution is observed in hot or cold concentrated hydrochloric acid or in aqueous ammonia.   It decomposes to give solutions in hot and cold concentrated nitric and sulfuric acids.   In concentrated sodium hydroxide solutions, decomposition occurs on heating, with the formation of violet-black precipitates.

References

1. A. ROSENHEIM, G. ABEL, and R. LEWY: *Z. anorg. u. allgem. Chem.*, **197**, 189 (1931).
2. K. H. LOHMANN and R. C. YOUNG: INORGANIC SYNTHESES, **4**, 97 (1953).

40. POTASSIUM OCTACYANOTUNGSTATE(IV) 2-HYDRATE

$$H_2WO_4 + K_2CO_3 \rightarrow K_2WO_4 + CO_2 + H_2O$$

$$K_2WO_4 + (2 + x)HCl \rightarrow$$
$$2KCl + WCl_x^{6-x} + 4H_2O + (x - 6)H^+$$
$$2WCl_x^{6-x} + 3Sn \rightarrow W_2Cl_9^{3-} + 3Sn^{++} + (2x - 9)Cl^-$$
$$W_2Cl_9^{3-} + 3K^+ \xrightarrow{C_2H_5OH} K_3W_2Cl_9$$
$$2K_3W_2Cl_9 + 32KCN + O_2 + 2H_2O \rightarrow$$
$$4K_4W(CN)_8 + 18KCl + 4KOH$$
$$K_4W(CN)_8 + 2H_2O \xrightarrow{C_2H_5OH} K_4W(CN)_8 \cdot 2H_2O$$

SUBMITTED BY EDWARD A. HEINTZ*
CHECKED BY WILMER J. STRATTON†

Although the structure,[1,2] properties,[2] and reactions[2] of potassium octacyanotungstate(IV), $K_4W(CN)_8$, are well

* Metals Research Laboratories, Union Carbide Metals Company, Division of Union Carbide Corporation, Niagara Falls, N.Y.; present address, University of Buffalo, Buffalo, N.Y.
† Earlham College, Richmond, Ind.

known, satisfactory methods for its preparation have not been completely developed. The difficulties center around the preparation of the intermediate chloride, tripotassium enneachloroditungstate(III), $K_3W_2Cl_9$. This synthesis may be accomplished by reduction of an acidic solution of tungsten(VI) either with tin[3,4,5] or by electrochemical methods.[6,7] The former method, which is employed here, has been found to be satisfactory with respect to yields and purity of the desired cyanide. In addition, the time of preparation has been shortened considerably over that required for the electrolytic method. The reduction with tin also has the advantage that no elaborate equipment or techniques are required.

Procedure

Twenty-eight grams (0.11 mol) of tungstic acid(VI) is mixed with 30 g. (0.22 mol) of potassium carbonate and 30 ml. of water. The mixture is stirred for a half-hour until a completely white slurry is formed and is then cooled to 0° in an ice bath.* The white slurry of potassium tungstate(VI) is added slowly over a period of 90 minutes to 500 ml. of concentrated hydrochloric acid (sp. gr. 1.19), which has also been precooled to 0° in an ice bath. After each addition, the solution is rapidly stirred until complete clarification is obtained. Toward the end of the addition, a slight turbidity may be present; this may be tolerated. When the addition of the tungstate is complete, an additional 200 ml. of concentrated hydrochloric acid is added, and the solution is allowed to stand for about 30 minutes at 0°.† One hundred grams (0.84 mol) of tin foil is added

---

* An equivalent quantity of tungsten(VI) oxide, WO_3, may be substituted for the tungstic acid but a completely white slurry will *never* be obtained and the steps following may proceed with some difficulty. Its use should be avoided if possible.

† The checker was unable to obtain clear solutions using this procedure but was still able to achieve satisfactory yields of the final product.

to the cooled solution.*   When the first tinge of blue color
appears, the solution is transferred to a water bath maintained at 40°, where it is permitted to stand for the duration
of the reduction (approximately 45 minutes).   The blue
solution rapidly becomes deep purple.   In order to determine whether reduction is complete, a sample of the solution
is withdrawn and diluted with water.   The formation of a
dark green solution that yields a dark green precipitate upon
the addition of 95% ethanol indicates the presence of the
$W_2Cl_9{}^{3-}$ ion.   If a red aqueous solution is obtained, the
reduction must be continued.   When a positive test is
observed, the acid solution is decanted from any unreacted
tin into twice its volume of 95% ethanol and rapidly filtered
by vacuum.   The dark green precipitate is washed with
ethanol and ether.   At this point the preparation may be
conveniently stopped and the $K_3W_2Cl_9$ stored in a vacuum
desiccator overnight.

This chloro salt is added to a solution of 100 g. (1.5 mol)
of potassium cyanide in 400 ml. of water, and the mixture
is heated on a steam bath for two hours.   During the heating, a stream of air is passed through the solution to oxidize
the tungsten to the tetrapositive state.   After the addition
of decolorizing charcoal, the solution is filtered while hot
and is then concentrated on a hot plate for crystallization.
The first crystals are a mixture of potassium chloride and
cyanide and these are removed by filtration.   The filtrate
is evaporated until additional crystals form and is then
allowed to cool to room temperature.   A second batch of
potassium chloride and cyanide crystals is obtained and
removed by filtration in the same manner.   The filtrate,
which by this time has a volume of approximately 200 ml.,
is added to twice its volume of 95% ethanol in order to
precipitate orange-yellow crystals of $K_4W(CN)_8 \cdot 2H_2O$.
The precipitate is filtered under vacuum and redissolved in
100 ml. of distilled water.   It is then reprecipitated by add-

* Granular or finely divided tin powder will not give as satisfactory
results as tin foil.

ing 200 ml. of 95% ethanol, filtered under vacuum, washed with two 25-ml. portions of ethanol, and placed in a vacuum desiccator to dry. On occasion, an orange "oil" may form upon the addition of ethanol. This "oil" can be made to crystallize by the simple addition of more ethanol. The yield is 18 to 31 grams (29 to 50%).

Analysis

The desired $K_4W(CN)_8$ was analyzed in the following manner. Potassium was precipitated as the tetraphenylborate salt and weighed as such. Tungsten was determined by fuming an aqueous solution of the salt with concentrated nitric and perchloric acids and then weighing the precipitated tungsten(VI) oxide. Cyanide was determined by fusion of a solid sample of the salt with sodium metal followed by an argentometric titration of the sodium cyanide formed. *Anal.* Calcd. for $K_4W(CN)_8 \cdot 2H_2O$: K, 26.76; W, 31.46; CN, 35.62. Found: K, 27.3, 26.9; W, 31.3, 31.4; CN, 35.7, 35.7.

Properties

Potassium octacyanotungstate(IV) 2-hydrate, $K_4W(CN)_8 \cdot 2H_2O$, is obtained as well-formed orange tetragonal crystals. The $W(CN)_8^{4-}$ ion is dodecahedral and is isomorphous with the more common $Mo(CN)_8^{4-}$ ion.[1,2] The free acid, $H_4W(CN)_8$, has been observed only in aqueous solution. It is a strong acid requiring 4 gram equivalents of base per formula weight of acid to yield one break in the titration curve. The tetrapositive tungsten salt is easily oxidized in aqueous solution with potassium permanganate or cerium(IV) sulfate to the pentapositive analog, potassium octacyanotungstate(V), $K_3W(CN)_8$. The measured standard potential of the $W(CN)_8^{3-}/W(CN)_8^{4-}$ couple is -0.457 volt vs. the normal hydrogen electrode at 25°.[2] The magnetic susceptibility of the solid has been found to be

$\chi_g = -3.58 \times 10^{-7}$, demonstrating the diamagnetism expected for tetrapositive tungsten with d^4sp^3 hybridization.[2]

References

1. J. R. HOARD and H. H. NORDSIECK: *J. Am. Chem. Soc.*, **61**, 2853 (1939).
2. H. BAADSGAARD and W. D. TREADWELL: *Helv. Chim. Acta*, **38**, 1669 (1955).
3. O. OLSSON: *Z. anorg. u. allgem. Chem.*, **88**, 49 (1914).
4. R. C. YOUNG: *J. Am. Chem. Soc.*, **54**, 4515 (1932).
5. R. A. LAUDISE and R. C. YOUNG: *ibid.*, **77**, 5288 (1955); INORGANIC SYNTHESES, **6**, 149 (1960).
6. O. O. COLLENBURG and J. BACKER: *Z. Elektrochem.*, **30**, 230 (1924).
7. H. B. JONASSEN, A. R. TARSEY, S. CANTOR, and G. F. HELFRICH: INORGANIC SYNTHESES, **5**, 139 (1957).

41. URANYL CHLORIDE 1-HYDRATE

(Dioxouranium(VI) Dichloride 1-Hydrate)

$$UO_2(NO_3)_2 \cdot 6H_2O + 2HCl \rightarrow UO_2Cl_2 \cdot 6H_2O + 2HNO_3$$
$$UO_2Cl_2 \cdot 6H_2O + 5SOCl_2 \rightarrow UO_2Cl_2 \cdot H_2O + 5SO_2 + 10HCl$$

SUBMITTED BY JACK D. HEFLEY,* DANIEL M. MATHEWS,* AND EDWARD S. AMIS*
CHECKED BY I. SHEFT† AND JOSEPH J. KATZ†

Anhydrous uranyl chloride has been prepared by reaction of oxygen with uranium(IV) chloride at 300° to 350°.[1] Other procedures for preparing uranyl chloride are:[2] reaction of chlorine with uranium(IV) oxide at 500°; reaction of carbon tetrachloride with uranium(VI) oxide at 290°; and reaction of hydrogen chloride with partially hydrated

* University of Arkansas, Fayetteville, Ark. Financial support for this research was received from the Atomic Energy Commission on Contract No. AT-(40-1)-2069.
† Argonne National Laboratory, Lemont, Ill.

uranium(VI) oxide to give the monohydrate, followed by the removal of this water in dry hydrogen chloride at 300°. The easiest way to prepare uranyl chloride 1-hydrate in a state of high purity is by the use of high-purity uranyl nitrate 6-hydrate* as a starting material.

Procedure

Two hundred and fifty grams, or any convenient weight depending on the weight of product desired, of pure uranyl nitrate 6-hydrate is treated with sufficient concentrated hydrochloric acid so that the salt is readily dissolved. Amounts of reagents in this preparation are not critical. The solution of the salt in the acid is evaporated by distillation until it becomes very viscous. At this point, concentrated hydrochloric acid is added in small portions and distillation continued until no brown oxides of nitrogen can be seen and until the brucine test[3] indicates that no nitrate is present in the solution.

At this point, the reaction vessel is transferred to an oil bath maintained at 180°, and dry hydrogen chloride gas is kept flowing over the product. The contents of the flask are stirred vigorously with a sturdy glass stirring rod while the hydrogen chloride is flowing to prevent the product from hardening into a rocklike mass. When the material is solid and appears dry, heating is stopped and the material is crushed and covered with freshly distilled thionyl chloride in a flask. Refluxing speeds up the further dehydration considerably, but is not essential. Upon dehydration, the lumps of uranyl chloride 1-hydrate form a light yellow powder having an appearance very similar to that of powdered sulfur. The excess thionyl chloride is decanted and the flask connected to a water aspirator through a drying tube. During the application of suction, the flask is warmed gently in a water bath until no liquid can be seen in the flask, at which time the product is transferred to a vacuum drying

* Mallinkrodt Chemical Co. reagent-grade.

oven maintained at 80° and allowed to dry there for an hour. The yield of product is essentially quantitative.

Since reagent-grade uranyl nitrate is used in the preparation, since no traces of nitrate are left in the product, and since the analyses for uranium, chlorine, and oxygen agree so well with theory, the criterion for per cent purity and for the composition of the compound can be based on the analyzed and theoretical percentages of uranium, chlorine, and oxygen in the product. No water analysis, as such, need be made since the one water molecule is bound so tightly by uranyl chloride that its determination would be of doubtful value. *Anal.* Calcd. for $UO_2Cl_2 \cdot H_2O$: U, 66.31; Cl, 20.82; O, 13.4. Found: U, 66.24, 66.20; Cl, 19.74, 19.72; O, 13.3. Ratio: $Cl/U = 2.001$. On the assumption that metallic impurities are absent, the formula is $UO_2Cl_2 \cdot 1.008H_2O$.

Properties

Uranyl chloride 1-hydrate is a yellow powderlike material resembling powdered sulfur in appearance. The compound is very hygroscopic, takes up water vapor from the air readily, and must be handled in a dry-box. Its other properties are similar to those listed for anhydrous uranyl chloride.[2] The monohydrate is soluble in polar solvents such as ethanol and acetone but does not dissolve in non-polar solvents. Its aqueous solutions are stable at room temperature and its alcoholic solutions are unstable. The anhydrous compound, several hydrates, and addition compounds with halides and amines have been described.

References

1. J. A. LEARY and J. F. SUTTLE: INORGANIC SYNTHESES, **5**, 148 (1957).
2. J. J. KATZ and E. RABINOWITCH: "The Chemistry of Uranium," Part I, National Nuclear Energy Series, Div. VII, Vol. 5, Part 8, pp. 577–587, McGraw-Hill Book Company, Inc., New York, 1951.
3. F. FEIGL: "Spot Tests," Vol. I, p. 300, Elsevier Publishing Co., New York, 1954.

CHAPTER VIIA

42. SODIUM FLUORIDE(F^{18})

Submitted by D. R. Stranks*
Checked by Floyd B. Baker†

One hundred-and-eighteen-minute F^{18} is the longest-lived radioisotope of fluorine and may be produced by one of three nuclear reactions:[1]

(1) $F^{19}(\gamma,n)F^{18}$, using 48- to 84-M.e.v. x-rays from a betatron and KHF_2 as a target material.

(2) $F^{19}(n,2n)F^{18}$, using fast neutrons from the $Li^6(d,n)Be^7$ reaction in a cyclotron and KHF_2 as a target.

(3) $O^{16}(t,n)F^{18}$, using the 2.65-M.e.v. tritons from the $Li^6(n,\alpha)H^3$ reaction in a nuclear reactor.

The most generally accessible machine is the nuclear reactor, and large activities of F^{18} can be induced by the neutron bombardment of oxygen salts of lithium [reaction (3)]. Lithium carbonate is the most convenient oxygen salt because of its high thermal stability (temperatures around 250° are developed by self-heating of lithium salts in an intense neutron flux), its ease of purification (since lithium carbonate has a negative temperature coefficient of solu-

* University of Melbourne, Victoria, Australia.
† Los Alamos Scientific Laboratory, Los Alamos, N.M.

bility), its nondeliquescent nature, and the relatively high yield of F^{18} produced per gram of material irradiated.

The recommended procedure yields NaF^{18} solutions of known chemical composition, from which other inorganic F^{18} compounds may be synthesized either by direct chemical methods or by isotopic exchange. The use of apparatus of polyethylene (or other comparable plastics) is recommended for most parts of the preparation, first to reduce contaminants in the target material and second to reduce losses of HF^{18} in the final purification stage.

Procedure

$$Li^6(n,\alpha)H^3; \qquad O^{16}(H^3,n)F^{18}$$

Fifteen grams of analytical-grade lithium carbonate* is dissolved in 1 l. of double-distilled water in a polyethylene beaker. The solution is first boiled on a steam bath and the beaker is then placed in an oven at 100° to allow the lithium carbonate crystals to settle. As much as possible of the hot supernatant solution is decanted and the remaining wet crystals are dried at 100°. Approximately 8 g. of recrystallized lithium carbonate is obtained.

A standard aluminum irradiation can (e.g., 1.2-cm. radius, 5-cm. length) is fitted with an aluminum liner tube (e.g., 0.9-cm. radius, 5-cm. length) to provide a 3-mm. annulus into which lithium carbonate can be packed.† Depending on the amount of F^{18} required (see below for the expected yield of F^{18} per gram) up to 10 g. of recrystallized lithium carbonate is packed into the annular space within

---

* The purification of lithium carbonate by taking advantage of its negative coefficient of solubility has been described by E. R. Caley and P. J. Elving, INORGANIC SYNTHESES, **1**, 1 (1939).

† Because of the high neutron cross section of lithium salts, the effective neutron flux at thicknesses of lithium exceeding 3 to 4 mm. is quite small.[2] Thus greater thicknesses of Li_2CO_3 do not improve the F^{18} yield yet lead to more serious radiation problems.

the irradiation can, which is irradiated in a nuclear reactor for up to 10 hours.*   After a half-hour "cooling period" for the decay of 2.27-minute Al^{28}, the contents of the can are transferred to a small glass beaker containing 5 ml. of a carrier solution consisting of 20 mg. of sodium fluoride and 5 mg. of sodium chloride.   The lithium carbonate is dissolved completely by the dropwise addition of concentrated nitric acid and the final solution transferred to a 15-ml. glass centrifuge tube.   Chloride ion is precipitated by the dropwise addition of silver nitrate until the coagulation of silver chloride (which scavenges most contaminant activities) is just complete.   After centrifugation, the supernatant solution is transferred by dropper pipet to a polyethylene centrifuge tube containing 50 mg. of magnesium chloride. The solution is made alkaline to methyl red by the dropwise addition of dilute sodium hydroxide solution, and complete precipitation of $\{Mg(OH)_2 + MgF_2\}$ is ensured by chilling the centrifuge tube for 5 minutes in ice.   After centrifugation, all but approximately 0.5 ml. of the supernatant liquid is removed by dropper pipet.   The centrifuge tube containing the wet fluoride precipitate is attached to a bubbling train consisting of polyethylene centrifuge tubes fitted with polyethylene plugs drilled for 2-mm.-i.d. polyethylene tubing (Fig. 15.).   The tubing is jointed by standard cones and sockets machined from polyethylene block. All plugs and standard joints are lightly lubricated with a silicone, or better, a fluorinated vacuum grease.   Tube I contains 5 ml. of concentrated sulfuric acid, tube II the wet fluoride sample, tube III acts as a simple spray tube, and tubes IV and V each contain 5 ml. of 0.1 N sodium hydroxide (carbonate-free).†

After the bubbling train is assembled, sulfuric acid is gently forced from tube I into II by nitrogen pressure, and

---

* Longer irradiation times do not increase significantly the F^{18} yield but produce more long-lived contaminants.

† If methanolic NaF^{18} is required, the sodium hydroxide can be prepared in anhydrous methanol.

evolution of HF^{18} commences immediately. Nitrogen is forced through the bubbling train at a rate of about two bubbles per second. After the initial reaction has abated (a few minutes), tube II is heated with a beaker of boiling water for a further fifteen minutes. Approximately 90% of the F^{18} activity is trapped in IV and the remainder in V. (The course of the reaction is readily followed by means of a

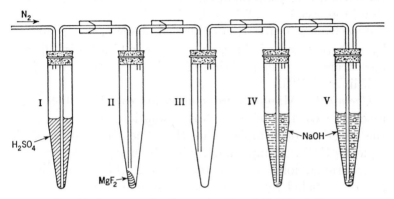

FIG. 15. Apparatus for the preparation of NaF^{18} solutions.

well-shielded portable Geiger counter or monitor.) Finally the solutions in IV and V are removed by suction pipet to a glass storage vessel. The combined solution will be 0.05 N in NaF^{18} and 0.05 N in NaOH. If desired, the alkali can be neutralized with the stoichiometric quantity of mineral acid or dilute hydrofluoric acid. The entire chemical treatment may be completed within an hour.

   Irradiation of 1 g. of lithium carbonate in a thermal neutron flux of 1×10^{12} neutrons cm.$^{-2}$ sec.$^{-1}$ produces approximately 0.5 millicurie of F^{18} at the time of removal from the reactor, but larger quantities of lithium carbonate or higher neutron fluxes will yield proportionately higher F^{18} activities. The efficiency of the $O^{16}(t,n)F^{18}$ reaction in lithium carbonate is 1.6×10^{-5}. Decay measurements show that the F^{18} samples usually contain less than 0.01% of radioactive contaminants. Chemical tracer work is usually possible with an initial 0.5 millicurie of F^{18} for 12 to 24 hours after irradiation has ceased.

Properties

Isotopic. Fluorine-18 exhibits a half-life of 112 minutes and emits 0.65-M.e.v. positrons, with which are associated the 0.51-M.e.v. γ-annihilation radiation. Samples are most simply assayed as solids or liquids with a Geiger counter, but positive identification of the isotope is best carried out by spectrometry of the γ-radiation combined with decay measurements over a period of at least 8 hours (i.e., four half-lives of F^{18}).

Chemical. Many fluoro complexes can be labeled by reaction with the acidified NaF^{18} solution, as for example, the reaction of complexes of the type $CoX_{4-5}CO_3$ with aqueous HF^{18}. Simple inorganic salts may be prepared by conventional ion-exchange techniques. Some compounds may be labeled by direct isotopic exchange as with HF^{18}_{aq} and H_2SiF_6,[3] although fluorinated methanes do not readily exchange.[4] The preparation of anhydrous HF^{18} and the halogen fluorides must be performed in metal vacuum apparatus by exchanging the gaseous fluoro compound directly with the irradiated lithium salt.[5]

References

1. R. B. BERNSTEIN and J. J. KATZ: *Nucleonics* **11**, No. 10, 46 (1953).
2. L. G. STANG, W. D. TUCKER, R. F. DOERING, A. J. WEISS, M. W. GREENE, and H. O. BANKS: "UNESCO International Conference on Radio-Isotopes (Paris 1957)," Pergamon Press, New York (1958).
3. A. H. W. ATEN, JR., and J. A. BIGOT: *Rec. trav. chim.*, **72**, 1002 (1953).
4. M. T. ROGERS and J. J. KATZ: *J. Am. Chem. Soc.*, **74**, 1375 (1952).
5. R. B. BERNSTEIN and J. J. KATZ: *J. Phys. Chem.*, **56**, 885 (1952).

43. CHLORINE(Cl^{36})-LABELED DEUTERIUM CHLORIDE

{Hydrogen-D Chloride(Cl^{36})}

$$D_2SO_4 + NaCl^{36} \rightarrow NaDSO_4 + DCl^{36}$$

SUBMITTED BY R. H. HERBER*
CHECKED BY B. J. MASTERS†

The investigation of isotope effects in chemical kinetics has come to play an important role in the study of reaction mechanisms. Doubly labeled hydrogen chloride is useful in the elucidation of isotope effects in isotopic exchange reaction studies.

In the preparation of DCl^{36}, it is important to avoid the introduction of either H_2SO_4 or H_2O into the sulfuric acid-D_2 (deuterosulfuric acid), D_2SO_4, used in the final step of the synthesis. For this reason, sulfur trioxide is first distilled from fuming sulfuric acid into an ice-cooled receiver. The sulfur trioxide is then revaporized into D_2O. Under these conditions any H_2SO_4 carried over in the first distillation step will remain behind in the sulfur trioxide reservoir. For maximum isotopic purity, it is necessary to use an all-glass system in the preparation of the D_2SO_4 since neither stopcock grease nor flexible tubing is inert to attack by sulfur trioxide.

Procedure

The synthesis of deuterium chloride (Cl^{36}) requires the preparation of completely deuterated sulfuric acid. This material is prepared from sulfur trioxide and 99% deuterium

* Rutgers—The State University, New Brunswick, N.J. Research supported in part by the U.S. Atomic Energy Commission.
† Los Alamos Scientific Laboratory, Los Alamos, N.M.

oxide as described below.*   The apparatus for obtaining
sulfur trioxide is shown in Fig. 16.   The boiler of the distilling set-up is charged with 58 ml. (100 g.) of fuming sulfuric acid (with 65% excess sulfur trioxide).   The boiler
is then warmed gently with a flame until the oxide (b.p.

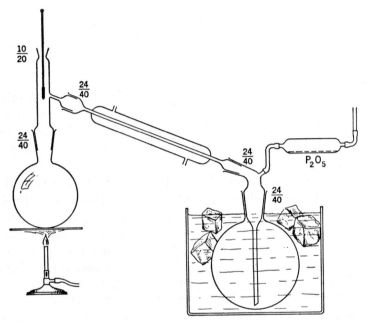

Fig. 16. Apparatus for the preparation of sulfur trioxide.

44.8°) is evolved.   There is usually considerable fuming
before all of the atmospheric moisture is eliminated from
the system.   (This initial fuming, although it does not
interfere with the synthesis, can be eliminated by flushing
the apparatus with dry nitrogen.)   The sulfur trioxide is
allowed to condense in the condenser (through which water
should be circulated only if the ambient temperature is in
excess of 32°) and flow into the ice-cooled receiver, where

* The procedure given for making D_2SO_4 is a modification of one described
by N. N. Greenwood and A. Thompson, INORGANIC SYNTHESES, **6,** 121
(1960).

it sets to a white crystalline mass composed of long needles. The distillation of the trioxide is continued until the temperature of the vapor exceeds 45°.

At this point the flask containing the solid sulfur trioxide is transferred to a warm water bath and connected via an all-glass delivery tube ending in a sintered-glass gas dispersion tip to a receiver containing 5 ml. of 99% D_2O (Fig. 17).

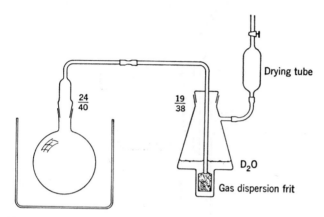

FIG. 17. Apparatus for the preparation of deuterosulfuric acid.

The receiver flask is vented through a drying tube containing a small amount of phosphorus(V) oxide to prevent back diffusion of atmospheric moisture into the D_2SO_4. The receiver flask, which is provided with a magnetic stirring bar, is set in an ice bath on top of a magnetic stirrer. After the assembly is completed, the water bath surrounding the sulfur trioxide is warmed gently until the oxide bubbles into the D_2O. The heat of the aquation reaction is sufficient to keep the pores of the fritted plug open, even though the temperature of the receiver flask is below the melting point of the trioxide. The transfer of gaseous trioxide is continued until the temperature of the water bath reaches about 70° or until the liquid volume in the receiver is 15 ml. At this point the D_2SO_4 in the ice-cooled receiver will correspond to about 100% sulfuric acid.

The sulfuric acid-D₂ is transferred to the separatory funnel of the apparatus shown in Fig. 18. Since this device will become part of a high-vacuum gas-handling system, both the funnel stopcock and the standard-taper ground

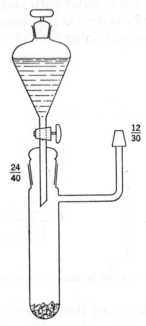

Fig. 18. Apparatus for the preparation of Cl³⁶-labeled deuterium chloride.

joint must be lubricated. Any nonprotonated stopcock grease* may be employed for this purpose to ensure a vacuum-tight seal. The reaction vessel is charged with 100 mg. (0.00171 mol) of c.p. sodium chloride dissolved in a minimal quantity (about 0.5 ml. is sufficient) of distilled water† to which has been added 0.2 ml. of HCl³⁶‡ having a

---

* For example, Kel-F grease, M. W. Kellogg Co., Item S-8076, Scientific Glass Supply Co.

† If the supply of D₂O is adequate, the use of heavy water as a solvent for the sodium chloride will avoid the possibility of contamination of the final product with HCl by occluded H₂O in the crystals.

‡ Obtained as an aqueous solution, about 1.5 molar, as Item 36-D, Oak Ridge National Laboratory.

specific activity of 35 microcuries per ml. The apparatus (Fig. 18) is attached by means of the male ground joint to a vacuum system, and the water removed by exposing the salt solution to vacuum. The solid residue so obtained may be dried thoroughly by cautious flaming of the salt under vacuum conditions. Care must be taken to avoid spattering.

The sulfuric acid-D_2 is then allowed to fall dropwise from the separatory funnel onto the dried $NaCl^{36}$. (*Care!* Foaming may occur at this point if the rate of addition is too rapid. This rapid gas evolution can be minimized if the cold-finger containing the $NaCl^{36}$ is cooled to about 0° with an ice bath.) The resultant DCl^{36} is condensed into a liquid-nitrogen-cooled cold-finger attached elsewhere on the vacuum line. Addition of the D_2SO_4 is continued dropwise until gas evolution ceases.

It should be noted that at some sacrifice of high specific activity, the total yield of DCl can be increased by increasing the quantity of sodium chloride used in the synthesis. Since the quantity of D_2SO_4 prepared is about 0.250 mol, the stoichiometric quantity of sodium chloride which can be used is about 14.6 grams. However, practical limitations of solubility and handling make the use of more than 2 to 3 g. of the salt impractical.

The DCl^{36} must be freed of small amounts of excess sulfur trioxide which may be present in the sulfuric acid and which will have been condensed by the liquid nitrogen. This is done by warming the cold-finger carefully to acetone–Dry Ice temperature ($-78°$) and transferring the DCl^{36} to a second nitrogen-cooled cold-finger by distillation. The sulfur trioxide will remain behind in the first receiver.

Analysis

The two analytical problems associated with the preparation of deuterium chloride (Cl^{36}) are analysis of the product for Cl^{36} content and for deuterium content. The radioassay can be carried out either by the precipitation and counting of solid samples (e.g., Hg_2Cl_2, $AgCl$)[1,2] or by gas-phase radioassay.[3]   The deuterium analysis of small samples requires mass spectrometric techniques.[4]   Such analyses should, however, be carried out on replicate DCl samples prepared in an identical manner from nonradioactive NaCl, or better with D_2O obtained from the original DCl sample. Such analyses will give only the maximum DCl/HCl ratio in the final sample, since this cannot exceed the deuterium purity of the initial heavy water.

References

1. A. J. FREEDMAN, J. R. FELTHAM, N. LARK, and M. KAHN: *Nucleonics,* **13**, No. 5, 58 (1955).
2. P. SORENSON: *Anal. Chem.,* **27**, 391 (1955).
3. R. H. HERBER: *Rev. Sci. Instr.,* **28**, 1049 (1957); M. T. ROGERS and J. J. KATZ: *J. Am. Chem. Soc.,* **74**, 1375 (1952); R. B. BERNSTEIN, *et al.*: *J. Chem. Phys.,* **23**, 1622 (1955).
4. E. M. ARNETT, *et al.*: *Science,* **131**, 1680 (1960).

44. CHLORINE(Cl^{36})-LABELED THIONYL CHLORIDE, SILICON TETRACHLORIDE, BORON CHLORIDE, GERMANIUM(IV) CHLORIDE, AND PHOSPHORUS(III) CHLORIDE

SUBMITTED BY R. H. HERBER*
CHECKED BY FLOYD B. BAKER†

A wide variety of volatile chlorides can be labeled with Cl^{36} radiotracer ($T_{\frac{1}{2}} = 3.08 \times 10^5$ years, $E_{max} = 0.714$ M.e.v.)

* Rutgers—The State University, New Brunswick, N.J.   Research supported in part by the U.S. Atomic Energy Commission.
† Los Alamos Scientific Laboratory, Los Alamos, N.M.

by taking advantage of the rapid isotopic exchange reaction of these halides with anhydrous tetramethylammonium chloride.

Procedure

A reaction vessel is constructed of a 30-ml. Pyrex test tube fitted with a 2-mm. stopcock and a male 10/30 standard-taper ground joint. About 110 mg. (0.001 mol) of reagent-grade tetramethylammonium chloride is dissolved in 5 ml. of distilled water and the solution is transferred via a capillary medicine dropper into the reaction vessel through the opened stopcock. Two drops (about 0.1 ml.) of chlorine-36 stock solution* are diluted with 1 ml. of distilled water and sufficient 6 M sodium hydroxide (about one drop) to give a basic solution, and this solution is introduced into the reaction vessel with the capillary dropper.

The reaction tube is shaken to mix the contents and is then attached to an all-glass vacuum system. The water is removed by pumping in the usual manner. After the salt has been sucked reasonably dry, it may be heated on a hot water bath and exposed to continued pumping until a static vacuum of 0.1 micron or less is attained (important in avoiding subsequent hydrolysis).

A measured quantity (normally 0.010 mol) of a volatile halide such as thionyl chloride, silicon tetrachloride, boron chloride, germanium(IV) chloride, or phosphorus(III) chloride is then dosed into the reaction vessel, with liquid nitrogen as a refrigerant. The reaction vessel is isolated from the vacuum manifold and warmed to 0° in an ice bath to bring about liquefaction of the volatile chloride. Intermittent shaking of the ice-bath-cooled reactants for a period of 1 to 4 hours usually ensures complete exchange of the radio-

* Item 36-P, Oak Ridge National Laboratory. Supplied as 1.64 N HCl with a specific activity of 0.035 to 0.004 mc./ml.

chlorine, even though the solubility of the tetramethyl-ammonium chloride in the chlorides is very limited.

At the end of this time, the volatile chloride is separated from the tetramethylammonium chloride by distillation, by again using high-vacuum gas-transfer techniques. Quantitative recovery of the volatile halide can be effected in all cases. The final specific activity of the labeled chloride depends upon the initial specific activity of the labeled tetramethylammonium salt and the quantity of volatile halide labeled. On the assumption of complete randomization of chlorine activity, the specific activity of the volatile halide is given by:

$$\frac{m \text{ mols of } (CH_3)_4NCl \times \text{ sp. activity of } (CH_3)_4NCl}{n \times m \text{ mols of volatile halide} + m \text{ mols of } (CH_3)_4NCl} = \frac{cpm.}{mg.} Cl$$

in which n is the number of replaceable chlorine atoms per molecule of volatile chloride.

Analysis

The specific radioactivity of the labeled product can be obtained either by solid-sample counting[1,2] of mercury(I) chloride or by gas-phase radioassay[3] of the volatile halide itself. In the former method it is necessary to distill an aliquot of the volatile halide into aqueous base and to isolate the chloride formed on hydrolysis by precipitation with mercury(I) nitrate. The gas-phase nondestructive radioassay yields a specific activity in terms of pressure rather than in terms of weight of mercury(I) chloride.

References

1. A. J. FREEDMAN, J. R. FELTHAM, N. LARK, and M. KAHN: *Nucleonics*, **13**, No. 5, 58 (1955).
2. P. SORENSON: *Anal. Chem.*, **27**, 391 (1955).
3. R. H. HERBER: *Rev. Sci. Instr.*, **28**, 1049 (1957).

45. ANHYDROUS METAL CHLORIDES*

$$M_2O_n + nCCl_4 \rightarrow 2MCl_n + nCOCl_2$$

Submitted by E. R. Epperson,[†] S. M. Horner,[‡] K. Knox,[§] and S. Y. Tyree, Jr.[‡]
Checked by J. R. Crook[¶] and George Gibson[¶]

The method of Michael and Murphy,[1] as modified by Knox *et al.*,[2] can be used to prepare several polyvalent metal chlorides. Oxides are converted to chlorides by heating with an excess of carbon tetrachloride in a sealed glass tube. The high pressures generated are balanced by placing the sealed tube inside a high-pressure steel reaction vessel containing the proper amount of liquid.

There are several advantages inherent in the method. Oxides of the metals are generally available or easily made in pure form. The reagents need not be excessively dry, because small amounts of water are converted to phosgene and hydrogen chloride. The convers on is complete and the only losses are manipulative ones. In most cases rather large crystals are formed which tend to be quite pure and are relatively insensitive to hydrolysis by virtue of their small surface-to-volume ratio.

Procedure

Metal oxide and reagent-grade carbon tetrachloride are placed in the glass reaction tube ($1\frac{1}{2}$-in. o.d. and 5 in. long) shown in Fig. 19. Eight milliliters of liquid carbon tetrachloride is used for every 26 ml. of internal volume of the

*For other communications on the general preparation of anhydrous metal halides see Inorganic Syntheses 4, 1953, synthesis 36; 5, 1957, synthesis 43.
† Elon College, Elon College, N.C.
‡ University of North Carolina, Chapel Hill, N.C.
§ Bell Telephone Laboratories, Murray Hill, N.J.
¶ Illinois Institute of Technology, Chicago, Ill.

glass reaction tube. The amount of metal oxide is that calculated to allow the presence of a five-fold excess of carbon tetrachloride, according to the equation for the reaction. The excess carbon tetrachloride is needed to dissolve and thereby reduce the final pressure of product gases, phosgene, and sometimes chlorine, and to dissolve the solid chlorocarbon by-products which would otherwise contaminate the product.

The neck of the reaction tube is sealed and heated carefully to give a uniformly thick seal. After flame-annealing the neck, the reaction tube is placed inside the steel bomb.* If standard-wall reaction tubes are used, the same proportion of carbon tetrachloride to free volume is maintained in the steel bomb as in the glass tube. If heavy-wall tubes are used, 66 ml. of liquid water at room temperature is used for every 1410 ml. of free volume in the steel bomb.

The steel bomb is closed and the assembly heated to 400° for 3 to 4 hours, the pressure developed being about 100 atmospheres. There is no danger of an explosion here, but the usual precautions taken in high-pressure, high-temperature work should be observed. If a leak should develop in the seal, obnoxious gases will escape. The assembly is allowed to cool to room temperature, and the steel bomb is opened in a hood or out-of-doors.

The reaction tube now contains gases under pressure, estimated to be about 1 to 2 atmospheres at room temperature, and so it should be handled carefully. It is opened in a hood by playing an oxy-gas flame on the sealed tip, which blows out because of the pressure inside the tube. (*Caution.* The tip should be heated on a side which will make it blow out in a safe direction.) The whole top of the tube is taken off. This is done by scratching the side of the tube with a sharp file just below the shoulder (before opening the tip with the flame) and leading the scratch around

---

* The bomb was obtained from the American Instrument Co., Silver Spring, Md. It had an i.d. of $3\frac{5}{16}$ in., an o.d. of $4\frac{3}{8}$ in., and a depth of 10 in. Its catalog description was Aminco Reaction Vessel no. 41-4150.

the tube with a red-hot glass rod.   These operations should be carried out as rapidly as possible so they will be completed before effervescence ceases and air enters the tube.

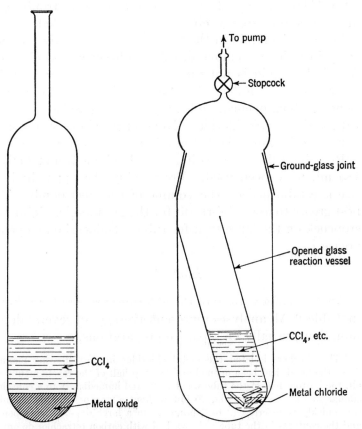

FIG. 19. Glass vessel for reaction of metal oxides with carbon tetrachloride.

FIG. 20. Container for removal of opened reaction vessel to dry-box.

The tube is placed inside another tube fitted with a groundglass joint and stopcock at the top (Fig. 20).   The stopcock is joined to a vacuum system by a rubber tube through a Dry Ice–acetone trap and a tower of sodium hydroxide pellets.   It is partly opened very carefully, by adjusting the stopcock so as to give a steady but not violent ebullition.

Rapid boiling causes cooling, which tends to decrease the rate of boiling to the point where bumping can be very bad. The external application of sufficient heat by means of an infrared lamp is very effective in overcoming the trouble and in maintaining steady ebullition. About one-half of the volume of the liquid in the reaction tube is slowly pumped away in order to remove dissolved phosgene and chlorine. All of the liquid is not pumped away, as otherwise solid chlorocarbons will deposit. The tube is removed to an efficient dry-box, opened, and the product filtered and washed with carbon tetrachloride. None of the chlorides reported appear to be appreciably soluble in carbon tetrachloride.*

Reaction tubes varying in internal volume from 22 ml. to 185 ml. have been used. Presumably the upper limit in size is established by the volume of the steel bomb. The best grease to use as lubricant for the ground-glass joint and stopcock on the large transfer tube is Halocarbon stopcock grease.†

Analysis

Analyses of a variety of the chlorides prepared are shown in Table I. All analyses represent averages of several determinations, usually on separate preparations.

* The checkers isolated the metal chlorides in the following manner. After the bomb had been opened and the top half of the reaction tube cut off, the bottom half of the tube was transferred immediately to a container similar to that shown in Fig. 20 but without a stopcock. This assembly was quickly transferred (2 to 3 minutes) to a large dry-box and opened, and the contents in the tube were washed with carbon tetrachloride onto a sintered-glass funnel and suction flask assembly connected to a suction system external to the dry-box. In this operation and subsequent washing with carbon tetrachloride, the chlorides were not drawn completely dry. After washing, the carbon tetrachloride-wet crystals were transferred to a smaller version of the container shown in Fig. 20 and pumped dry on a conventional vacuum line. The dried product and container (under vacuum) were then transferred to a smaller dry-box, where samples were taken for analysis. Both dry-boxes were kept flushed with P_4O_{10}-dried, purified nitrogen.

† Obtainable from Halocarbon Products Corp., North Bergen, N.J.

TABLE I

Chloride	Starting oxide	Analyses*				Cl/M
		Metal		Chlorine		
		Calcd.	Found	Calcd.	Found	
FeCl$_3$	Fe$_2$O$_3$	34.43	34.43	65.57	65.41	2.99
ReCl$_5$	Re$_2$O$_7$	51.23	51.18	48.77	48.11	4.92†
MoCl$_5$	MoO$_3$	35.12	35.44	64.88	64.62	4.93†
WCl$_6$	WO$_3$	46.36	46.25	53.64	53.50	6.00
NbCl$_5$	Nb$_2$O$_5$	34.39	34.52	65.61	65.44	4.97
TaCl$_5$	Ta$_2$O$_5$	50.51	50.84	49.49	49.32	4.95
ZrCl$_4$	ZrO$_2$	39.43	39.54	60.57	60.43	3.98‡
AlCl$_3$	Al$_2$O$_3$	20.23	20.31	79.77	79.64	2.98

* In the preparation of samples for analysis they are hydrolyzed for several hours in tubes designed to prevent loss of chloride (as HCl) in the fumes frequently formed on reaction with water.

† It is the belief of one of us (S.Y.T.) that these low ratios are due to surface reaction of these two chlorides with small amounts of oxygen in the dry-box chamber, and that the method itself yields pure products in both cases.

‡ The atomic weight of 92.3 was used for zirconium, since the ZrO$_2$ sample is assumed to contain about 2% hafnium as in natural zirconium ores.

Comments on Individual Preparations

Iron(III) chloride crystals are large flat dark green plates. Some of the very thin plates appear red by transmitted light although dark green by reflected light.

Rhenium(VII) oxide must be sublimed into the glass reaction tube, the pressure in the system brought to just above atmospheric pressure, the connecting tube cut, and the carbon tetrachloride quickly poured in through a funnel. The rhenium(V) chloride product is in the form of large green-black crystals, under a green liquid, indicating some slight solubility in the mother liquor.

Molybdenum(V) chloride crystals are very dark-colored beneath a brown solution. Upon sucking the crystals dry during the washing procedure, the surfaces of the crystals turn a very pale green, which color is removed by soaking the crystals in a fresh portion of carbon tetrachloride. It is believed that the crystals pick up oxygen (in the dry-box), forming the dioxide chloride. The checkers note that with their procedure for isolation of products the green color is not observed.

The tungsten(VI) chloride product forms large black crystals underneath a reddish liquid. The crystals are not easily soluble in water, as reported for the direct-synthesis product.[3] Digestion with hot aqueous ammonia for one hour is necessary to dissolve completely samples of the hexachloride prepared by this procedure.

Lemon-yellow needles of niobium(V) chloride are obtained under a pale yellow solution. Usually a few small dirty-white pellets are observed in the product. They are easily picked out, and upon grinding in the dry-box they turn yellow. Emission spectra of the ground pellets show only lines characteristic of niobium, and the pellets are completely soluble in water. Since only very small amounts of the white pellets are found in any one preparation, it is not possible to analyze the material quantitatively, but it is believed that they are essentially niobium(V) chloride also.

Pure white crystals of tantalum(V) chloride, zirconium-(IV) chloride, and aluminum chloride are obtained. The supernatant liquids are pale yellow in these cases owing to dissolved chlorine.

Under the experimental conditions described above, zinc oxide, lanthanum(III) oxide, cadmium oxide, and thorium-(IV) oxide are partially converted to the corresponding chlorides.

Properties

The properties of tungsten(VI) chloride,[3] iron(III) chloride,[4] niobium(V) chloride,[5] tantalum(V) chloride,[5] rhenium(V) chloride,[6] molybdenum(V) chloride,[7] zirconium-

(IV) chloride,[8] and aluminum chloride[9] have been described elsewhere.

References

1. A. MICHAEL and A. MURPHY: *Am. Chem. J.*, **44**, 365 (1910).
2. K. KNOX, *et al.*: *J. Am. Chem. Soc.*, **79**, 3358 (1957).
3. M. H. LIETZKE and M. L. HOLT: INORGANIC SYNTHESES, **3**, 163 (1950).
4. B. R. TARR: *ibid.*, **3**, 191 (1950).
5. K. M. ALEXANDER and F. FAIRBROTHER: *J. Chem. Soc.*, **1949**, 233.
6. L. C. HURD and E. BRIMM: INORGANIC SYNTHESES, **1**, 180 (1939).
7. O. HÖNIGSCHMID and G. WITTMAN: *Z. anorg. u. allgem. Chem.*, **229**, 65 (1936).
8. W. S. HUMMERS, S. Y. TYREE, JR., and S. YOLLES: INORGANIC SYNTHESES, **4**, 121 (1953).
9. R. E. DODD and R. L. ROBINSON: "Experimental Inorganic Chemistry," p. 205, Elsevier Publishing Co., Amsterdam, 1954.

46. UNIPOSITIVE HALOGEN COMPLEXES

As is well known, the electronegativities of the halogens decrease with increasing atomic weight. Studies[1-4] have shown that positive halogen ions such as X^+ or $X(H_2O)_y^+$ do not exist in appreciable concentration in aqueous solution, even for bromine and iodine. However, unipositive halogen cations can be stabilized by coordination, and Carlsohn[5] has made extensive studies of unipositive iodine salts in which pyridine or its homologs are the stabilizing ligands. The corresponding bromine(I) compounds have also been obtained.[6,7] In addition to the work cited above, a number of recent investigations on positive halogen complexes have been reported.[8,9,10,11]

A common method for the preparation of these compounds involves the reaction of a silver salt with the halogen in a dry, mildly polar solvent such as chloroform, in the presence of the coordinating base, e.g., pyridine or quinoline. The silver salt may be used in the form of its complex with the coordinating base. The silver halide precipitate is separated by filtration and the complex is salted out with anhydrous ether or petroleum ether. Procedures are given below for the preparation of monoquinolineiodine(I) benzoate, dipyridinebromine(I) nitrate, and dipyridinebromine(I) perchlorate, as representative examples of positive halogen complexes.

Evidence indicates that the adduct of iod ne(I) chloride and pyridine (synthesis 47) contains unipositive iodine stabilized by coordination with pyridine.

A. MONOQUINOLINEIODINE(I) BENZOATE

[Benzoato(quinoline)iodine(I)]

$$AgC_7H_5O_2 + I_2 + C_9H_7N \rightarrow [I(C_9H_7N)(C_7H_5O_2)] + AgI$$

SUBMITTED BY R. A. ZINGARO* AND W. B. WITMER*
CHECKED BY ALEXANDER I. POPOV†

Procedure

In a carefully dried, 500-ml. glass-stoppered Erlenmeyer flask, 11.5 g. (0.05 mol) of dry powdered silver benzoate is suspended in 100 ml. of chloroform which has been previously dried and distilled from calcium chloride. To the suspension of the silver salt is added a solution of 7 g. (slightly in excess of 0.05 mol) of quinoline in 100 ml. of chloroform. Dry powdered iodine is added in small portions with vigorous shaking, until a total of 12.7 g. (0.1 mol) has been added over a period of 5 minutes. After continued vigorous shaking for an additional 10 minutes the suspension is transferred rapidly to a sintered-glass filter of medium porosity through which dried air can be drawn (Fig. 21).

* Texas A. and M. College, College Station, Tex.
† Northern Illinois University, De Kalb, Ill.; present address, Michigan State University, East Lansing, Mich.

The chloroform filtrate is separated and transferred to a 1-l. flask, and 500 ml. of dry, low-boiling petroleum ether is added. The pale yellow crystalline precipitate is separated by filtration in a moisture-free atmosphere (Fig. 21) and

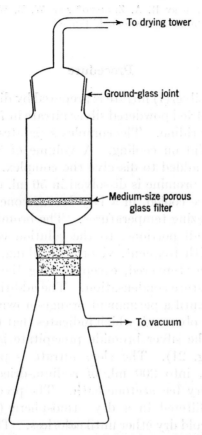

Fɪɢ. 21. Apparatus for moisture-free filtration.

washed with ethyl ether which has been dried over sodium. The product is then dried, and stored *in vacuo* over sulfuric acid. The yield is about 70%. The product melts over the range 140 to 150°, with decomposition. *Anal.* Calcd. for $[I(C_9H_7N)(C_7H_5O_2)]$: I, 33.7; C_9H_7N, 34.2. Found: I, 33.5, 33.6; C_9H_7N, 34.2.

B. DIPYRIDINEBROMINE(I) NITRATE

$$[Ag(C_5H_5N)_2]NO_3 + Br_2 \rightarrow [Br(C_5H_5N)_2]NO_3 + AgBr$$

SUBMITTED BY R. A. ZINGARO* AND W. B. WITMER*
CHECKED BY ALEXANDER I. POPOV†

Procedure

Dipyridinesilver(I) nitrate is prepared by dissolving 8.5 g. (0.05 mol) of dried powdered silver nitrate in 7.9 g. (0.1 mol) of pure dry pyridine. The complex separates as a colorless crystalline solid on cooling. A volume of 30 ml. of dry chloroform is added to dissolve the complex. In a second flask, 10 g. of bromine is dissolved in 50 ml. of chloroform. Both flasks are cooled, in a Dry Ice–acetone bath, to just above the freezing temperatures. The bromine solution is added, in small portions, to the solution containing the silver salt, with frequent, vigorous shaking. Both flasks should remain stoppered, except during the additions, to minimize moisture condensation. The addition of bromine is continued until a permanent orange-brown coloration of the halogen is observed, which indicates that the reaction is complete. The silver bromide precipitate is removed by filtration (Fig. 21). The clear filtrate is poured slowly, with shaking, into 200 ml. of sodium-dried ethyl ether cooled in a Dry Ice–acetone bath. The precipitate which separates is filtered in a dry atmosphere (Fig. 21) and washed with cold dry ether until colorless. The dipyridine-bromine(I) nitrate acquires a very pale yellowish cast as soon as all the ether is removed. The product, obtained in a yield in excess of 90%, melts at 79 to 80°. *Anal.* Calcd. for $[Br(C_5H_5N)_2]NO_3$: Br, 26.6; C_5H_5N, 52.7. Found: Br, 26.0; C_5H_5N, 52.5, 52.3.

* Texas A. and M. College, College Station, Tex.
† Northern Illinois University, De Kalb, Ill.; present address, Michigan State University, East Lansing, Mich.

C. DIPYRIDINEBROMINE(I) PERCHLORATE

$$[Ag(C_5H_5N)_2]ClO_4 + Br_2 \rightarrow [Br(C_5H_5N)_2]ClO_4 + AgBr$$

SUBMITTED BY GEORGE B. KAUFFMAN* AND KENNETH L. STEVENS*
CHECKED BY SIGEO KIDA† AND J. V. QUAGLIANO†

Procedure

Seven and thirty-one hundredths grams (0.02 mol) of dipyridinesilver(I) perchlorate[12] is dissolved in a mixture of 15 ml. of dry chloroform‡ and 1.5 ml. of dry pyridine‡ contained in a 125-ml. Erlenmeyer flask. To this solution,§ which has been cooled in an ice bath,‖ is slowly added dropwise with continuous stirring a solution of 1.05 ml. (3.27 g. is slightly >0.02 mol¶) of bromine dissolved in 20 ml. (30 g.) of dry chloroform. The resulting cream-colored precipitate of silver bromide is removed by suction filtration on a sintered-glass funnel and washed with two 5-ml. portions of a chloroform-pyridine mixture (*20:1 by volume*),** and the washings are added to the yellow filtrate. About 40 ml. of *absolute* ethyl ether is then added with stirring to the filtrate, whereupon the product precipitates as a fine, white, crystalline powder tinged yellow by occluded bromine.†† The

* Fresno State College, Fresno, Calif.
† Florida State University, Tallahassee, Fla.
‡ This solvent may be conveniently dried by shaking with anhydrous granular sodium sulfate and decanting the clear liquid.
§ Since this solution is somewhat light-sensitive, the reaction is run without excessive delay.
‖ Inadequate cooling may result in a partially decomposed brownish product. However, a pure white product will be obtained by recrystallization from warm methanol as directed below.
¶ A slight excess of bromine is recommended in order to avoid contamination of the product with unreacted dipyridinesilver(I) perchlorate. Thus, when the reaction has been completed, the supernatant liquid should be tinged yellow.
** Dipyridinebromine(I) perchlorate is not soluble in pure chloroform.
†† The checkers report that the yield of precipitate is improved by cooling to about 10°.

crystals are collected on a small sintered-glass or Büchner funnel, washed free of bromine with several 10-ml. portions of *absolute* ether, and air-dried. The product may be further dried *in vacuo* over sulfuric acid, giving a yield of 5.75 g. (85.2%), or the air-dried product may be recrystallized by dissolving in a minimum amount (about 40 ml.) of warm (40°) methanol, cooling the solution in an ice-salt bath for 5 to 10 minutes, collecting the white fluffy needles by suction filtration, washing with several 10-ml. portions of *absolute* ether, and finally drying *in vacuo* over sulfuric acid for one hour. The yield of recrystallized product (m.p. 120 to 123°, with decomposition) is 4.15 g. (61.5%). The product should be stored in a refrigerator. *Anal.* Calcd. for $[Br(C_5H_5N)_2]ClO_4$: Br, 23.7; C_5H_5N, 46.9. Found: Br, 23.5, 23.4, 23.7; C_5H_5N, 46.7, 46.6.

Analysis

Positive iodine and bromine are determined by the oxidation of iodide ion to free iodine, in accordance with the following equations:

$$I^+ + I^- \rightarrow I_2$$
$$Br^+ + 2I^- \rightarrow Br^- + I_2$$

In the analysis of monoquinolineiodine(I) benzoate and dipyridinebromine(I) nitrate, a sample of about 0.1 g. was added to a solution containing 2 g. of potassium iodide and a few drops of hydrochloric acid in 50 ml. of water, and the liberated iodine was titrated with a standard sodium thiosulfate solution in the presence of starch as indicator. In the analysis of dipyridinebromine(I) perchlorate, a 0.2-g. sample was dissolved in 25 ml. of 0.5 N sodium hydroxide solution to which 0.5 g. of potassium iodide had been added. The solution was then acidified with 10 ml. of 2 N sulfuric acid and the liberated iodine titrated immediately with thiosulfate.

For the determination of amine in the first two compounds, the following procedure was employed. One-tenth gram of the complex was dissolved in 100 ml. of glacial acetic acid.   The amine was titrated with a 0.2 N solution of perchloric acid in glacial acetic acid, the titration being followed by means of a high-frequency titrating device, e.g., a Sargent-Jensen High Frequency Titrator.   Pyridine was determined in dipyridinebromine(I) perchlorate in the following manner.   To a 0.5-g. sample was added 30 ml. of a potassium iodide–sodium thiosulfate solution containing 1 g. of potassium iodide and 1.5 g. of sodium thiosulfate 5-hydrate.   The liberated iodine was decolorized by the sodium thiosulfate.   The liberated pyridine was then titrated with 0.1 N hydrochloric acid to a gray-blue end point using bromophenol blue indicator.   A blank is recommended to establish the color of the solution at the end point.

Properties

The complexes of unipositive iodine and bromine are either colorless or pale yellow.   It is conceivable that the yellow color may be due to the release of some free halogen. They decompose slowly if stored in a dark, dry, moisture-free atmosphere, but will generally hydrolyze rapidly on exposure to light and moist air.   They are generally soluble in chloroform, ethanol, acetic acid, pyridine, and related polar solvents, and may also react with these solvents. They are only very slightly soluble in such solvents as ethyl ether, carbon tetrachloride, carbon disulfide, and aliphatic hydrocarbons.   In methanol or pyridine, the positive character of the halogen can be demonstrated, since, on electrolysis, the halogen migrates quantitatively to the cathode in these solvents.   The complexes have been reported to be useful as brominating or iodinating agents in some organic reactions.   With few exceptions the melting points are not sharp, but decomposition occurs over a wide temperature range.

It is interesting to note that whereas dipyridinebromine(I) nitrate is hygroscopic and extremely unstable in air and water, the corresponding perchlorate is a nonhygroscopic, relatively stable solid.   In fact, it apparently can be recrystallized from water at 40° without decomposition.

With pyridine as ligand, two types of complexes have been isolated: $I(C_5H_5N)X$ (X = acid radical) and $I(C_5H_5N)_2X$. The former type has been formulated as a nonelectrolyte, $[I(C_5H_5N)X]$, and the latter as an electrolyte, $[I(C_5H_5N)_2]X$.[5]

References

1. A. ROBERTSON and W. A. WATERS: *J. Chem. Soc.*, **1947**, 492.
2. F. KOROSY and G. SZÉKELY: *Nature*, **168**, 77 (1951); *Magyar Kém. Folyóirat*, **57**, 110 (1951).
3. R. P. BELL and E. GELLES: *J. Chem. Soc.*, **1951**, 2734.
4. P. FRESENIUS: *Angew. Chem.*, **64**, 470 (1933).
5. H. CARLSOHN: "Über eine neue Klasse von Verbindungen des positiv einvertigen Iods," Verlag Hirzl, Leipzig 1932; *Angew. Chem.*, **46**, 747 (1933).
6. M. I. USCHAKOW, W. O. TCHISTOW, and N. D. ZELINSKII: *Ber.*, **68B**, 824 (1935).
7. H. CARLSOHN: *ibid.*, **68B**, 2209, 2212 (1935).
8. R. A. ZINGARO, J. E. GOODRICH, J. KLEINBERG, and C. A. VANDER-WERF: *J. Am. Chem. Soc.*, **71**, 575 (1949).
9. R. A. ZINGARO, C. A. VANDERWERF, and J. KLEINBERG: *ibid.*, **72**, 5341 (1950).
10. E. COLTON: *ibid.*, **77**, 6190 (1955).
11. W. B. WITMER, "Studies on Positive Bromine," Ph.D. dissertation, Agricultural and Mechanical College of Texas, 1960.
12. G. B. KAUFFMAN and R. P. PINNELL, INORGANIC SYNTHESES, **6**, 6 (1960).

47. MONOPYRIDINEIODINE(I) CHLORIDE

[Chloro(pyridine)iodine(I)]

$$C_5H_5N + ICl \rightarrow [I(C_5H_5N)]Cl \text{ or } [I(C_5H_5N)Cl]$$

SUBMITTED BY GEORGE B. KAUFFMAN* AND KENNETH L. STEVENS*
CHECKED BY DONALD J. ROYER†

Addition compounds of pyridine and similar organic bases with halogens and interhalogens have been known for

* Fresno State College, Fresno, Calif.
† Georgia Institute of Technology, Atlanta, Ga.

some time.[1-15] A systematic study[7] of the possible compounds of empirical formula $C_5H_5N \cdot XY$, where both X and Y are halogens, reveals that the stability of such compounds follows the order: $C_5H_5N \cdot ICl > C_5H_5N \cdot IBr > C_5H_5N \cdot BrCl > C_5H_5N \cdot Br_2 > C_5H_5N \cdot Cl_2 > C_5H_5N \cdot I_2$. The compounds may be obtained from carbon tetrachloride solution by adding pyridine to the corresponding halogen or interhalogen.

This synthesis of monopyridineiodine(I) chloride, the most stable member of the series, is based on the work of Williams.[7] Because of its extremely low conductivity in pyridine solution, he considered the compound to be a nonelectrolyte, $[C_5H_5N\text{-}I\text{-}Cl]$, a structure in which the iodine atom becomes dicovalent by absorption of two of its valence electrons into its core.[16,17] On the other hand, physicochemical studies (conductivity, thermal analysis, and electrolysis of the system iodine(I) chloride–pyridine led Fialkov and Muzyka[10] to formulate the compound as an electrolyte, $[C_5H_5N:I]^+Cl^-$, in concurrence with an earlier view of Audrieth and Birr.[18] Both views agree that the compound contains unipositive iodine. Fialkov and Muzyka[10] report the existence of another compound, $C_5H_5N \cdot 2ICl$, which they formulate as $[C_5H_5N:I]^+ICl_2^-$.

Procedure

Four and four-tenths milliliters (slightly > 0.05 mol) of *dry* pyridine* is mixed with 10 ml. of *dry* carbon tetrachloride* in a 250-ml. Erlenmeyer flask. A solution of 8.12 g. (0.05 mol) of iodine(I) chloride[19]† in 100 ml. of *dry* carbon tetrachloride is slowly added dropwise with constant swirling.‡ The resulting yellow precipitate is collected by suc-

* Conveniently dried by shaking with anhydrous granular sodium sulfate and decanting the clear liquid.

† The checker suggests that if iodine(I) chloride is not available, one may substitute a solution prepared by bubbling about 1.77 g. (0.025 mol) of chlorine into 100 ml. of carbon tetrachloride containing 6.35 g. (0.025 mol) of iodine.

‡ The reverse addition of pyridine to iodine(I) chloride results in a product contaminated with occluded iodine(I) chloride. To prevent contamination, pyridine rather than iodine(I) chloride is used in excess.

tion filtration, washed with several small portions of carbon tetrachloride, and air-dried.   The yield of crude product is quantitative (based on iodine(I) chloride).   This is added to a 300-ml. Erlenmeyer flask containing 250 ml. of 95% ethanol, and the mixture is heated on a water bath until the compound has dissolved (about 5 to 10 minutes).   Partial decomposition is evidenced by the reddish brown color of the resulting solution.*   The solution is then cooled in an ice bath (about 10 to 15 minutes), and the bright yellow needles are collected by suction filtration, washed with several small portions of carbon tetrachloride, air-dried, and finally dried *in vacuo* over phosphorus(V) oxide for 48 hours. The yield may vary from 6.04 g. to 8.46 g. (50 to 70%). *Anal.* Calcd. for $[I(C_5H_5N)]Cl$: I, 52.56; C_5H_5N, 32.76; Cl, 14.68.   Found: I, 52.73, 52.56, 52.57; C_5H_5N, 32.58, 32.78, 32.47; Cl, 14.55, 14.43, 14.74.

Analysis

Iodine.   To a 0.25-g. sample is added a solution of 0.5 g. of potassium iodide in 20 ml. of distilled water, followed by 0.5 ml. of 6 M sulfuric acid to neutralize the pyridine.   The liberated iodine is *immediately* titrated with 0.1 N sodium thiosulfate in the presence of starch indicator.

Pyridine.   To a 0.25-g. sample is added 20 ml. of a potassium iodide–sodium thiosulfate solution containing 0.5 g. of KI and 0.75 g. of $Na_2S_2O_3 \cdot 5H_2O$.   The liberated iodine is decomposed by the thiosulfate.   The liberated pyridine is then titrated *immediately* with 0.1 N hydrochloric acid to a gray-blue end point with bromophenol blue as indicator.   A blank is recommended to establish the color of the solution at the end point.

Chlorine.   A Dry Ice–acetone-cooled condenser is fitted onto one neck of a two-necked 200-ml. flask, while *ca.* 30 ml.

---

* The standard recrystallization technique using a *minimum* amount of hot solvent requires the use of higher temperatures to dissolve the crude product, resulting in more extensive decomposition and an impure (reddish yellow) product.

of liquid ammonia is introduced through the other neck. A 0.2-g. sample is then added, followed by enough freshly cut sodium to preserve the dark blue color of the mixture for one-half hour. The condenser is then removed, the ammonia allowed to evaporate, and the excess sodium decomposed by addition of ethanol. The solution is diluted with water, filtered if necessary, and acidified with dilute nitric acid, and the chloride and iodide are precipitated with 0.1 N silver nitrate. From the weight of the combined silver halides and the percentage of iodine (*see above*), the percentage of chlorine can be calculated:

$$\% \text{ Cl} = \frac{(24.737 \times \text{wt. AgX}) - (45.763 \times \% \text{ I} \times \text{g. of sample})}{\text{g. of sample}}$$

Properties[7]

Monopyridineiodine(I) chloride, as recrystallized from ethanol, consists of pale yellow fluffy needles, which melt at 134 to 135°. It is very sparingly soluble in water, benzene, and carbon tetrachloride, slightly more soluble in nitrobenzene, and readily soluble in pyridine, cold acetone, and hot ethanol. It reacts slowly with cold ethanol and acetone to liberate iodine.

In ethanol solution the compound reacts with silver nitrate to yield an immediate precipitate of silver chloride. In agreement with expectations for unipositive iodine, electrolysis of an alcoholic solution gives iodine and pyridine at the cathode and chlorine at the anode. The compound also dissolves in aqueous potassium iodide to liberate iodine. In warm carbon tetrachloride solution it reacts with phenol to give a white precipitate of *sym*-triiodophenol.

References

1. A. W. HOFMANN: *Ber.*, **12**, 988 (1879).
2. A. DITTMAR: *ibid.*, **18**, 1612 (1885).

3. A. PICTET and G. KRAFFT: *Bull. soc. chim. France*, [3], **7**, 73 (1892).
4. P. F. TROWBRIDGE and O. C. DIEHL: *J. Am. Chem. Soc.*, **19**, 558 (1897).
5. A. MOUNEYRAT: *Compt. rend.*, **136**, 1471 (1903); **139**, 1470 (1904).
6. H. W. CREMER and D. R. DUNCAN: *J. Chem. Soc.*, **1931**, 1857.
7. D. M. WILLIAMS: *ibid.*, **1931**, 2783.
8. "Beilstein's Handbuch der organischen Chemie," 4th ed., Vol. XX, p. 2189, Verlag von Julius Springer, Berlin, 1935.
9. K. GLEU and W. JAGEMANN: *J. prakt. Chem.*, **145**, 257 (1936).
10. YA. A. FIALKOV and I. D. MUZYKA: *Zhur. Obshcheĭ Khim.*, **18**, 1205 (1948); **19**, 1416 (1949); **20**, 385 (1950).
11. A. I. POPOV and R. T. PFLAUM: *J. Am. Chem. Soc.*, **79**, 570 (1957).
12. A. I. POPOV and R. H. RYGG: *ibid.*, **79**, 5622 (1957).
13. A. I. POPOV, C. I. BISI, and M. CRAFT: *ibid.*, **80**, 6513 (1958).
14. W. B. PERSON, R. E. HUMPHREY, W. A. DESKIN, and A. I. POPOV: *ibid.*, **80**, 2049 (1958).
15. R. D. WHITAKER, J. R. AMBROSE, and C. W. HICKAM: *J. Inorg. & Nuclear Chem.*, **17**, 254 (1960).
16. G. M. BENNETT and G. H. WILLIS: *J. Chem. Soc.*, **1929**, 263.
17. N. V. SIDGWICK: "The Electronic Theory of Valency," p. 292, Clarendon Press, Oxford, 1927.
18. L. F. AUDRIETH and E. J. BIRR: *J. Am. Chem. Soc.*, **55**, 572 (footnote 16) (1933).
19. J. CORNOG and R. A. KARGES: INORGANIC SYNTHESES, **1**, 165 (1939).

48. ANHYDROUS HYDROGEN IODIDE

$$C_{10}H_{12} + 2I_2 \rightarrow C_{10}H_8 + 4HI$$

SUBMITTED BY C. J. HOFFMAN*
CHECKED BY EDWARD A. HEINTZ†

Gaseous anhydrous hydrogen iodide can be prepared by the catalytic union of the elements[1,2] and by the reaction of solid iodine with boiling tetrahydronaphthalene.[3] The apparatus required for the direct combination of the elements requires considerable time to fabricate and, although

* Lockheed Missiles and Space Division, Sunnyvale, Calif.
† Metals Research Laboratories, Union Carbide Metals Co., a Division of Union Carbide Corp., Niagara Falls, N.Y.; present address, University of Buffalo, Buffalo, N.Y.

the alternative synthesis requires no special apparatus, difficulty is often experienced in controlling the rate of gas evolution. The synthesis described below is a modification of the second method, with the advantage that a steady uniform stream of hydrogen iodide can be generated. Based on the conversion of all the iodine to the hydrogen halide, the yield of hydrogen iodide obtained by this method is nearly quantitative. This is in contrast to the yield of hydrogen bromide by an analogous method,[4] which results in conversion of only one-half of the bromine to hydrogen bromide.

Procedure

A 500-ml. three-necked ground-joint flask nested in a heating mantle is connected to a reflux condenser, to an inlet gas-delivery tube extending to about 1 in. from the flask bottom, and to a dropping funnel fitted with a Teflon stopper. Two cold traps fitted with stopcocks are assembled in series to the exit of the reflux condenser through ground-glass joints. The exit from the last trap is connected to a mercury flow bubbler. All joints are lightly coated with Halocarbon grease.* The trap connected directly to the reflux condenser is immersed in an ice bath to limit entrainment; the succeeding trap, cooled by liquid nitrogen, is used to collect the anhydrous hydrogen iodide.

The reaction flask is charged with 50 ml. of tetrahydronaphthalene and the hydrocarbon is slowly brought to the boiling point, while a solution of 2.56 g. (0.01 mol) of iodine in 100 ml. of the same hydrocarbon is made and transferred to the dropping funnel. The hydrogen iodide is generated by dropwise addition of the iodine solution to the moderately boiling tetrahydronaphthalene; the rate of addition is sufficient to maintain a slight iodine coloration in the reaction flask. To sweep the hydrogen iodide from the reaction flask, a stream of dry nitrogen is passed into the flask and

* Obtainable from Halocarbon Products, Inc., Hackensack, N.J.

through the train during the entire reaction. After the addition of the entire iodine charge, the contents of the flask are boiled for a few minutes to remove the residual iodine coloration. The usual vacuum-line techniques[5] are used to transfer the hydrogen iodide from the train by distilling through a trap maintained at 0° and into a storage bulb. The yield of hydrogen iodide is 90%, based on the quantity of iodine employed.

Analysis

The exit gas from the generator ice trap is dissolved directly in water. The hydrogen-ion concentration of the resulting solution is determined by titration with standard base, and the iodide-ion concentration by the precipitation of silver iodide. Only traces of tetrahydronaphthalene are detected by the very slight carbon-hydrogen bond-infrared absorption in the samples of the anhydrous gas prepared by this procedure.

References

1. E. R. CALEY and M. G. BURFORD: INORGANIC SYNTHESES, 1, 159 (1939).
2. G. BAUER: "Handbuch der präparativen anorganischen Chemie," p. 262, Ferdinard Enke, Stuttgart, (1960).
3. J. HOUBEN, J. BOEDLER, and W. FISCHER: *Ber.*, 69B, 1766 (1936).
4. D. R. DUNCAN: INORGANIC SYNTHESES, 1, 151 (1939).
5. R. T. SANDERSON: "Vacuum Manipulation of Volatile Compounds," John Wiley & Sons, Inc., New York (1948).

CHAPTER VIIB

See also: Cyclopentadienyl metal carbonyls and some derivatives, synthesis 31

Anhydrous metal chlorides, synthesis 45

Sodium salts of carbonyl hydrides prepared in ethereal media, synthesis 53

49. ACETYLACETONATOMANGANESE(III)

[Tris(2,4-pentanedionato)manganese(III)]

$$MnCl_2 + 2HC_5H_7O_2 + 2NaC_2H_3O_2 \rightarrow$$
$$Mn(C_5H_7O_2)_2 + 2NaCl + 2HC_2H_3O_2$$
$$4Mn(C_5H_7O_2)_2 + KMnO_4 + 7HC_5H_7O_2 + HC_2H_3O_2 \rightarrow$$
$$5Mn(C_5H_7O_2)_3 + KC_2H_3O_2 + 4H_2O$$

SUBMITTED BY ROBERT G. CHARLES*

CHECKED BY B. E. BRYANT†

Acetylacetonatomanganese(III) has been made by the reaction of hydrous manganese(III) oxide on acetylacetone (2,4-pentanedione),[1] by the air oxidation of a mixture of hydrous manganese(II) oxide and aqueous acetylacetone,[2] and by the interaction of manganese(II) sulfate with potassium permanganate in an ammoniacal solution of acetylacetone.[3] The present procedure is similar to the last-mentioned method.

* Westinghouse Research Laboratories, Pittsburgh 35, Pa.

† Dow Chemical Co., Freeport, Tex.; present address, North Texas State University, Denton, Texas.

Procedure

To a solution of 5.2 g. (0.026 mol) of manganese(II) chloride 4-hydrate and 13.6 g. (0.1 mol) of sodium acetate 3-hydrate in 200 ml. of water is added 20.0 g. (0.2 mol) of acetylacetone. To the resulting mixture a solution of 1.04 g. (0.0066 mol) of potassium permanganate in 50 ml. of water is slowly added at room temperature, with stirring. After stirring a few minutes, a solution of 13.6 g. (0.1 mol) of sodium acetate 3-hydrate in 50 ml. of water is added in small amounts, with stirring. The mixture is heated on the hot plate for about 10 minutes and cooled to room temperature, and the dark solid is filtered on a Büchner funnel. The product is washed with water and dried *in vacuo* over anhydrous calcium sulfate. The yield is 6.5 g. (70% of theory). The dried chelate is dissolved in 20 ml. of warm benzene, the solution filtered, and the chelate reprecipitated by cooling the solution and adding 75 ml. of petroleum ether. The recrystallized material is dried at room temperature *in vacuo* over anhydrous calcium sulfate. *Anal.* Calcd. for $Mn(C_5H_7O_2)_3$: C, 51.1; H. 6.01; ash (as Mn_3O_4), 21.6. Found: C, 51.2; H, 6.34; ash, 22.0.

Properties

Acetylacetonatomanganese(III) forms lustrous crystals which are black to dark brown by reflected light and green by transmitted light.[1,2] It does not melt sharply, but decomposes above 150°. The molecular weight in such solvents as amyl benzoate is normal.[1,2] The compound is soluble in such solvents as benzene, chloroform, and ethyl acetate and is only slightly soluble in water.

References

1. G. URBAIN and A. DEBIERNE: *Compt. rend.*, **129**, 302 (1899).
2. F. GACH: *Monatsh.*, **21**, 98 (1900).
3. G. H. CARTLEDGE: *J. Am. Chem. Soc.*, **73**, 4416 (1951).

50. RHENIUM(III) IODIDE

(Rhenium Triiodide)

Two methods for the preparation of rhenium(III) iodide are described below. In one procedure (A), perrhenic acid, obtained by reaction of 30% hydrogen peroxide on powdered rhenium metal, is reduced directly to the triiodide by the action of concentrated hydriodic acid and ethanol at elevated temperatures. The second procedure (B) utilizes the controlled thermal decomposition of rhenium(IV) iodide in an atmosphere of iodine.[1] The tetraiodide is prepared by reduction of perrhenic acid with concentrated aqueous hydriodic acid, followed by dehydration of the initial product.

Procedure A

SUBMITTED BY L. MALATESTA*
CHECKED BY COLIN LOCK† AND GEOFFREY WILKINSON†

The preparation is best carried out in the flask shown in Fig. 22, but an Erlenmeyer flask covered by a funnel can be used instead. To a suspension of 1 g. (0.00536 mol) of powdered rhenium metal in 4 ml. of water, there is added dropwise 4 ml. of 30% hydrogen peroxide. The colorless solution is evaporated to a sirupy consistency on a sand bath. Four milliliters of water is then added and the solution is evaporated again. The process is repeated twice more with 4-ml. portions of water to ensure removal of excess hydrogen peroxide.

The sirupy solution is treated with 20 ml. of a 55% solution of hydriodic acid and 20 ml. of ethanol and the resulting mixture is evaporated on a sand bath so that its volume is

* Institute for General Chemistry, University of Milan, Milan, Italy.
† Imperial College of Science and Technology, London, England.

reduced to about 5 ml. in one hour.* The solution is then
permitted to come to room temperature, and the black
crystalline precipitate is filtered by suction on a Büchner
funnel. The crystals are washed with 5 ml. of cold absolute

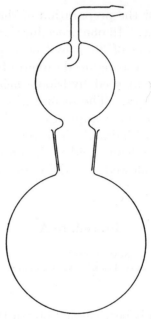

FIG. 22. Apparatus for the preparation of rhenium(III) iodide.

ethanol and transferred on the Büchner funnel to a desiccator. The mother liquor is evaporated nearly to dryness on
a sand bath, a few milliliters of ethanol is added, and the
precipitate is filtered over that previously obtained. The
product is washed first with 25 ml. of absolute ethanol and
then with 10 ml. of carbon tetrachloride to remove excess
iodine. The yield is 2.16 g. or 71% based on the amount of
rhenium used.† *Anal.* Calcd. for ReI_3: Re, 32.8; I, 67.2.
Found: Re, 32.9; I, 67.0.

* The checkers report that if an Erlenmeyer flask is used for the preparation, considerable sputtering may occur at this point, even though the
evaporation is carried out carefully. They have found that the use of an
air jet in the evaporation process helps to cut down sputtering.

† The checkers found yields of 55 to 60%.

Procedure B

$$KReO_4 + HR \rightarrow HReO_4 + KR$$
(R = resin anion)
$$2HReO_4 + 14HI \rightarrow 2ReI_4 + 3I_2 + 8H_2O$$
$$2ReI_4 \rightarrow 2ReI_3 + I_2$$

SUBMITTED BY GEORGE W. WATT* AND RICHARD J. THOMPSON††
CHECKED BY CHARLES L. RULFS,§ DEAN W. COOKE,§ AND BERNARD
SPIELVOGEL§

A tube 40 cm. in length and 20 mm. i.d. is fitted with a stopcock. The tube is charged with 50 g. of 50–100-mesh Dowex 50 W-X1 cation-exchange resin above a 1-cm. layer of Pyrex wool. The resin is washed with 20 ml. of 6 M hydrochloric acid and rinsed with pure hot (100°) water until the effluent is colorless and does not give any turbidity with silver nitrate solution. (About 200 ml. of water is required.) A 10.0-g. sample (0.0356 mol) of finely ground potassium perrhenate is dissolved in 120 ml. of pure hot (100°) water. The hot solution is added to the resin in four 30-ml. portions and the column is then rinsed with pure water (boiling, if undissolved potassium perrhenate is observed). The effluent is collected at the rate of 15 to 20 ml. per minute. The initial neutral portion of the effluent (*ca.* 50 ml.) is discarded and the fraction which is acid to litmus (*ca.* 130 ml.) is collected in a 250-ml. beaker.

The acidic solution is concentrated to a volume of 20 ml. and cooled, and 50 ml. of concentrated (54%) hydriodic acid is added. (The hydriodic acid is distilled from red phosphorus just before use.) The beaker is placed in a

* The University of Texas, Austin, Tex.
† North Texas State University, Denton, Tex.
‡ Financial support of the Research Corporation, the Atomic Energy Commission, Contract At-(40-1)-1639, and The Robert A. Welch Foundation is gratefully acknowledged.
§ The University of Michigan, Ann Arbor, Mich.

vacuum desiccator charged with a mixture of solid sodium hydroxide and phosphorus(V) oxide and the pressure is reduced by means of a water aspirator. The desiccants are changed as necessary and the reduced pressure is maintained. About 48 hours is required to remove the water from the product (ReI_4).*

The hard black rhenium(IV) iodide is transferred to a test tube 30 cm. long and 25 mm. o.d., which has been constricted to about 10-mm. i.d. at the center. Five grams of iodine is placed on the tetraiodide and the tube is evacuated (oil-pump) and sealed. The tube is heated at $350 \pm 5°$ for 8 hours in a furnace. The tube is then adjusted in such a manner that the rhenium(III) iodide which has formed is maintained in one portion in the furnace at 220° while the other portion protrudes from the furnace. The latter portion is allowed to cool slowly at first and is then cooled further by a jet of air. When all the iodine has apparently collected in the cooled portion, the entire tube is allowed to cool to room temperature. The tube is then scored in the center with a file and broken. (Care is taken to effect a break without introducing shards of glass into the product.) The glistening black crystals are transferred onto the fritted-glass plate of a tared crucible and washed with carbon tetrachloride until the washings are colorless. (About 400 ml. of solvent is required.) The product is then rinsed with two 20-ml. portions each of ethanol and ethyl ether and dried at 110°. The yield is 16.3 g. or 83%. *Anal.* Calcd. for ReI_3: Re, 32.8: I, 67.2. Found: Re, 33.0; I, 67.0.

Properties

Rhenium(III) iodide forms lustrous black needlelike crystals. It is only sparingly soluble in water and dilute

* The checkers found that the drying process required considerably more time than that reported. They suggest that the product be given a preliminary drying with calcium chloride in the desiccator and that this be followed by several changes of phosphorus(V) oxide. With such a procedure, drying can be effected in about 3 days.

acids and nearly insoluble in methanol, ethanol, petroleum ether, ethyl ether, and carbon tetrachloride. The compound evolves iodine slowly in a vacuum, the rate of evolution increasing with temperature. It dissolves readily in liquid ammonia, but undergoes extensive solvolysis in this medium.[2] The corresponding chloride and bromide are soluble and apparently stable in liquid ammonia.[3]

References

1. R. D. PEACOCK, A. J. E. WELCH, and L. T. WILSON: *J. Chem. Soc.*, **1958,** 2901.
2. R. J. THOMPSON: dissertation, The University of Texas, Austin, p. 63, 1959.
3. W. KLEMM and G. FRISCHMUTH: *Z. anorg. u. allgem. Chem.*, **230,** 209 (1937).

51. POTASSIUM HEXACHLORORHENATE(IV) AND POTASSIUM HEXABROMORHENATE(IV)

$$2KX + 2KReO_4 + 10HX + 3H_3PO_2 \rightarrow$$
$$2K_2ReX_6 + 3H_3PO_3 + 5H_2O$$
$$(X = Cl, Br)$$

SUBMITTED BY GEORGE W. WATT* AND RICHARD J. THOMPSON†‡
CHECKED BY JEAN M. GIBBONS§

Potassium hexahalorhenate(IV) complexes have been prepared by reduction of potassium perrhenate in concentrated hydrohalic acid media. Among the reducing agents which have been employed are iodide ion,[1] chromium(II),[2]

* University of Texas, Austin, Tex.
† North Texas State University, Denton, Tex.
‡ Financial support of the Research Corporation, the Atomic Energy Commission, Contract At-(40-1)-1639, and The Robert A. Welch Foundation is gratefully acknowledged.
§ University of Kansas, Lawrence, Kan.

sulfur dioxide, hydrazine, formaldehyde, and hypophosphorous acid.[3] The chloro and bromo complexes have been obtained in highest yield and highest purity by use of hypophosphorous acid as the reductant.

Procedure

A. POTASSIUM HEXACHLORORHENATE(IV)

Ten grams (0.0346 mol) of potassium perrhenate, 2.58 g. (0.0346 mol) of potassium chloride, 25 ml. of 50% hypophosphorous acid, and 500 ml. of concentrated hydrochloric acid are placed in a covered 600-ml. beaker. The stirred mixture is heated until dissolution of the salts occurs. (The use of a Teflon-sheathed stirrer-bar, in conjunction with a stirrer-hot plate, facilitates the procedure.) The temperature is maintained at $95 \pm 5°$.

The solution changes in color from a pale yellow through a dark, almost opaque, green to an intense emerald green, and finally to a pale emerald green. The final color is attained in about 2 hours. A ribbed watch glass is then placed over the beaker and the material is concentrated at $95 \pm 5°$ to about 50 ml. (The total elapsed time is about 16 hours.)

The material is allowed to cool slowly to room temperature and the pale green crystals are transferred to a sintered-glass filter and suction-dried. The product is covered and stirred well three times with chilled 6 N hydrochloric acid, suction drying being effected at the end of each operation. The salt is then washed with two 20-ml. volumes each of acetone and of ethyl ether. The washed material is freed of solvents with suction and dried at 110°. The yield is 15.3 g. (0.032 mol) or 93% of theoretical. *Anal.* Calcd. for K_2ReCl_6: Cl, 44.6; Re, 39.0. Found: Cl, 44.3; Re, 39.4.

The salt is dissolved in 400 ml. of concentrated hydrochloric acid to which two drops of hydrazine have been added. The heated mixture is concentrated to 25 ml. at just below the boiling point, and the recrystallized material is isolated, washed, and dried as above. The yield is 13.5 g. (0.0283 mol or 82%) of pure crystals. *Anal.* Found: Cl, 44.6; Re, 39.0.

B. POTASSIUM HEXABROMORHENATE(IV)

A 600-ml. beaker is charged with 10.0 g. (0.0346 mol) of potassium perrhenate, 4.11 g. (0.0345 mol) of potassium bromide, 400 ml. of concentrated hydrobromic acid (49% HBr), and 10 ml. of 50% hypophosphorous acid. The heated mixture is held at $110 \pm 5°$ until a volume of 25 ml. is attained (about 16 hours). (The color of the mixture changes from yellow to an intense dark red within 2 hours; the intensity of the dark red mixture then fades appreciably.) The mixture is chilled and the dark red crystals are transferred onto a sintered-glass filter and suction-dried. The product is covered with chilled 4 N hydrobromic acid and stirred well, and the acid is removed with suction; the washing procedure is repeated twice. The salt is then washed with two 20-ml. volumes each of acetone and of ethyl ether, freed of solvents with suction, and dried at 110°. A yield of 24.4 g. (0.0328 mol; 95%) of the bromide is obtained.

The crude material is dissolved in 250 ml. of concentrated hydrobromic acid to which a drop of hydrazine has been added. The volume is reduced to 25 ml. at just below the boiling point, and the recrystallized salt is isolated and washed and dried as above. The yield of purified salt is 22.0 g. (0.0296 mol; 86% based on potassium perrhenate). *Anal.* Calcd. for K_2ReBr_6: Re, 25.0; Br, 64.5. Found: Re, 25.1; Br, 64.4.

Properties

Compounds of the type K_2ReX_6, in which X represents I, Br, or Cl, are hydrolyzed by water, the hydrolysis proceeding more readily with increasing atomic number of the halogen. The emerald-green chloride hydrolyzes only slowly in water at room temperature, the dark red bromide reacts within minutes, and the black iodide, it is reported, cannot be obtained free from hydrolysis products.[4] In hot neutral media, hydrolysis of the chloride is accompanied by air oxidation or disproportionation, as evidenced by the formation of a white precipitate containing perrhenate ion when tetraphenylarsonium chloride is added to the filtrate of the hydrolytic mixture. In the presence of alkalies, the hexachloro compound disproportionates in a complex manner.[5] More rapid concentration than that described in the procedure above can yield yellow-green crystals of the hexachloro complex which give low chloride values. Similar treatment of the bromo complex yields a rust-brown product which gives low bromide values. Both salts can be obtained as beautiful large rhombs by slow evaporation of the appropriate solutions.

References

1. L. C. Hurd and V. A. Reinders: Inorganic Syntheses, **1**, 178 (1939) (and references cited therein).
2. V. W. Meloche and R. Martin: *J. Am. Chem. Soc.*, **78**, 5955 (1956).
3. C. L. Rulfs and R. J. Mayer: *ibid.*, **77**, 4505 (1955).
4. J. C. Morrow: *J. Phys. Chem.*, **60**, 19 (1956).
5. N. V. Sidgwick: "The Chemical Elements and Their Compounds," Vol. II, p. 1309, Oxford University Press, London, 1950.

CHAPTER VIII

See also: Cyclopentadienyl metal carbonyls and some derivatives, synthesis 31

Anhydrous metal chlorides, synthesis 45

52. TRIIRON DODECACARBONYL

$$Fe(CO)_5 + 3OH^- \rightarrow HFe(CO)_4^- + CO_3^{--} + H_2O$$
$$3HFe(CO)_4^- + 3MnO_2 + 3H_2O \rightarrow$$
$$Fe_3(CO)_{12} + 3Mn^{++} + 9OH^-$$

Submitted by R. B. King*† and F. G. A. Stone*§
Checked by R. S. Summitt‡ and W. E. Edgell‡

Triiron dodecacarbonyl has been obtained by three different methods: the action of heat on the iron carbonyl $Fe_2(CO)_9$,[1] oxidation of the anion $HFe(CO)_4^-$ by various oxidizing agents,[2] and treatment of iron pentacarbonyl with triethylamine followed by acidification of the reaction mixture.[3] The method described below is based on the oxidation of the anion $HFe(CO)_4^-$ with manganese dioxide.

Procedure

The reaction is carried out in a well-ventilated hood using a 2-l. three-necked flask fitted with a stirrer, nitrogen inlet,

* Harvard University, Cambridge, Mass.
† Present address, E. I. du Pont de Nemours & Co., Wilmington, Del.
§ Present address, Queen Mary College, London, England.
‡ Purdue University, Lafayette, Ind.

and reflux condenser.   A safety pan is placed under the reaction flask.   After flushing out the system with nitrogen, 42 ml. (60 g.; 0.3 mol) of commercial iron pentacarbonyl and 170 ml. of methanol are placed in the flask and treated with a solution of 45 g. of sodium hydroxide in 90 ml. of water. An exothermic reaction occurs.   The mixture is stirred for about 30 minutes and then treated with 125 ml. of saturated ammonium chloride solution.

Meanwhile a thick brown aqueous paste of manganese dioxide is prepared by cautiously treating 67 g. (0.4 mol) of potassium permanganate and 300 ml. of water with 100 ml. of 95% ethanol in a large beaker covered with a watch glass.*   The mixture is heated† on a steam bath until reaction begins, as evidenced by formation of a brown precipitate of manganese dioxide.   It should be noted that reaction is vigorous, and the beaker must be kept covered to avoid spattering.   Reaction is complete when no more purple permanganate is observed.

The suspension of manganese dioxide thus obtained is added to the buffered $HFe(CO)_4^-$ solution.   Heat is evolved, and the mixture becomes dark red in color.   The oxidation process is allowed to proceed for 1 to 2 hours with stirring of the mixture and the excess of manganese dioxide is then decomposed by gradual addition of a solution of 40 g. of iron(II) sulfate 7-hydrate dissolved in 250 ml. of dilute sulfuric acid (about 2 N).   The mixture, still red in color, is then treated with 300 ml. of 1:1 sulfuric acid. Stirring is continued until the black precipitate of triiron dodecacarbonyl is present in only a weakly colored, usually very pale green, supernatant solution.   The product is then filtered and washed successively with 400 ml. of hot dilute ($\sim$2 N) sulfuric acid, 200 ml. of 95% ethanol, and 150 ml.

---

* It is necessary to use freshly prepared manganese dioxide, obtained as described.   Commercial manganese dioxide cannot be used.

† Note added by checkers: The reaction to prepare MnO_2 often starts spontaneously with stirring.   Heating therefore should be delayed until it is certain that the reaction will not start without it.

of pentane, isohexane, or petroleum ether. The ethanol and pentane washings are dark green, but this represents negligible loss of product. The yield of triiron dodecacarbonyl is 35 to 45 g. (70 to 90%). The iron carbonyl should be stored under nitrogen. Stability of the product is improved if traces of ethanol or water are allowed to remain in contact with it. Triiron dodecacarbonyl thus obtained is pure enough for most purposes. If necessary, the last traces of water or ethanol may be removed by application of high vacuum. If highly pure triiron dodecacarbonyl is required, it may be obtained by sublimation (60° at 0.1 mm.) of the crude material, or by placing the crude material in a Soxhlet apparatus and extracting with pentane under nitrogen, with filtration of the product after it separates from the extracts.

Properties

Triiron dodecacarbonyl[4] is a black crystalline solid, very sparingly soluble in organic solvents and affording intensely dark green solutions. On standing in air the carbonyl is gradually oxidized to brown iron(III) oxide and thus should be stored under nitrogen. On prolonged storage, decomposition to pyrophoric products has occasionally been observed. The compound is appreciably volatile, giving a black crystalline sublimate. Heating somewhat higher than 60° results in production of a mirror of metallic iron.

Triiron dodecacarbonyl is a precursor to a great variety of organoiron compounds. In this respect, it is frequently a superior reagent to iron pentacarbonyl.[5,6]

References

1. J. Dewar and H. O. Jones: *Proc. Roy. Soc. (London)*, **A76**, 558 (1905); **A79**, 66 (1907).
2. W. Hieber: *Z. anorg. u. allgem. Chem.*, **204**, 165 (1932); W. Hieber and G. Brendel: *ibid.*, **289**, 324 (1957).
3. M. Heintzelor: Ger. patent, 928044 (1955).
4. J. Chatt, P. L. Pauson, and L. M. Venanzi: "Organometallic Chemistry," H. Zeiss (ed.), Chap. 10, Am. Chem. Soc. Monograph, Reinhold

Publishing Corporation, New York, 1960. A review of the chemistry of this and other metal carbonyls.
5. W. Hubel, E. H. Braye, A. Clauss, E. Weiss, U. Kruerke, D. A. Brown, G. S. D. King, and C. Hoogzand: *J. Inorg. & Nuclear Chem.*, **9**, 204 (1959); W. Hubel and E. H. Braye: *ibid.*, **10**, 250 (1959).
6. R. B. King, T. A. Manuel, and F. G. A. Stone: *ibid.*, **16**, 233 (1961); R. B. King, P. M. Treichel, and F. G. A. Stone: *J. Am. Chem. Soc.*, **83**, 3600 (1961).

53. SODIUM SALTS OF CARBONYL HYDRIDES PREPARED IN ETHEREAL MEDIA

Submitted by R. B. King* and F. G. A. Stone†

Sodium salts of carbonyl hydrides of general formula $Na_xM(CO)_y$ or $Na_xM(CO)_yC_5H_5$, prepared from metal carbonyls and bases, have been known for some time in aqueous or alcoholic media.[1] More recently the salts have been synthesized in liquid ammonia[2] or in ethereal media[3] by the action of sodium or sodium amalgams on various metal carbonyls. The ethereal solutions are especially useful for synthetic purposes because of the re ative inertness of the solvent. Tetrahydrofuran is a convenient ether to use, and carbonyls or carbonyl derivatives which will form salts include $Co_2(CO)_8$, $Mn_2(CO)_{10}$, $(C_5H_5)_2Fe_2(CO)_4$, $Re_2(CO)_{10}$, $(C_5H_5)_2Mo_2(CO)_6$, $R_3PMn(CO)_4$, $V(CO)_6$, and $Fe_3(CO)_{12}$. The sodium compounds produced are usually extremely air-sensitive and are best used *in situ* for further reactions, e.g.:

$$NaMn(CO)_5 + CH_3COCl \xrightarrow{\text{tetrahydrofuran}}$$
$$CH_3COMn(CO)_5 + NaCl$$
$$NaFe(CO)_2C_5H_5 + CF_2{=}CFCF_2Cl \rightarrow$$
$$CF_3CF{=}CFFe(CO)_2C_5H_5 + NaCl$$
$$NaCo(CO)_4 + CH_2{=}CHCH_2Cl \rightarrow$$
$$\pi\text{-}CH_2{=}CHCH_2Co(CO)_3 + NaCl + CO$$

* Explosives Department, Experimental Station, E. I. du Pont de Nemours & Company, Wilmington, Del.

† Harvard University, Cambridge, Mass.; present address, Queen Mary College, London, England.

The first synthesis described below illustrates the preparation of a salt using a sodium dispersion, whereas the second preparation illustrates the use of sodium amalgam. Usually a more satisfactory reaction results when sodium amalgam is used, but the method has the disadvantage of requiring relatively large quantities of mercury (which, however, may be recovered).

A. SODIUM SALT OF IRON CARBONYL HYDRIDE

{Sodium Tetracarbonylferrate(-II)}

CHECKED BY R. P. M. WERNER*

$$Fe_3(CO)_{12} + 6Na \xrightarrow{\text{tetrahydrofuran}} 3Na_2Fe(CO)_4$$

Procedure

The triiron dodecacarbonyl required for this synthesis may be prepared by manganese dioxide oxidation of basic solutions of iron pentacarbonyl (synthesis 52).† The tetrahydrofuran should be freshly redistilled over lithium aluminum hydride (lithium tetrahydroaluminate) before use. Sodium dispersions may be obtained commercially, or prepared by the method described in an earlier synthesis.[4]

The reaction is carried out in a 1-l. three-necked flask fitted with a stirrer, reflux condenser, and nitrogen inlet. After flushing the apparatus with nitrogen, 500 ml. of tetrahydrofuran, 9.2 g. of 50% sodium dispersion in mineral oi (equivalent to 4.6 g. or 0.2 mol of sodium), and 17 g. (0.033 mol) of triiron dodecacarbonyl are placed in the flask. The mixture is first stirred under nitrogen for an hour while the color changes from green through red to red-brown and

---

* Ethyl Corporation, Detroit, Mich.

† The checker has drawn attention to an alternative method for preparing triiron dodecacarbonyl involving acid decomposition of iron carbonyl hydride complexes of the type $H_2Fe_3(CO)_{11} \cdot NR_3$, which are easily obtainable from iron pentacarbonyl and an amine. See German patent 928044 and also W. H. Hieber, J. Sedlmeier, and R. Werner: *Ber.*, **90**, 278 (1957).

then is refluxed under nitrogen for about 6 hours, when the color becomes somewhat lighter.*

B. SODIUM SALT OF MANGANESE PENTACARBONYL HYDRIDE AND MANGANESE PENTACARBONYL HYDRIDE

{Sodium Pentacarbonylmanganate(-I) and
Hydrogen Pentacarbonylmanganate(-I)}

$$Mn_2(CO)_{10} + 2Na \xrightarrow{\text{tetrahydrofuran}} 2NaMn(CO)_5$$
$$NaMn(CO)_5 + H_3PO_4 \rightarrow HMn(CO)_5 + NaH_2PO_4$$

CHECKED BY G. BURCAL† AND W. BURNS†

The manganese carbonyl required for this synthesis may be obtained by treating anhydrous manganese(II) chloride with a tetrahydrofuran solution of the sodium ketyl of benzophenone, followed by carbonylation of the resulting solution at elevated temperatures and pressures.[5] An alternative method for preparing manganese carbonyl involves the reaction between anhydrous manganese(II) acetate, triethylaluminum in appropriate ethers, and carbon monoxide at high pressure.[6] Although this method gives higher yields, it requires the handling of large amounts of pyrophoric triethylaluminum.

The preparation is carried out in a 100-ml. three-necked flask fitted with a reflux condenser, stirrer, and nitrogen inlet, and the entire experiment is conducted under nitrogen.   The flask should have a slight bulge of about 0.5-cc. volume at the bottom in order to facilitate removal of excess amalgam with a hypodermic syringe.   After the flask has been flushed out with nitrogen, 4 ml. (54 g.) of

---

* The checker points out that the red color of the solution is due to the presence of polynuclear carbonylferrates, especially $Fe_3(CO)_{11}^{2-}$, which are very intensely colored.   The purity of the desired tetracarbonylferrate(-II), however, is not affected much by these.

The desired $Na_2Fe(CO)_4$ at this time and after cooling the mixture to room temperature will be present partially in the solid state.

† Ethyl Corporation, Detroit, Mich.

mercury is placed in it and 0.45 g. (0.0195 mol) of sodium is added in about 0.1-g. portions. The sodium reacts vigorously with the mercury, evolving heat and smoke. After the sodium amalgam has cooled to room temperature it is treated with 3.0 g. (0.0077 mol) of manganese carbonyl in 50 ml. of tetrahydrofuran and the mixture is stirred at room temperature for at least 45 minutes. In general, the solution is colorless and contains suspended gray matter, probably finely divided mercury. Sometimes a green or blue solution may be obtained but this does not affect the preparation.

Excess amalgam is removed from the solution by using a syringe, the process being facilitated somewhat by placing the tip of the needle in the bulge at the bottom of the flask.* The solution of $NaMn(CO)_5$ is then "washed" with 2 ml. of fresh mercury, which is removed as before. The sodium salt $NaMn(CO)_5$ is very air-sensitive and should always be kept or transferred under nitrogen.

After the mercury has been removed from the flask, the stirrer is replaced by a stopper in order to minimize leakage of air when the flask is evacuated. When the solvent is removed at room temperature, by using an aspirator vacuum,† a grayish residue remains. Nitrogen is admitted and the flask is fitted with a dropping funnel containing 30 ml. of 85% phosphoric acid. The apparatus is connected to a vacuum system through a trap cooled to $-196°$ and containing phosphorus(V) oxide. The apparatus is evacuated, and the phosphoric acid is added slowly (1 hour), the product and water distilling into the trap cooled to $-196°$. At the end of the addition of acid, the reaction

---

* The mercury may be easily recovered for future reactions of a similar type. This is conveniently done by washing the recovered mercury first with 95% ethanol to remove the sodium and then with water until the water washings are clear and colorless. The mercury is then suitable for additional sodium amalgam experiments without redistillation.

† The checkers find that removal of the last traces of tetrahydrofuran at room temperature under the vacuum of a good oil pump makes purification of the final product unnecessary.

flask should be warmed to 50°. The product is conveniently purified by fractional condensation at 45° in the vacuum system to remove tetrahydrofuran, which is not condensed under these conditions. The product is dried again over phosphorus(V) oxide to give about 2.5 g. (83% yield) of manganese pentacarbonyl hydride.

If it is desired to run reactions with 1% sodium amalgam on a larger scale than that described in the above preparation, it is convenient to use a flask with a stopcock attached to the bottom, rather than one with a bulge, as described. After the sodium derivative is formed, the excess of amalgam may be conveniently drained into a small beaker by opening the stopcock. The authors have found such a flask useful in reactions involving 0.1 mol or more of 1% sodium amalgam.

Properties

The sodium salt $NaMn(CO)_5$ may be used to prepare a variety of organomanganese compounds.[1]

Manganese pentacarbonyl hydride is a liquid, colorless when pure, but usually yellow from traces of manganese carbonyl due to decomposition. Its extrapolated boiling point is about 100°. Since it is quite air-sensitive and volatile, it is most conveniently handled in a vacuum system. With diazomethane it gives $CH_3Mn(CO)_5$[7] and with tetrafluoroethylene it gives $HCF_2CF_2Mn(CO)_5$.[8]

References

1. J. CHATT, P. L. PAUSON, and L. M. VENANZI: "Organometallic Chemistry," H. Zeiss (ed.), Chap. 10, Am. Chem. Soc. Monograph, Reinhold Publishing Corporation, New York, 1960.
2. H. BEHRENS: *Z. Naturforsch.*, **7b**, 321 (1952); H. BEHRENS and W. HAAG: *ibid.*, **14b**, 600 (1959); H. BEHRENS and R. WEBER: *Z. anorg. u. allgem. Chem.*, **281**, 190 (1955); **291**, 122 (1957); E. O. FISHER and S. VIGOUREUX: *Ber.*, **91**, 2205 (1958).
3. R. D. CLOSSON, J. KOZIKOWSKI, and T. H. COFFIELD: *J. Org. Chem.*, **22**, 598 (1957); W. HIEBER, O. VOHLER, and G. BROWN: *Z. Naturforsch.*, **13b**, 192 (1958); W. HIEBER and G. WAGNER: *ibid.*, **12b**, 478

(1957); T. S. PIPER and G. WILKINSON: *J. Inorg. & Nuclear Chem.*, **3**, 104 (1956); W. HIEBER and G. BRAUN: *Z. Naturforsch.*, **14b**, 132 (1959); E. W. ABEL, A. SINGH, and G. WILKINSON: *J. Chem. Soc.*, **1960**, 1321; W. HIEBER, G. FAULHABER, and F. THEUBERT: *Z. Naturforsch.*, **15b**, 326 (1960); R. ERCOLI, R. CALDERAZZO, and A. ALBEROLA: *J. Am. Chem. Soc.*, **82**, 2966 (1960); R. B. KING, S. L. STAFFORD, P. M. TREICHEL, and F. G. A. STONE, *ibid.*, **83**, 3604 (1961); T. H. COFFIELD, U.S. patent 2,967,087 (Jan. 3, 1961).

4. T. P. WHALEY: INORGANIC SYNTHESES, **5**, 6 (1957).

5. R. D. CLOSSON, L. R. BUZBEE, and G. G. ECKE: *J. Am. Chem. Soc.*, **80**, 6167 (1958).

6. H. E. PODALL, J. H. DUNN, and H. SHAPIRO: *ibid.*, **82**, 1325 (1960).

7. W. HIEBER and G. WAGNER: *Z. Naturforsch.*, **12b**, 478 (1957); *Ann.*, **618**, 24 (1958).

8. R. B. KING, E. PITCHER, S. L. STAFFORD, P. M. TREICHEL, and F. G. A. STONE: "Advances in the Chemistry of Coordination Compounds," S. Kirschner (ed.), p. 619, The Macmillan Company, New York, 1961.

54. IRON-LABELED CYCLOPENTADIENYL IRON COMPLEXES

SUBMITTED BY D. R. STRANKS*
CHECKED BY FLOYD B. BAKER†

In principle, radioactive ferrocene [bis(cyclopentadienyl)-iron] might be synthesized from iron(II)[Fe[55] + Fe[59]] chloride and cyclopentadienylsodium in tetrahydrofuran, from the acetylacetonatoiron(II)[2,4-pentanedionatoiron(II)]-[Fe[55] + Fe[59]]–pyridine complex and cyclopentadienylmagnesium bromide,[2] or from iron(Fe[55] + Fe[59]) metal and cyclopentadiene vapor.[3] The last procedure in particular is not readily adapted to a semimicro preparation of high-specific-activity material in high yield. A simpler method is to bombard inactive ferrocene with neutrons and take advantage of the relatively high retention of (Fe[55] + Fe[59]) as ferrocene in the ensuing Szilard-Chalmers reaction.[4] Labeled "ferricinium" [bis(cyclopentadienyl)-iron(III)]

* University of Melbourne, Victoria, Australia.
† Los Alamos Scientific Laboratory, Los Alamos, N.M.

salts may then be obtained from the active ferrocene either by the "instantaneous" isotopic exchange with ferricinium salts[5] or by direct oxidation. As the former involves an unavoidable dilution of specific activity and the ferricinium salt must be prepared from ferrocene in the first instance, electrolytic oxidation (which yields a more nearly pure product than chemical oxidation) is recommended.

Procedure

A. IRON-LABELED FERROCENE

$$Fe(C_5H_5)_2 + n \rightarrow Fe^{55}(C_5H_5)_2 + Fe^{59}(C_5H_5)_2 + \gamma$$

Inactive ferrocene, synthesized from iron(II) chloride containing less than 0.05% of other transition metals, is purified by two steam distillations in an all-glass distillation assembly and oven-dried at 70°. One gram of the purified ferrocene is transferred to a small silica test tube (e.g., 5 cm. long, 6 mm. i.d.), the end is closed with a tight wad of silica wool, and the tube is inserted in an aluminum irradiation can.* The can is inserted in a reactor, preferably in a high-flux irradiation position where a large fast-neutron flux exists, and is irradiated for six days. After a two-day "cooling" period,† the sample is annealed for 8 hours in an oven at 105 to 110°. The active ferrocene is then dissolved in 25 ml. of hexane and is extracted in a glass separatory funnel four times with 25-ml. portions of 0.1 N hydrochloric acid.‡ The hexane solution is steam-distilled, the active ferrocene is filtered off on a sintered-glass disk, washed with distilled water, and finally dried in a vacuum desiccator.

* No advantage is gained by performing irradiations in an inert atmosphere within a sealed silica ampul.

† Shielding from radiation should be unnecessary after this time.

‡ This acidic extract contains roughly half of the total iron activity existing mainly as Fe(III) of high specific activity. Another fifth of the total activity is adsorbed on the glass walls of the separatory funnel and may be removed by shaking with acetone; the chemical form of this activity has not been identified.

Chemical yield: 95% or better.   Isotopic yield: 20% of the total (Fe^{55} + Fe^{59}) activity is isolated as ferrocene. With a thermal-neutron flux of 1×10^{12} neutrons cm.$^{-2}$/ sec.$^{-1}$, six days' irradiation produces a total of 140 μC./g. of Fe^{55} and 70 μC./g. of Fe^{59}.   (Higher neutron fluxes will yield proportionately higher specific activities.)   The specific activity of the ferrocene is one-fifth of these values.

B. IRON-LABELED FERRICINIUM PERCHLORATE

$$Fe^{55,59}(C_5H_5)_2 \rightarrow Fe^{55,59}(C_5H_5)_2^+ + e^-$$

Active ferrocene (0.185 g.; 0.001 mol) is added to 0.244 g. of sodium perchlorate dissolved in 20 ml. of fractionated methanol and the solution is transferred to the anode compartment (A) of the electrolytic cell illustrated in Fig. 23. A mercury pool (M) serves as the anode and a platinum wire (P) as the cathode.   The cathode compartment (C) contains 30 ml. of 0.1 M perchloric acid.   The electrode

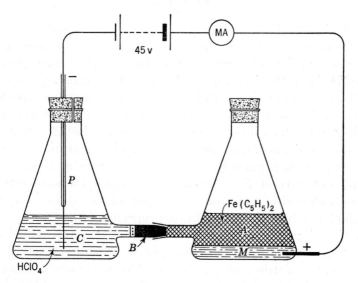

FIG. 23. Electrolytic cell for the preparation of iron-labeled ferricinium perchlorate.

compartments are separated by a sintered-glass disk and a saturated sodium perchlorate–agar plug (*B*). A 45-volt radio battery is connected to the cell and a current of 3 to 4 milliamp. is passed for 2 to 3 hours, when the development of the blue ferricinium color should be complete. The course of oxidation may be judged by adding one drop of the anode solution to 1 ml. of water; the absence of a turbidity indicates complete oxidation but it is advisable to pass the current for an additional 15 minutes beyond this stage. The final anode solution contains 0.05 *M* ferricinium perchlorate and 0.1 *M* sodium perchlorate. The final water content of the methanol solvent does not exceed 0.5 *M* and is usually much less.

If a solid salt is required, the anode solution is poured into a five-fold excess of petroleum ether, which is cooled in a Dry-Ice bath. The precipitated ferricinium perchlorate may then be removed by centrifugation and dried.

Properties

Isotopic. Iron-55 is an electron-capture isotope with a half-life of 2.94 years. Iron-59 is a mixed β-γ emitter the main radiations of which are 0.27 M.e.v. β (46%), 0.46 M.e.v. β (54%), 1.10 M.e.v. γ (57%), and 1.29 M.e.v. γ (43%). The half-life of Fe^{59} is 45.1 days. The radioactive samples are most readily assayed with a standard thin-mica-window Geiger counter which will detect mainly the Fe^{59} β-particles. Decomposition of ferrocene and ferricinium salts in a boiling mixture of four parts by volume of concentrated nitric acid and one part of 75% perchloric acid and the subsequent electrodeposition of iron on copper disks[6] gives samples which exhibit excellent counting reproducibility.

Chemical. Ferrocene is an orange solid (m.p. 172.6 to 173°), which sublimes at atmospheric pressure at 100° and is steam-volatile and readily soluble in common organic solvents but insoluble in water. The vapor is stable up to 400°. Ferrocene is oxidized, for example, by benzoquinone and iron(III) chloride to the Fe(III) state. The "sand-wich" structure of ferrocene is typical of many cyclopenta-dienyl transition-metal complexes.

Ferricinium perchlorate, nitrate, and chloride are readily soluble in water and alcohols, somewhat soluble in hydro-carbons, but insoluble in ether-type solvents. The ferrici-nium ion is blue, and it may be precipitated from solution as the triiodide, tungstosilicate, picrate, reineckate, etc. Ferricinium salts may be reduced to ferrocene by tin(II) chloride.

References

1. G. WILKINSON and J. M. BIRMINGHAM: *J. Am. Chem. Soc.*, **76**, 4281 (1954).
2. G. WILKINSON, P. L. PAUSON, and F. A. COTTON: *ibid.*, **76**, 1970 (1954).
3. S. A. MILLER, J. A. TEBBOTH, and J. F. TREMAINE: *J. Chem. Soc.*, **1952**, 632.
4. N. SUTIN and R. W. DODSON: *J. Inorg. & Nuclear Chem.*, **6**, 91 (1958).
5. F. S. DAINTON, G. S. LAURENCE, W. SCHNEIDER, D. R. STRANKS, and M. S. VAIDYA: UNESCO "International Conference on Radio-Iso-topes" (Paris, 1957).
6. G. J. VOSBURGH, L. B. FLEXNER, and D. B. COWIE: *J. Biol. Chem.*, **175**, 391 (1948).

55. TRIS(3-NITROACETYLACETONATO)COBALT(III)

[Tris(3-nitro-2,4-pentanedionato)cobalt(III)]

$$[(CH_3CO)_2CH]_3Co \xrightarrow[\text{(CH}_3\text{CO)}_2\text{O}]{\text{Cu(NO}_3\text{)}_2\cdot3H_2O} [(CH_3CO)_2CNO_2]_3Co$$

SUBMITTED BY JAMES P. COLLMAN* AND WILLIAM L. YOUNG, III*
CHECKED BY GEORGE B. KAUFFMAN† AND MICHAEL F. CITRO†

Tris(3-nitroacetylacetonato)cobalt(III) has been pre-pared only by direct nitration of cobalt(III) acetylacetonate [2,4-pentanedionatocobalt(III)] under mildly acidic condi-

* The University of North Carolina, Chapel Hill, N.C.
† Fresno State College, Fresno 26, California.

tions.[1]   A mixture of copper(II) nitrate and acetic anhydride effects this nitration in high yield.   It has been
suggested that this mixture contains acetyl nitrate.[2]
Copper(II) nitrate has been found to be more effective
than other metal nitrates, suggesting that a copper complex may be involved.   Reactive benzenoid systems have
been nitrated by this mild reagent.   The procedure
described here is easy to perform and can also be used to
prepare tris(3-nitroacetylacetonato)chromium(III).

Procedure

A mixture of 10.75 g. (0.04 mol) of finely ground copper-
(II) nitrate 3-hydrate* and 200 ml. of acetic anhydride in a
500-ml. Erlenmeyer flask fitted with a calcium chloride drying tube is stirred for 15 minutes at 0°.   The stirring is best
effected by a magnetic stirrer operating through an ice-water
bath.   At the end of this time a portion of the copper(II)
nitrate has dissolved to form a deep blue solution.   To this
slurry is added 5.0 g. (0.014 mol) of cobalt(III) acetylacetonate[3] and the resulting mixture is stirred for two hours
at 0°.   The cooling bath is then removed and the mixture
is stirred for one hour at room temperature.   The blue-
green solution is then mixed with 600 ml. of water, 600 g. of
ice, and 15 g. of sodium acetate.   The two-phase liquid
mixture is stirred for 2 hours, during which time a finely
divided green precipitate appears.   At this point, the mixture should consist of a green solution and a fine green
powder.   If any gummy material remains in the mixture,
it should be stirred until the gummy substance disappears.

The green precipitate is collected on a suction filter and
washed with two 50-ml. portions of water and one 15-ml.
portion of cold ethanol.   The air-dried green solid is dissolved in 40 ml. of boiling chloroform† and this solution is

---

* The checkers found that dehydrated copper(II) nitrate (a white powder
prepared by heating the hydrate to constant weight at 105°) is insoluble
in acetic anhydride.

† Dichloromethane can be used instead of chloroform in this step.

combined with 40 ml. of hot ethanol in an open beaker. The solution is heated to a gentle boil in a hood, and chloroform allowed to distill off until the volume of the solution is 55 to 60 ml. At this point, crystals appear in the solution. The green mixture is allowed to cool to room temperature, then is chilled in an ice bath, and the green precipitate is collected on a filter. The green crystals are washed with two 20-ml. portions of cold ethanol and air-dried. The air-dried green needles weigh at least 4.9 g. (71% yield) and decompose at 198°. *Anal.* Calcd. for $Co(C_5H_6NO_4)_3$: C, 36.67; H, 3.69; N, 8.68. Found: C, 36.42; H, 3.82; N, 8.63.

Properties

Tris(3-nitroacetylacetonato)cobalt(III) forms dark green needles that do not melt but decompose reproducibly at 198°. This substance exhibits an ultraviolet spectrum in chloroform with λ_{max} 262 mμ(ϵ = 29,400). This chelate is slightly soluble in most organic solvents.

References

1. J. P. COLLMAN, R. A. MOSS, S. D. GOLDBY, and W. S. TRAHANOVSKY: *Chem. & Ind. (London)*, **1960**, 1213.
2. G. BACHARACH: *J. Am. Chem. Soc.*, **49**, 1527 (1927).
3. B. E. BRYANT and W. C. FERNELIUS: INORGANIC SYNTHESES, **5**, 188 (1957).

56. INNER COMPLEXES OF COBALT(III) WITH DIETHYLENETRIAMINE

SUBMITTED BY PHILIP H. CRAYTON*
CHECKED BY FRED ZITOMER† AND JACK LAMBERT†

Complexes of the terdentate diethylenetriamine (dien) have been known for some time.[1] The existence of com-

* Carborundum Co., Research Dept., Niagara Falls, N.Y.
† Kansas State University, Manhattan, Kan.

paratively stable chelates of this amine with tripositive metal ions exhibiting a coordination number of six presents a unique opportunity to study the properties of the "inner complexes" with a variety of anions completing the coordination sphere. Since bond angles and distances are favorable for the assumption of either a planar or "bent" configuration, two possible types of structures, cis and trans, are possible. The compounds are prepared by mixing the constituents in aqueous solution. The relative water insolubility of the inner complexes permits their easy separation and purification. The pH of the solutions is of utmost importance in direct synthesis from simple salts. This is most dramatically shown in the case of the thiocyanato complexes, where the use of water prevents the formation of a trithiocyanato complex. It is shown less dramatically in the low yields of thiocyanato hydroxo and trinitro compounds obtained when the proper pH is not attained.

Procedure

A. DITHIOCYANATOHYDROXO(DIETHYLENETRIAMINE)-COBALT(III)

$$4Co(NO_3)_2 + 8KSCN + 4(H_2NC_2H_4)_2NH + O_2 + 2H_2O \rightarrow$$
$$4[Co(dien)(SCN)_2OH] + 8KNO_3$$

Twenty milliliters of a 10% aqueous solution of diethylenetriamine is slowly added to a solution made by dissolving 5 g. (0.017 mol) of cobalt(II) nitrate 6-hydrate and 5.5 g. (0.057 mol) of potassium thiocyanate in 50 ml. of water. The solution is brought to a pH in the range of 4 to 6. Aeration for one hour causes a dull red noncrystalline solid to separate. The precipitate is allowed to stand overnight, then is filtered, washed with water, and dried at 110°. The compound may be purified by dissolving 4 g. in 100 ml. of 2 *M* sodium hydroxide solution and then neutralizing the solution. A yield of 3.7 g. (60%) is obtained. *Anal.* Calcd.

for [Co(dien)(SCN)$_2$OH]: Co, 19.96; C, 24.39; S, 21.72.
Found: Co, 20.01; C, 24.22; S, 21.60.

B. TRITHIOCYANATO(DIETHYLENETRIAMINE)COBALT(III)

$$4Co(SCN)_2 + 4KSCN + 4(H_2NC_2H_4)_2NH + O_2 + 4C_2H_5OH$$
$$\rightarrow 4[Co(dien)(SCN)_3] + 4C_2H_5OK + 2H_2O$$

A solution of 6 ml. of diethylenetriamine in 50 ml. of
absolute ethanol is slowly added to a solution of 10 g.
(0.057 mol) of cobalt(II) thiocyanate and 5 g. (0.051 mol)
of potassium thiocyanate in 200 ml. of absolute ethanol.
A tan precipitate begins to form almost immediately. Air,
dried by passage through a bed of a desiccant, is bubbled
through the mixture for one hour. The precipitate is filtered with suction and washed with absolute ethanol until
the washings are colorless. Care must be taken not to suck
the precipitate dry. A final wash is made with ether and
the compound is stored in a desiccator. The yield is 18 g.
(95%). *Anal.* Calcd. for [Co(dien)(SCN)$_3$]: Co, 17.50; C,
24.98; S, 28.60. Found: Co, 17.55; C, 24.90; S, 28.40.

C. TRINITRO(DIETHYLENETRIAMINE)COBALT(III)[2]

1. FROM COBALT(II) NITRATE

$$4Co(NO_3)_2 + 12NaNO_2 + 4(H_2NC_2H_4)_2NH + O_2 + 4HC_2H_3O_2$$
$$\rightarrow 4[Co(dien)(NO_2)_3] + 8NaNO_3 + 4NaC_2H_3O_2 + 2H_2O$$

A solution is prepared by adding 10.5 g. (0.036 mol) of
cobalt(II) nitrate 6-hydrate, 11 g. (0.16 mol) of sodium
nitrite, 2.9 g. (0.072 mol) of sodium hydroxide, and 8.7 g.
(0.145 mol) of acetic acid to 15 ml. of water. Aeration of
the solution is begun and a solution of 3 ml. of diethylenetriamine in 12 ml. of water is added slowly. The buffer
system maintains the pH between 5 and 6. The pH
should be checked after the amine has been added and is
adjusted if necessary. The formation of a green precipitate
indicates that the amine is being added too rapidly or that

the pH is too high.   After aeration for one hour, the solution is filtered and the yellow precipitate washed several times with water and then with ethanol.   The yield is 10.3 g. (78%).   *Anal.* Calcd. for [Co(dien)(NO$_2$)$_3$]: Co, 19.63; N, 27.99.   Found: Co, 19.50; N, 27.95.

2. From *trans*-Trinitrotriamminecobalt(III)

$$[Co(NH_3)_3(NO_2)_3] + (H_2NC_2H_4)_2NH \rightarrow$$
$$[Co(dien)(NO_2)_3] + 3NH_3\uparrow$$

Ten grams (0.036 mol) of *trans*-trinitrotriamminecobalt-(III)[3,4] is dissolved in 15 ml. of water by heating.   To the hot solution there is added 2.5 ml. of diethylenetriamine. A stream of air is passed through the solution, which is kept at about 60° for 45 to 60 minutes or until the odor of ammonia cannot be detected.   The solution is cooled and the crystals which form are filtered and washed several times with water and ethanol.   The yield is ten grams (80%).

3. From Sodium Hexanitrocobaltate(III)

$$Na_3[Co(NO_2)_6] + (H_2NC_2H_4)_2NH \rightarrow$$
$$[Co(dien)(NO_2)_3] + 3NaNO_2$$

Seven grams (0.017 mol) of sodium hexanitrocobaltate-(III) is dissolved in 15 ml. of water, the solution is heated to 50°, and 2.7 ml. of diethylenetriamine is added.   A yellow crystalline precipitate forms, which grows as the solution is cooled.   The precipitate is filtered with suction and washed several times with water and then with ethanol.   A second crop of crystals can be obtained by concentrating the mother liquor.   The yield is 3 g. (59%).

D. DINITROCHLORO(DIETHYLENETRIAMINE)COBALT(III)

$$2[Co(dien)(NO_2)_3] + 2HCl \rightarrow$$
$$2[Co(dien)(NO_2)_2Cl] + H_2O + NO\uparrow + NO_2\uparrow$$

Ten grams (0.033 mol) of trinitro(diethylenetriamine)-cobalt(III) is permitted to stand for 24 hours under 100 ml.

of 6 M hydrochloric acid, whereupon red-brown crystals appear under a green solution. The crystals are filtered and washed with warm water until the wash water has only a faint yellow color. The crystals are dried at 110°. The yield is 8 g. (82%). *Anal.* Calcd. for [Co(dien)(NO$_2$)$_2$Cl]: Co, 20.40; C, 16.60; N, 14.50; Cl, 12.25. Found: Co, 20.50; C, 16.50; N, 14.45; Cl, 12.25.

E. DINITROAMMINE(DIETHYLENETRIAMINE)COBALT(III) CHLORIDE

$$[Co(dien)(NO_2)_2Cl] + NH_4OH \rightarrow$$
$$[Co(dien)(NH_3)(NO_2)_2]Cl + H_2O$$

Five grams (0.017 mol) of the dinitro chloro complex is placed in a solution of 25 ml. of water and 5 ml. of concentrated ammonium hydroxide. The solution is heated nearly to boiling and held there for about 30 minutes, after which time only a faint odor of ammonia persists. The solution is allowed to cool overnight and any unconverted starting material is filtered off. The solution is evaporated until crystals begin to appear and is then allowed to cool. The crystals are collected on a filter and washed first with 20% ethanol and then with absolute ethanol. The product is dried at 110°. The yield is approximately 4.5 g. (90%). *Anal.* Calcd. for [Co(dien)(NH$_3$)(NO$_2$)$_2$]Cl: Co, 19.25; N, 18.25; Cl, 11.60. Found: Co, 19.25; N, 18.00; Cl, 11.40.

F. TRICHLORO(DIETHYLENETRIAMINE)COBALT(III)

$$2[Co(dien)(NO_2)_3] + 6HCl \rightarrow$$
$$2[Co(dien)Cl_3] + 3H_2O + 3NO\uparrow + 3NO_2\uparrow$$

Ten grams (0.033 mol) of trinitro(diethylenetriamine)-cobalt(III) is gently heated with 250 ml. of concentrated hydrochloric acid until nitrogen(IV) oxide evolution ceases. The resulting solution is cooled and allowed to stand overnight. The fine brown crystals of trichloro(diethylenetriamine)cobalt(III) are removed by filtration on a Büchner funnel and washed with acetone until the washings are colorless. The washings and additional acetone are added to the mother liquor to give a final volume of about 1 l. A second crop of crystals can be recovered after 2 to 3 days. A yield of 8.6 g. (81%) is obtained. *Anal.* Calcd. for [Co(dien)Cl$_3$]: Co, 21.94; C, 17.87; N, 15.64; Cl, 38.75. Found: Co, 22.00; C, 18.87; N, 15.45; Cl, 38.70.

G. TRINITRATO(DIETHYLENETRIAMINE)COBALT(III)

$$2[Co(dien)(NO_2)_3] + 6HNO_3 \rightarrow$$
$$2[Co(dien)(NO_3)_3] + 3H_2O + 3NO\uparrow + 3NO_2\uparrow$$

Five grams (0.017 mol) of trinitro(diethylenetriamine)-cobalt(III) is warmed with 5 ml. of concentrated nitric acid (sp. gr. 1.42); nitrogen(IV) oxide is evolved and a deep violet solution is formed. This solution is allowed to evaporate to a slurry at room temperature. By mixing 25 ml. of acetone with the slurry and filtering on a Büchner funnel, violet crystals of trinitrato(diethylenetriamine)-cobalt(III) are left on the paper. These are washed with acetone and dried at 110°. The yield is 5.2 g. (90%). *Anal.* Calcd. for [Co(dien)(NO$_3$)$_3$]: Co, 16.95; C, 13.80. Found: Co, 17.00; C, 13.70.

Properties

Of the complexes prepared, only the trinitro complex is stable toward water. This compound is relatively insoluble in organic solvents, as well as in water. Hydrolysis to form the more stable hydroxo or aquo complexes occurs with the trithiocyanato and trichloro complexes. The compound [Co(dien)(SCN)$_2$(OH)] has the rather remarkable property of being insoluble in acids and soluble in bases; it can be recovered from basic solution by precipitation with acids.

Absorption spectra have been obtained for those compounds with sufficient solubility and stability in water to make such information meaningful. Spectral data are summarized in Table I.

TABLE I

Compound	Absorption maxima					
	mμ	log ϵ	mμ	log ϵ	mμ	log ϵ
[Co(dien)(NO₂)₃]	250	4.38	340	3.68	433	2.50
[Co(dien)(NH₃)(NO₂)₂Cl]	250	4.25	346	3.49	447	2.27
[Co(dien)(NO₂)₂Cl]	245	4.20	336	3.57	449	2.32
[Co(dien)(NO₃)₃]	...	....	318	2.75	520	1.95

The reaction of [Co(dien)(NO₂)₃] with both acids and bases is of considerable interest. Acids replace first one nitro group and then the remaining two simultaneously. The first group replaced is presumably trans to the secondary amine group in diethylenetriamine. Replacement of one nitro group by an amine group can be easily accomplished, but all three nitro groups apparently cannot be replaced. Reaction of propylenediamine(1,2-propanediamine) with the complex leads to the formation of a solid which behaves as though only one amine group of the diamine had entered the coordination sphere.

References

1. F. G. Mann: *J. Chem. Soc.*, **1930**, 1734; *ibid.*, **1934**, 466; J. A. Mattern: thesis, University of Illinois, 1942; Ph.D. thesis, 1946.
2. P. H. Crayton and J. A. Mattern: *J. Inorg. & Nuclear Chem.*, **13**, 248 (1960).
3. S. M. Jörgensen: *Z. anorg. Chem.*, **5**, 185 (1894); H. Sueda: *Bull. Chem. Soc. Japan*, **13**, 449 (1956).
4. W. E. Cooley, C. F. Liu, and J. C. Bailar, Jr.: *J. Am. Chem. Soc.*, **81**, 4189 (1959).

57. HYDRATED RHODIUM(III) CHLORIDE, CHLOROAMMINERHODIUM(III) SALTS, AND A NOTE ON THE RECOVERY OF RHODIUM WASTES

SUBMITTED BY SUSAN N. ANDERSON* AND FRED BASOLO*
CHECKED BY E. I. ONSTOTT†

A. HYDRATED RHODIUM(III) CHLORIDE

$$2Rh + 6KCl + 3Cl_2 \xrightarrow{575°} 2K_3RhCl_6$$
$$K_3RhCl_6 + H_2O \rightarrow K_2[Rh(H_2O)Cl_5] + KCl$$
$$2K_2[Rh(H_2O)Cl_5] + 6KOH \rightarrow Rh_2O_3 \cdot 5H_2O + 10KCl$$
$$Rh_2O_3 \cdot 5H_2O + 6HCl \rightarrow 2RhCl_3 \cdot 3H_2O + 2H_2O$$

Hydrated rhodium(III) chloride, $RhCl_3 \cdot 3H_2O$, has been found to be the best starting material for the preparation of complex rhodium compounds. Although anhydrous rhodium(III) chloride may be obtained directly from the elements, it is insoluble in water and difficult to use as a starting material. The soluble hydrate modification is obtained by a more circuitous route. The first step in the synthesis of $RhCl_3 \cdot 3H_2O$ is an adaptation of the method of Gutbier and Huttlinger[1] for the preparation of $K_2[Rh(H_2O)Cl_5]$. The second step is the conversion of the latter compound to $RhCl_3 \cdot 3H_2O$ according to the procedure of Delépine.[2]

Procedure

Five grams (0.048 mol) of rhodium sponge and 10.9 g. (0.146 mol) of finely pulverized potassium chloride are ground together in a mortar. The mixture is then placed in an unglazed porcelain boat in the center of a ceramic tube inserted in a furnace heated to 550 to 575°. This temperature is maintained for 45 to 60 minutes while chlorine is

* Northwestern University, Evanston, Ill.
† Los Alamos Scientific Laboratory, Los Alamos, N.M.

bubbled first through water, then through the reaction tube, and out into a solution of potassium hydroxide used as a trap. After cooling, the dark red product is extracted with 300 ml. of water and the unreacted rhodium is removed on a filter. (At this point $K_2[Rh(H_2O)Cl_5]$ may be isolated from the filtrate by evaporating the solution on the steam bath until crystallization begins. It can be recrystallized from water containing a drop of concentrated hydrochloric acid. However, the use of this salt for the synthesis of certain rhodium complexes leads to difficulty in the removal of the additional potassium chloride from the desired reaction product.)

To the wine-red filtrate, after removal of unreacted rhodium, solid potassium hydroxide is added slowly until the red color just disappears and the golden yellow hydroxide, $Rh_2O_3·5H_2O$ or $Rh(OH)_3·H_2O$ precipitates. Excess base should be avoided because it causes dissolution of the amphoteric hydroxide. The precipitate is then collected on a fritted-glass filter,* washed with 20 ml. of water to remove the potassium chloride and excess potassium hydroxide, and dissolved in the minimum amount of concentrated hydrochloric acid. Upon evaporation to dryness on the steam bath the resulting wine-red solution gives $RhCl_3·3H_2O$.

It is important that the product be left on the steam bath until there is no longer a noticeable odor of hydrogen chloride. No attempt should be made to dry the product further, as it begins to decompose above 100° into rhodium(III) oxide and hydrogen chloride. Yield, 8.2 g. (64%).†

Hydrated rhodium(III) chloride prepared in this way contains some potassium chloride as a result of the adsorption of potassium hydroxide during the precipitation of $Rh_2O_3·5H_2O$; it also contains a small amount of hydro-

---

* The first 50 ml. of filtrate may be refiltered to remove the traces of $Rh_2O_3·5H_2O$ which pass through the filter. Likewise the filterability may be improved by allowing the precipitate to stand overnight.

† The checker obtained a 23% yield of rhodium(III) chloride. The only apparent difference in procedure was that dry chlorine was used instead of first passing it through water as described here.

chloric acid which cannot be completely removed by heating the compound on the steam bath. A typical analysis showed 42% Rh and 44% Cl. However, for all synthetic work described here, further purification is not necessary.

B. CHLOROAMMINERHODIUM(III) SALTS

1. Chloropentaamminerhodium(III) Chloride and *trans*-Dichlorotetraamminerhodium(III) Chloride

$$2RhCl_3 \cdot 3H_2O + 5(NH_4)_2CO_3 \rightarrow$$
$$2[Rh(NH_3)_5Cl]Cl_2 + 5CO_2 + 11H_2O$$
$$2RhCl_3 \cdot 3H_2O + 4(NH_4)_2CO_3 \rightarrow$$
$$2[Rh(NH_3)_4Cl_2]Cl + 4CO_2 + 10H_2O$$

The method used to prepare chloropentaamminerhodium-(III) chloride and dichlorotetraamminerhodium(III) chloride is a modification of that reported by Lebedinski[3] for the synthesis of the former compound.

Procedure

Three grams (0.011 mol) of $RhCl_3 \cdot 3H_2O$ is dissolved in 40 ml. of water. To this are added 10 g. (0.187 mol) of ammonium chloride and 7.5 g. (0.078 mol) of ammonium carbonate, the latter as a finely pulverized powder. The mixture is allowed to stand on the steam bath for 3 hours and is then cooled and allowed to crystallize. The golden yellow product is collected on a filter and then extracted with 100 ml. of boiling hydrochloric acid: water (2:1 by volume). Dichlorotetraamminerhodium(III) chloride dissolves but chloropentaamminerhodium(III) chloride is insoluble and is left on the filter. The filtrate is allowed to cool to room temperature, and $[Rh(NH_3)_4Cl_2]Cl$ precipitates. Before analysis, the tetraammine complex is converted into the less soluble nitrate, $[Rh(NH_3)_4Cl_2]NO_3 \cdot H_2O$ by dissolving the chloride in a minimum amount of water and filtering into 3 ml. of ice-cold concentrated nitric acid.

Yield, 0.5 g. (13%).* *Anal.* Calcd. for $[Rh(NH_3)_4Cl_2]NO_3 \cdot$-$H_2O$: N, 21.69; H, 4.37; Cl, 22.0 Found: N, 21.88; H, 4.14; Cl, 21.9.

The residue of pale yellow $[Rh(NH_3)_5Cl]Cl_2$ is recrystallized from a minimum amount of boiling water. (Care must be taken to keep the solution as concentrated as possible to prevent aquation of the complex.) Yield, 1.4 g. (42%). *Anal.* Calcd. for $[Rh(NH_3)_5Cl]Cl_2$: Cl (ionic), 24.0; Cl(total), 36.1. Found: Cl (ionic), 24.5; Cl (total), 36.1.

2. *cis*- and *trans*-Dichlorobis(ethylenediamine)rhodium-(III) Nitrate

$$RhCl_3 \cdot 3H_2O + 2(C_2H_4(NH_2)_2 \cdot 2HCl) + 4KOH \rightarrow$$
$$[Rh(en)_2Cl_2]Cl + 4KCl + 7H_2O$$
$$[Rh(en)_2Cl_2]Cl + HNO_3 \rightarrow [Rh(en)_2Cl_2]NO_3 + HCl$$

The cis and trans forms of dichlorobis(ethylenediamine)-rhodium(III) nitrate are obtained from solutions of the corresponding chlorides by reaction with concentrated nitric acid. Solutions of the chlorides are prepared from hydrated rhodium(III) chloride by treatment with ethylenediamine dihydrochloride, the hydrochloric acid set free being neutralized with potassium hydroxide in such a manner that no excess base is ever present.[4]

Procedure

A mixture of 1.0 g. (0.0038 mol) of $RhCl_3 \cdot 3H_2O$ and 1.01 g. (0.0076 mol) of ethylenediamine dihydrochloride† in 50 ml. of water containing 0.426 g. (0.0076 mol) of potassium hydroxide is refluxed until the solution becomes clear. To the refluxing solution there is added, through the top of a water-cooled condenser, another 0.426 g. of potas-

---

* The checker's yields were 0.25 g. of $[Rh(NH_3)_4Cl_2]NO_3 \cdot H_2O$ and 0.8 g. of $[Rh(NH_3)_5Cl]Cl_2$.

† Ethylenediamine dihydrochloride is made by adding alcoholic hydrochloric acid to alcoholic ethylenediamine in an ice bath until precipitation is complete.

sium hydroxide in 50 ml. of water (about 5 ml. at a time every 1 to 2 minutes). The resulting golden yellow solution is evaporated on a steam bath to about one-half its original volume and is cooled to room temperature. Then 20 ml. of concentrated nitric acid is added and the solution is allowed to stand for about 2 hours, during which time the less soluble *trans*-[Rh(en)$_2$Cl$_2$]NO$_3$ is precipitated almost quantitatively in the form of golden yellow crystals. The product is removed by filtration, washed with a little dilute nitric acid, and air-dried. The trans isomer may be recrystallized by dissolving it in a minimum amount of water and filtering into ice-cold concentrated nitric acid. The yield is 0.45 g. (33%). *Anal.* Calcd. for [Rh(en)$_2$Cl$_2$]NO$_3$: C, 13.49; H, 4.53. Found: C, 13.87; H, 4.63.

Upon further standing and evaporation at room temperature for 24 to 48 hours, the filtrate remaining after removal of the trans isomer yields bright yellow *cis*-[Rh(en)$_2$Cl$_2$]NO$_3$. The product is removed by filtration and purified exactly as was the trans isomer. The yield is 0.15 g. (11%).* *Anal.* Calcd. for [Rh(en)$_2$Cl$_2$]NO$_3$: C, 13.49; H, 4.53. Found: C, 13.98; H, 4.31.

3. *cis*- and *trans*-Dichlorobis(ethylenediamine)rhodium-(III) Chloride

Procedure†

Either form of the chloride may be prepared by passing a concentrated aqueous solution of the appropriate nitrate through an anion-exchange resin (e.g., Dowex 1-X4) in the chloride form. The solution containing the chloride is then concentrated on a steam bath to the point of crystallization and cooled to room temperature. The product is collected

* The checker obtained yields of 0.25 g. of the trans and 0.05 g. of the cis compound.

† Inasmuch as the cis and trans forms of this compound are very soluble in water and are difficult to separate from each other and from potassium chloride, they cannot be conveniently obtained by the initial reaction described in the procedure for the preparation of the nitrates.

on a filter and recrystallized by dissolving in the smallest possible amount of water and filtering into a little ice-cold concentrated hydrochloric acid.

cis-[Rh(en)$_2$Cl$_2$] may be resolved into its optical isomers through the *d*-α-bromocamphor-π-sulfonate salt. A solution of 0.45 g. (0.0014 mol) of cis-[Rh(en)$_2$Cl$_2$]Cl and 0.9 g. of ammonium *d*-α-bromocamphor-π-sulfonate in 15 ml. of water is frozen in an ice-salt bath. After melting, the *l*-cis-[Rh(en)$_2$Cl$_2$][*d*-C$_{10}$H$_{10}$O$_4$SBr] is collected on a filter and washed with a few drops of ice-cold water. This salt is ground thoroughly with 2 ml. of a 1:1:1 mixture of ethanol: ethyl ether: concentrated hydrochloric acid and the *l*-cis-[Rh(en)$_2$Cl$_2$]Cl removed by filtration. The yield is 0.13 g. (59% of levo salt). *Anal.* Calcd. for [Rh(en)$_2$Cl$_2$]Cl: C, 14.58; H, 5.89. Found: C, 14.50; H, 5.08.

Properties

The cis and trans isomers of [Rh(en)$_2$Cl$_2$]Cl may be conveniently distinguished from each other since their infrared spectra differ significantly in the 3, 6, and 9μ regions, the cis isomer in each case showing a higher degree of splitting. The specific optical rotation of a 0.4% aqueous solution of this isomer has values of $[\alpha]_{577}$mμ $= -50°$ and $[\alpha]_{535}$mμ $= -58°$.

C. RECOVERY OF RHODIUM WASTES

Two means of recovering rhodium wastes have been used successfully. One is to reduce the rhodium(III) in a water solution to rhodium metal by means of zinc and hydrochloric acid. The other is to heat a solid residue containing rhodium(III) to about 800° (with a Meker burner) and decompose it. In either case, the residue is extracted with water and then with aqua regia, to remove any impurity. Rhodium obtained in this way may contain traces of rhodium(III) oxide, Rh$_2$O$_3$. Pure rhodium metal may be

prepared by heating the oxide in hydrogen to about 600°
and allowing it to cool in a hydrogen atmosphere.

References

1. A. GUTBIER and A. HUTTLINGER: *Ber.*, **41**, 212 (1908).
2. M. DELÉPINE: *Bull. soc. chim. Belges*, **36**, 108 (1927).
3. W. W. LEBEDINSKI: *Ann. secteur platine*, **13**, 9 (1936).
4. S. ANDERSON and F. BASOLO: *J. Am. Chem. Soc.*, **82**, 4423 (1960).

58. cis- AND trans-TETRACHLORO- (DIPYRIDINE)IRIDIUM(IV)

cis- or $trans$-$C_5H_5NH[Ir(C_5H_5N)_2Cl_4]$ + $NH_3 \rightarrow$
$\qquad cis$- or $trans$-$NH_4[Ir(C_5H_5N)_2Cl_4]$ + C_5H_5N
cis- or $trans$-$NH_4[Ir(C_5H_5N)_2Cl_4]$ + $4HNO_3 \rightarrow$
$\qquad cis$- or $trans$-$[Ir(C_5H_5N)_2Cl_4]$ + $4NO_2$ + $\frac{1}{2}N_2$ + $4H_2O$

SUBMITTED BY GEORGE B. KAUFFMAN[*]
CHECKED BY J. W. HOGARTH[†] AND F. P. DWYER[†]

The complexes of iridium(IV), fewer in number than
those of iridium(III), often contain pyridine as a ligand.[1]
An impure substance with the reported composition
$Ir(C_5H_5N)_2Cl_4$, prepared by the action of pyridine on an
iridium(IV) chloride solution, was described first by Renz[2]
and later by Gutbier and Hoyermann.[3,4] Since the composition was based entirely on iridium content without any
allusion to isomerism and since the color was inconsistent
with his findings, Delépine[5,6] concluded that the product
was not a pure substance.

* Fresno State College, Fresno, Calif. Financial support of the Research
Corporation and the National Science Foundation (Grant NSF-G11241)
is gratefully acknowledged.
† John Curtin School of Medical Research, Australian National University, Canberra, A.C.T., Australia.

The cis and trans forms of tetrachloro(dipyridine)-iridium(IV) were first prepared in pure form by Delépine[5,6,7] by oxidation of the corresponding isomeric tetrachloro-(dipyridine)iridates(III). Ogawa[8] later obtained them by oxidation of (C_5H_5NH)$_2$[Ir(C_5H_5N)Cl$_5$] and [Ir(C_5H_5N)$_3$Cl$_3$]. The trans isomer has also been synthesized by aqua regia oxidation of *trans*-K[Ir(C_5H_5N)$_2$(C_2O_4)$_2$].[9,10]

The sensitivity of the isomeric tetrachloro(dipyridine)-iridates(III) to oxidation differs markedly, the red trans salts being more easily oxidized than the orange cis salts. Thus the trans isomers are oxidized to *trans*-tetrachloro-(dipyridine)iridium(IV) almost immediately at room temperature by nitric acid, aqua regia, chlorine water, or bromine water. On the other hand, oxidation of the cis isomers with nitric acid requires heating to dryness. Although the reaction is facilitated by using aqua regia or chlorine water, a very large excess of these oxidants is required. Oxidation does not occur at all with bromine water. This difference in ease of oxidation between the isomeric tetrachloro(dipyridine)iridates(III) is reflected in the difference in ease of reduction between the corresponding tetrachloro(dipyridine)iridium(IV) compounds (see Properties).

The present synthesis employs oxidation of the isomeric tetrachloro(dipyridine)iridates(III) after conversion of the relatively water-insoluble pyridinium salts (cis, 1 g./65 ml. at 18°; trans, 1 g./770 ml. at 18°) (see synthesis 60) to the easily water-soluble ammonium salts (cis, 1 g./10 ml. at 19°; trans, 1 g./30 ml. at 19°).

Procedure

A. *cis*-TETRACHLORO(DIPYRIDINE)IRIDIUM(IV)

Two and one-hundredth grams (0.0035 mol) of orange *cis*-pyridinium tetrachloro(dipyridine)iridate(III)[11] is dissolved with stirring in 45 ml. of 2 N aqueous ammonia contained in a 250-ml. evaporating dish. Thirty milliliters of nitric acid and 10 ml. of hydrochloric acid are added, and the solution is evaporated to dryness on a steam bath (*hood!*). The resulting violet-black residue is washed by decantation with three 40-ml. portions of hot water. The crystals are transferred to a small Büchner funnel, washed with two successive 20-ml. portions of water, ethanol, and ethyl ether, air-dried, and finally dried at 110° for one hour. The yield is 1.60 g. (92.5%). *Anal.* Calcd. for $Ir(C_5H_5N)_2Cl_4$: Ir, 39.16; C, 24.39; H, 2.01; N, 5.67. Found: Ir, 39.10; C, 24.22;* H, 1.93;* N, 5.55.*

B. *trans*-TETRACHLORO(DIPYRIDINE)IRIDIUM(IV)

Two and twenty-nine hundredths grams (0.004 mol) of red *trans*-pyridinium tetrachloro(dipyridine)iridate(III)[11] is dissolved with stirring in 75 ml. of 1 N aqueous ammonia contained in a 150-ml. beaker. The solution is warmed, and a mixture of 25 ml. of nitric acid and 5 ml. of hydrochloric acid is added, whereupon a deep purple powder immediately precipitates. After the mixture has been allowed to stand at room temperature for a half-hour, the precipitate is collected by suction filtration on a small sintered-glass funnel (fine porosity), washed with 25-ml. portions of water, ethanol, and ethyl ether, air-dried, and finally dried at 110° for one hour. The yield is 1.86 g. (94.3%). *Anal.* Calcd. for $Ir(C_5H_5N)_2Cl_4$: Ir, 39.16; C, 24.39; H, 2.01; N, 5.67. Found: Ir, 38.98; C, 24.36*; H, 1.97*; N, 5.67.*

Properties

Both isomers of tetrachloro(dipyridine)iridium(IV) are nonelectrolytes, which are insoluble in water, ethanol, and ethyl ether but slightly soluble in chloroform, yielding violet solutions. Both are deep violet, the cis compound being somewhat darker than the trans compound.

Both isomers behave as oxidizing agents; the cis com-

* Values supplied by the checkers.

pound is the stronger oxidant and falls between chlorine and bromine, whereas the trans isomer falls between bromine and iodine. Thus, both isomers liberate iodine from potassium iodide solution and are reduced to the corresponding isomers of $K[Ir(C_5H_5N)_2Cl_4]$, whereas only the cis isomer reacts with potassium bromide solution to liberate bromine. Similarly, the cis compound dissolves in warm ethanol to form a yellow solution of cis-$H[Ir(C_5H_5N)_2Cl_4]$, whereas the trans compound is not reduced even by boiling ethanol. Both isomers oxidize aqueous ammonia to elementary nitrogen and are reduced to the corresponding isomers of $NH_4[Ir(C_5H_5N)_2Cl_4]$, but the reaction is more complex with the trans isomer. An interesting reaction illustrating relative oxidizing power occurs when the cis isomer is triturated with a solution of a $trans$-tetrachloro(dipyridine)iridate(III):

$$cis\text{-}[Ir(C_5H_5N)_2Cl_4] + trans\text{-}M[Ir(C_5H_5N)_2Cl_4](red) \rightarrow$$
$$trans\text{-}[Ir(C_5H_5N)_2Cl_4] + cis\text{-}M[Ir(C_5H_5N)_2Cl_4]\ (orange)$$

Although the trans isomer is insoluble in boiling nitric acid, the cis isomer dissolves, giving a brown-violet solution. On evaporation, the cis isomer is recovered as strongly dichroic green-violet rhomboids. The trans isomer is not dichroic. Syncrystallization of the cis isomer with cis-$[Pt(C_5H_5N)_2Cl_4]$ ("Anderson's salt"), with which it is isomorphous and to which it communicates its dichroism, enabled Delépine[5,6] to establish the configuration of not only the tetrachloro(dipyridine)iridium(IV) compounds, but the tetrachloro(dipyridine)iridates(III) as well.

References

1. "Gmelins Handbuch der anorganischen Chemie," 8th ed., System-Number 67, Verlag Chemie, Weinheim/Bergstr. und Berlin, 1939.
2. C. RENZ: Z. anorg. Chem., **36**, 105 (1903).
3. D. HOYERMANN: Sitzber. physik.-med. Sozietät Erlangen, **42**, 275 (1910).
4. A. GUTBIER and D. HOYERMANN: Z. anorg. Chem., **89**, 340 (1914).
5. M. DELÉPINE: Ann. chim. (Paris), [9], **19**, 5 (1923).
6. M. DELÉPINE: Compt. rend., **175**, 1211 (1922).
7. M. DELÉPINE: Z. physik. Chem., **130**, 222 (1927).

8. E. Ogawa: *J. Chem. Soc. Japan*, **51**, 190 (1930).
9. M. Delépine: *Compt. rend.*, **176**, 445 (1923).
10. M. Delépine: *Ann. chim. (Paris)*, [9], **19**, 145 (1923).
11. G. B. Kauffman: Inorganic Syntheses, **7**, 228 (1963).

59. cis- AND trans-TRICHLOROTRIS(DIETHYL SULFIDE)IRIDIUM(III)

$$(NH_4)_2[IrCl_6] + 3(C_2H_5)_2S \xrightarrow{\Delta}$$
$$cis\text{- and } trans\text{-}[Ir\{(C_2H_5)_2S\}_3Cl_3] + 2NH_4Cl + \tfrac{1}{2}Cl_2$$

Submitted by George B. Kauffman*
Checked by J. W. Hogarth† and F. P. Dwyer†

Iridium(III) compounds are generally more stable than those of iridium(IV), and iridium(III) coordination compounds include some of the most stable complexes known. On treatment with diethyl sulfide, iridium(IV) chloride loses chlorine, and the thio ether coordinates with the resulting iridium(III) chloride to form a mixture of stable, nonelectrolytic isomers of formula $[Ir\{(C_2H_5)_2S\}_3Cl_3]$.[1-3] The reaction is strongly dependent on the solvent; it is accelerated in ethanol or acetone but inhibited completely in chloroform or benzene. Even in the presence of aqua regia, the same isomers are obtained—an indication of the extraordinary stability of iridium(III) complexes.

In the present synthesis, the more readily available ammonium hexachloroiridate(IV) is substituted for iridium-(IV) chloride. An alternative synthesis involving preliminary reduction of ammonium hexachloroiridate(IV) to hexachloroiridate(III) with ammonium oxalate has been found to give substantially the same total yield of both isomers, but the amount of cis isomer obtained was about twice that of the trans isomer.[4]

* Fresno State College, Fresno, Calif. Financial support of the Research Corporation and the National Science Foundation (Grant NSF-G11241) is gratefully acknowledged.

† John Curtin School of Medical Research, Australian National University, Canberra, A.C.T., Australia.

Generalizing from Delépine's observations on the colors of a number of iridium(III) isomers, the original investigators[2] concluded that the orange compound was the cis (1,2,3) isomer and the red compound, the trans (1,2,6) isomer. In view of the fact that the red compound exhibits solubilities and a melting point that might be expected to be characteristic of the cis isomer (see Properties) and the fact that of the two isomers the red compound is preferentially adsorbed by a polar adsorbent (silica gel),[4] further stereochemical investigations such as measurements of dipole moments or absorption spectra would be desirable.*

Procedure

To 300 ml. of distilled water contained in a 500-ml. round-bottomed flask is added 5.00 g. (0.0113 mol) of ammonium hexachloroiridate(IV),† followed by 5.00 ml. (4.19 g.; 0.0465 mol) of freshly distilled diethyl sulfide (b.p., 92.1°; density, 0.837) dissolved in 30 ml. of 95% ethanol. A long reflux condenser is attached, and the deep red mixture is heated on the water bath at 75 to 80° for about 12 hours. The mixture, which now contains orange-yellow crystals, is refrigerated for several hours, filtered by suction filtration, and the light yellow filtrate (A) is set aside to be reworked later in obtaining a second crop of cis isomer. After the crystals have been washed with three 10-ml. portions of water and air-dried,‡ the cis isomer is extracted by washing it with 5-ml. portions of hot benzene until the originally bright yellow washings are colorless (six portions should be sufficient). The dirty brown residue is set aside for extraction of the trans isomer.

---

* Note added in proof: A recent study of dipole moment, electrophoretic behavior, conductance, n.m.r. and absorption spectra, and derivative formation by G. B. Kauffman, J. H. Tsai, R. M. Kallo, R. C. Fay, and C. K. Jørgensen has demonstrated conclusively that while the yellow isomer is indeed cis, the red compound is an electrolytic "polymerization" isomer, trans-[Ir{(C₂H₅)₂S}₄Cl₂] trans-[Ir{(C₂H₅)₂S}₂Cl₄].

† The commercial product may be used.

‡ The washings (B) should be set aside.

A. cis-TRICHLOROTRIS(DIETHYL SULFIDE)IRIDIUM(III)

Since the cis isomer is too soluble in benzene to be crystallized efficiently from this solvent, the benzene washings are transferred to an evaporating dish and evaporated to dryness by directing an air stream across the surface of the liquid. The residue is dissolved with stirring in a minimum amount (about 35 ml.) of boiling 95% ethanol, transferred to a 150-ml. beaker, and about 40 ml. of boiling water is added. The solution is allowed to cool without being stirred, whereupon large yellow crystals begin to form. When crystallization appears nearly complete (about half an hour), the mixture is cooled for an additional half-hour in an ice bath with frequent stirring.* The crystals are collected by suction filtration, washed with a little ice-cold 95% ethanol and ice water, and then air-dried. The yield is 1.90 g. (29.5%) of yellow crystals melting at 131 to 132°.

The supernatant liquid (A) and washings (B) are combined, evaporated to a volume of about 75 ml., and extracted in a 125-ml. separatory funnel with three 10-ml. portions of hot benzene. The combined benzene extracts are evaporated, and the residue is recrystallized from an ethanol-water mixture as before (about $\frac{1}{5}$ scale), yielding a second crop (0.30 g.; 4.7%) of less pure crystals (m.p., 125 to 128°).* The total yield of cis isomer is 2.20 g. (34.2%). *Anal.* Calcd. for $IrC_{12}H_{30}S_3Cl_3$: Ir, 33.88; C, 25.33; H, 5.31. Found: Ir, 34.12; C, 25.53;† H, 5.36.†

B. trans-TRICHLOROTRIS(DIETHYL SULFIDE)IRIDIUM(III)

The dirty brown, benzene-insoluble residue is dissolved with stirring in a boiling mixture of 50 ml. of benzene and 40 ml. of 95% ethanol, and the resulting red solution is filtered through a Büchner funnel while still hot to remove the small amount of black residue. After the filtrate has

---

* The checkers report that recrystallization from ethanol produces very small crystals; they recommend instead dissolution in cold acetone (about 5 ml.), followed by addition of cold water to incipient cloudiness. Crystallization occurs readily on scratching the sides of the vessel with a glass rod.

† Values supplied by the checkers.

been cooled in an ice bath for about half an hour, the resulting flesh-colored precipitate is collected by suction filtration, washed with two 10-ml. portions of benzene, and air-dried. The yield is 3.00 g. (46.6%; m.p., 165 to 168°).* The filtrate and washings are evaporated (air stream) to about 20 ml., whereupon a few crystals form. When collected by suction filtration and washed and dried as above, this second crop of trans isomer weighs 0.50 g. (7.8%; m.p., 158 to 161°). The total yield of trans isomer is 3.50 g. (55.4%). *Anal.* Calcd. for $IrC_{12}H_{30}S_3Cl_3$: Ir, 33.88. Found: Ir, 33.37. The combined yield of both cis and trans isomers is 5.70 g. (88.6%). All solutions and residues remaining after completion of the synthesis may be added to iridium residues.

Properties

cis-Trichlorotris(diethyl sulfide)iridium(III) reportedly melts at 131°.[2] Although reported as an orange solid, it is obtained in this synthesis in the form of yellow crystals. It is insoluble in water, sparingly soluble in ethanol, but very soluble in benzene, chloroform, and acetone. It is also soluble in ethyl ether and most organic solvents.

The diethyl sulfide molecules can be replaced by other ligands. Thus treatment with aqueous ammonia forms complexes such as [$Ir(NH_3)\{(C_2H_5)_2S\}_2Cl_3$], [$Ir(NH_3)_2\{(C_2H_5)_2S\}Cl_3$], and [$Ir(NH_3)_5Cl]Cl_2$, while ethylamine yields [$Ir(C_2H_5NH_2)_5Cl]Cl_2$. In benzene solution, treatment with pyridine gives *cis*-[$Ir(C_5H_5N)\{(C_2H_5)_2S\}_2Cl_3$] at room temperature or *cis*-[$Ir(C_5H_5N)_2\{(C_2H_5)_2S\}Cl_3$] on heating. The third diethyl sulfide molecule cannot be replaced by pyridine even on long heating although replacement is possible with ammonia or ethylamine; the substitution seems more dependent upon the basicity of the displacing ligand than upon the reaction temperature.

trans-Trichlorotris(diethyl sulfide)iridium(III) reportedly melts at 171°,[2,3] but is stable to 200°. Although reported

* The checkers report 165.5°(cor.).

as a bright red solid, it is obtained in this synthesis in the form of a flesh-colored powder. It is insoluble in water, but slightly soluble in ethanol and acetone. Recrystallization from chloroform, in which it is very soluble, yields an addition compound *trans*-[Ir{(C$_2$H$_5$)$_2$S}$_3$Cl$_3$]·CHCl$_3$, which loses chloroform of crystallization spontaneously at room temperature, forming a reddish white opaque mass of the anhydrous compound.

The two isomers have been separated by adsorption chromatography on silica gel columns; the cis isomer is first eluted with chloroform, and the trans isomer is then eluted with ethanol.[4]

References

1. P. C. RÂY and N. ADHIKARI: *J. Indian Chem. Soc.*, **9**, 251 (1932).
2. P. C. RÂY, N. ADHIKARI, and R. GHOSH: *ibid.*, **10**, 275 (1933).
3. P. C. RÂY and N. N. GHOSH: *ibid.*, **13**, 138 (1936).
4. L. A. TETER: master's thesis, Fresno State College, 1960.

60. *cis*- AND *trans*-PYRIDINIUM TETRACHLORO(DIPYRIDINE)IRIDATE(III)

$$2(NH_4)_2[IrCl_6] + (NH_4)_2C_2O_4 \cdot H_2O \rightarrow$$
$$2(NH_4)_3[IrCl_6] + 2CO_2 + H_2O$$
$$C_5H_5N + HCl \rightarrow [C_5H_5NH]Cl$$
$$[C_5H_5NH]Cl + (NH_4)_3[IrCl_6] + 2C_5H_5N \overset{\Delta}{\rightarrow}$$
$$cis\text{- and } trans\text{-}C_5H_5NH[Ir(C_5H_5N)_2Cl_4] + 3NH_4Cl$$

SUBMITTED BY GEORGE B. KAUFFMAN*
CHECKED BY J. W. HOGARTH† AND F. P. DWYER†

Pyridine reacts almost immediately at 100° with hexachloroiridates(III), M$_3$[IrCl$_6$], or pentachloroaquoiridates-

* Fresno State College, Fresno, Calif. Financial support of the Research Corporation and the National Science Foundation (Grant NSF-G11241) is gratefully acknowledged.

† John Curtin School of Medical Research, Australian National University, Canberra, A.C.T., Australia.

(III), $M_2[Ir(H_2O)Cl_5]$, to form pentachloro(pyridine)iridates(III), $M_2[IrC_5H_5NCl_5]$.[1] If the reaction time is increased to one hour, tetrachloro(dipyridine)iridates(III), $M[Ir(C_5H_5N)_2Cl_4]$, result.[2] The third pyridine molecule required to produce the nonelectrolytic trichloro(tripyridine)iridium, $[Ir(C_5H_5N)_3Cl_3]$, is coordinated only after long heating with excess pyridine.[3]

Since 6-coordinated iridium has an octahedral configuration, tetrachloro(dipyridine)iridates(III) occur in two isomeric forms—cis (orange) and trans (red). The sparingly soluble pyridinium salts are readily isolated and hence are convenient starting materials for the synthesis of other members of the series. Because of their widely differing solubilities in water, the cis and trans pyridinium salts are easily separated. The procedure given below, which is modified from Delépine's original preparation,[4] employs readily available ammonium hexachloroiridate(IV), which is converted to hexachloroiridate(III) by reduction with ammonium oxalate.

Procedure

A solution of 0.711 g. (0.005 mol) of ammonium oxalate 1-hydrate in 20 ml. of boiling water is added in 1-ml. portions* with continuous stirring to 4.42 g. (0.010 mol) of ammonium hexachloroiridate(IV)† contained in a 100-ml. round-bottomed flask (*Caution.* Effervescence). The dark reddish brown solution is warmed on the steam bath for 10 minutes to ensure complete reduction.‡ After the solution has cooled to room temperature, 8.06 ml. (7.91 g.; 0.100 mol) of pyridine (density, 0.892) dissolved in 3.33 ml.

* Stepwise addition prevents possible formation of iridium oxalate complexes.

† The commercial product may be used.

‡ The solution contains ammonium pentachloroaquoiridate(III) as well as hexachloroiridate(III) owing to the aquation reaction:

$$(NH_4)_3[IrCl_6] + H_2O \rightleftharpoons (NH_4)_2[Ir(H_2O)Cl_5] + NH_4Cl.$$

As mentioned above, both substances react with pyridine to give the desired product.

(0.040 mol) of concentrated hydrochloric acid is added, and the flask is fitted with a long condenser. The mixture is refluxed for one hour on a boiling water bath, and the *hot* orange supernatant liquid, which contains most of the more soluble cis isomer, is decanted through a small Büchner funnel. The mass of orange-red crystals, which consists of trans isomer contaminated with some cis isomer, is extracted four times with 20-ml. portions of boiling water in order to dissolve the cis isomer. The first three extracts are decanted through the Büchner funnel. After the fourth extraction, the entire mixture is filtered through the funnel, leaving a residue of red crystals on the filter paper.

The extracts, which are now combined in the filter flask with the original supernatant liquid, are cooled for several hours in an ice bath, the resulting crop of orange crystals is collected by suction filtration, and the orange filtrate set aside. These crystals are redissolved in a minimum amount (about 50 ml.) of boiling water, the orange solution is allowed to cool to room temperature, and the red crystalline deposit of trans isomer is collected on the Büchner funnel with the red crystals previously obtained. The combined orange solutions are concentrated to a volume of about 15 ml. on a water bath, and a few drops of hydrochloric acid are added to neutralize any remaining pyridine and thus decrease the solubility of the cis isomer. After the solution has been cooled in an ice bath for about half an hour, the orange crystals are collected by suction filtration, washed with ethanol and ethyl ether, and air-dried. The filtrate may be added to iridium residues. The yield of cis isomer is 2.12 g. (37.0%). The red crystals are washed with two 25-ml. portions of ice water and air-dried. The yield of trans isomer is 2.31 g. (40.3%). The total yield of both isomers is 4.43 g. (77.3%). Both isomers may be recrystallized from boiling water.* *Anal.* Calcd. for

---

* The checkers report that the trans isomer does not readily dissolve in boiling water; they recommend recrystallization of this isomer from a hot dilute aqueous ethanol solution.

$C_{15}H_{16}N_3IrCl_4$: Ir, 33.69; C, 31.48; H, 2.82; N, 7.34.
Found: (cis) Ir, 33.21; C, 30.03;* H, 2.81;* N, 7.12;* (trans)
Ir, 32.99; C, 31.36;* H, 2.80;* N, 7.41.*

Properties

Unlike most tetrachloro(dipyridine)iridates(III), which
contain water of hydration, the pyridinium salts crystallize
in the anhydrous condition. The cis (orange) isomer is
much more soluble in water (1 part/65 parts at 18°) than
the trans (red) isomer (1 part/770 parts at 18°). Both
salts increase in solubility with increasing temperatures.

Although long refluxing with pyridine produces the corresponding cis and trans isomers of trichloro(tripyridine)-
iridium, the tetrachloro(dipyridine)iridates(III) are relatively stable towards acids and bases. Acids remove the
coordinated pyridine only with the greatest difficulty.
Bases alone fail to expel the coordinated pyridine, and even
in the presence of sodium sulfide they liberate pyridine
slowly on long boiling from the trans salt but not from the
cis.

Oxidizing agents convert both salts to the corresponding
isomers of tetrachloro(dipyridine)iridium(IV) (synthesis
58). Delépine[4] established the structure of the tetrachloro-
(dipyridine)iridates(III) by oxidizing the orange salts and
syncrystallizing the $[Ir(C_5H_5N)_2Cl_4]$ thus obtained with
"Anderson's salt," $[Pt(C_5H_5N)_2Cl_4]$, which is known to
possess the cis configuration.

References

1. M. Delépine: Compt. rend., **152**, 1390, 1589 (1911).
2. M. Delépine: ibid., **175**, 1075 (1922).
3. M. Delépine: Ann. chim. (Paris), [9], **19**, 145 (1923).
4. M. Delépine: ibid., [9], **19**, 5 (1923).

* Values supplied by the checkers.

61. RECOVERY OF PLATINUM FROM LABORATORY RESIDUES

$$\text{Pt compounds} \xrightarrow{\Delta} \text{Pt}$$
$$\text{Pt} + 4\text{HNO}_3 + 6\text{HCl} \rightarrow \text{H}_2[\text{PtCl}_6] + 4\text{NO}_2 + 4\text{H}_2\text{O}$$
$$\text{H}_2[\text{PtCl}_6] + 2\text{NaCl} \xrightarrow{\Delta} \text{Na}_2[\text{PtCl}_6] + 2\text{HCl}$$
$$2\text{NH}_4\text{Cl} + \text{Na}_2[\text{PtCl}_6] \rightarrow (\text{NH}_4)_2[\text{PtCl}_6] + 2\text{NaCl}$$
$$3(\text{NH}_4)_2[\text{PtCl}_6] \xrightarrow{\Delta} 3\text{Pt} + 2\text{N}_2 + 2\text{NH}_4\text{Cl} + 16\text{HCl}$$
$$\text{H}_2[\text{PtCl}_6] + 3\text{Zn} \rightarrow \text{Pt} + 3\text{ZnCl}_2 + \text{H}_2$$

Submitted by George B. Kauffman* and Larry A. Teter*
Checked by Richard N. Rhoda†

Although many procedures for recovering platinum appear in the literature, they are not generally applicable to laboratory residues. Since those intended for ores assume the presence of other platinum metals, they are unnecessarily complicated. On the other hand, simpler methods involving only treatment with formaldehyde, formic acid, sodium dithionite, iron, magnesium, zinc, or other reducing agents reduce other inactive metals such as copper or silver. Furthermore, standard reduction methods are seldom directly applicable to the more stable platinum complexes.

The following procedure, modified from Gilchrist's method,[1] is intended for the recovery of platinum from residues containing base metals and noble metals (other than those of the platinum group) as well as strong complexing agents. A preliminary separation of base metals as hydrated oxides considerably reduces the time required to obtain pure platinum by the precipitation of ammonium hexachloroplatinate(IV). The authors have tested the procedure both with actual laboratory residues and with syn-

* Fresno State College, Fresno, Calif. Financial support of the Research Corporation and the National Science Foundation (Grant NSF-G 11241) is gratefully acknowledged.
† The International Nickel Company, Inc., Bayonne, N.J.

thetic platinum mixtures containing as much as 50% of the following combined impurities: aluminum, ammonium, cobalt, chromium, copper, iron, mercury, potassium, silver, and sodium ions as well as ethylenediamine, diethyl sulfide, pyridine, tri-*n*-butylphosphine, urea, thiourea.

Procedure

The dried residue is heated to redness in a large porcelain casserole or evaporating dish over a Meker burner, and ignition is continued until fuming has ceased.* Most of the soluble salts are now removed by thoroughly washing and decanting the ignited and powdered residue several times with five times its volume of boiling water for each operation.† Since the washings may contain some finely divided platinum, they should be filtered. After the filter paper has been charred in a covered crucible, the residue should be added to the ignited and washed mixture.

The residue is treated with five times its volume of aqua regia ($1HNO_3:4HCl$). After the initial effervescence has subsided, the mixture is gently heated on a hot plate for about half an hour. It is then allowed to settle, and the liquid is carefully decanted into a beaker. The residue is similarly treated with 5-volume portions of aqua regia until all the platinum has dissolved, i.e., until the decanted liquid, originally dark reddish orange, is a pale straw color. A total of about 30 ml. of aqua regia per gram of platinum should be sufficient. The combined portions of the aqua regia solution are cooled with running water (not an ice bath),‡ and the precipitate of insoluble chlorides is removed

---

* Ignition removes ammonium salts and volatile substances and decomposes platinum complexes to metallic platinum. *All ignitions and evaporations should be carried out under the hood!*

† If potassium salts are present in considerable amounts, much potassium hexachloroplatinate(IV) will be precipitated when the mixture is boiled with aqua regia.

‡ If the solution becomes too cold, a considerable amount of sparingly soluble potassium hexachloroplatinate(IV) may precipitate.

by suction filtration through a sintered-glass funnel (medium porosity). The insoluble chlorides are added to the residue insoluble in aqua regia and boiled for a few minutes with twice the total volume of water. The mixture is filtered by suction through coarse paper, and the yellow filtrate, which contains potassium hexachloroplatinate(IV), is added to the aqua regia solution. The entire process is repeated until the filtrate is colorless, whereupon the residue is discarded.

The aqua regia filtrate is transferred to a very large beaker, sodium chloride (commercial salt) (1.2 g./g. of platinum) is added, and the solution is evaporated to near dryness on a steam bath.* An air stream directed across the surface of the liquid increases the rate of evaporation and reduces foaming. The residue is barely covered with hydrochloric acid and evaporated to dryness in order to destroy any nitro complexes. It is next just covered with water, again evaporated on the steam bath, and dried in an oven at 110° for one hour.†

The residue is dissolved in sufficient water to yield a concentration of about 50 g. of platinum per liter, the solution heated nearly to boiling, and sufficient sodium hydrogen carbonate (commercial baking soda) added (*caution:* effervescence) until the resulting solution just turns red litmus blue. After being cooled with running water for about 10 minutes, the mixture is filtered through a Büchner (*not sintered-glass*) funnel to remove the precipitate of hydrated base metal oxides which has settled. Any platinum-containing solution is removed by washing the precipitate twice

---

* A Meker burner or hot plate, although faster, would require constant stirring and swirling to prevent spattering. Sodium hexachloroplatinate(IV) is easier to handle than hexachloroplatinic(IV) acid, because the latter may decompose to insoluble products on being heated to dryness. If a reddish orange sirup rather than a yellowish green crystalline mass is obtained, the amount of sodium chloride was insufficient.

† This step is intended to remove most of the hydrochloric acid in order to avoid excessive consumption of sodium hydrogen carbonate and subsequent excess foaming, as well as contamination of ammonium hexachloroplatinate(IV) with coprecipitated sodium chloride.

with two times its volume of cold water for each operation. The washings are added to the filtrate.

A slight excess of solid ammonium chloride (0.6 g./g. of platinum) is then added to the solution to precipitate the platinum. The solubility of the ammonium hexachloroplatinate(IV) is reduced by adding an amount of 95% ethanol equal to about one-tenth the volume of the solution and by cooling in an ice bath for about 10 minutes. The yellow precipitate is collected on a Büchner funnel, and the filtrate is tested for complete precipitation by adding more ammonium chloride and setting it aside. The ammonium hexachloroplatinate(IV) is washed with several one-volume portions (relative to the filtrate) of *ice-cold* 20% ammonium chloride solution, 95% ethanol, and ethyl ether and then air-dried. The precipitate is removed from the filter paper, placed in a partially covered crucible, and ignited to metallic platinum over a Meker burner, gently at first, but then more strongly. The residue is washed several times with 5-volume portions of 6 N nitric acid and water to remove any coprecipitated sodium chloride. The platinum is dried in an oven at 110° for one hour.

Some platinum is still present as hexachloroplatinate(IV) in the light yellow filtrate. It is recovered by strongly acidifying this solution with hydrochloric acid (pH about 1),* adding excess mossy zinc, and allowing the mixture to stand until reduction appears complete (about one hour), with occasional stirring if necessary to remove precipitated platinum from the zinc and expose fresh metal surface. Additional acid is added, if necessary, to dissolve any excess zinc, and the platinum is collected on a Büchner funnel and washed and dried as was the previously recovered platinum. Since the metal produced by reduction with zinc is not as pure as that produced by ignition of ammonium hexachloroplatinate(IV), the products should be kept separate.

In general, the percentage recovery of platinum increases

---

* Use of an acid solution considerably reduces the time required for reduction and avoids evolution of ammonia and precipitation of basic salts.

with increasing percentage of platinum in the residue. For example, with a mixture containing 50% platinum, 77.1% recovery (53.6% by precipitation and 23.5% by reduction) was attained, while with a mixture containing 75% platinum, the recovery rose to 95.7% (80.7% by precipitation and 15.0% by reduction). If platinum of higher purity is desired, the recovered material may be dissolved in aqua regia, reprecipitated as ammonium hexachloroplatinate(IV), and reignited.

Reference

1. R. GILCHRIST: *Chem. Revs.*, **32**, 306 (1943).

62. *cis-* AND *trans-*TETRACHLORODIAMMINE-PLATINUM(IV)

SUBMITTED BY GEORGE B. KAUFFMAN*
CHECKED BY GEORGE SLUSARCZUK† AND STANLEY KIRSCHNER†

In the conversion of a planar tetracovalent compound to a hexacovalent compound, the two added groups usually occupy trans positions in the resulting octahedron.[1] Thus, oxidation of *cis-* or *trans-*dichlorodiammineplatinum(II) with chlorine results in formation of the corresponding isomers of tetrachlorodiammineplatinum(IV).[1-3] Aqua regia,[4,5] potassium permanganate,[4,5] ozone,[6] and nitric acid[4] have also been used as oxidizing agents. Oxidation with chlorine, which is convenient and yields a pure product, is employed here.

* Fresno State College, Fresno, Calif. Financial support of the Research Corporation and the National Science Foundation (Grant NSF-G11241) is gratefully acknowledged.

† Wayne State University, Detroit, Mich.

Procedure

A. *cis*-TETRACHLORODIAMMINEPLATINUM(IV)

$$cis\text{-}[Pt(NH_3)_2Cl_2] + Cl_2 \rightarrow cis\text{-}[Pt(NH_3)_2Cl_4]$$

A suspension of 1.50 g. (0.005 mol) of *cis*-dichlorodiammineplatinum(II) (synthesis 63) in 10 ml. of water in a 50-ml. beaker is heated to 75 to 80°* on a water bath. This temperature is maintained while chlorine is slowly bubbled through the mechanically stirred mixture, the volume of which is kept at about 10 ml. by addition of hot water. After one-half hour, the supernatant liquid, originally a pale yellow, has become dark orange, while the solid has changed from pale yellow to lemon yellow. After 3 hours, the flow of chlorine is stopped and the mixture boiled to remove excess chlorine. The mixture is then cooled in an ice bath and filtered through a sintered-glass funnel. The lemon-yellow crystals are washed with several 5-ml. portions of cold water and air-dried. The yield is 1.04 g. (56%). *Anal.* Calcd. for $[Pt(NH_3)_2Cl_4]$: Pt, 52.61; N, 7.55; H, 1.63; Cl, 38.22. Found: Pt, 52.64; N, 7.56, 7.72;† H, 1.84;† Cl, 38.02.

B. *trans*-TETRACHLORODIAMMINEPLATINUM(IV)

$$trans\text{-}[Pt(NH_3)_2Cl_2] + Cl_2 \rightarrow trans\text{-}[Pt(NH_3)_2Cl_4]$$

The procedure is the same as that given for the cis isomer (Procedure A) except that the starting material is 1.50 g. (0.005 mol) of *trans*-dichlorodiammineplatinum(II) (Synthesis 63), the reaction temperature is 100° (boiling-water bath), and reaction time is only one hour. The yield is 1.63 g. (88%). *Anal.* Calcd. for $[Pt(NH_3)_2Cl_4]$: Pt, 52.61;

---

* Use of a higher temperature may result in formation of a soluble hexachloroplatinate(IV).

† Values reported by checkers.

N, 7.55; H, 1.63; Cl, 38.22.   Found: Pt, 52.23; N, 7.50;*
H, 1.68;* Cl, 38.09.

Properties[7]

The cis and trans compounds are both lemon-yellow
crystalline powders.   Upon heating, the cis isomer becomes
olive green at 160° and dark green at 210°.   Slow decomposition of the cis isomer begins at about 240°, whereas that
of the trans isomer starts at 200 to 216°.   Both are only
slightly soluble in cold water, the symmetrical trans form
being the more soluble.[4]   The solubility of both compounds
in water increases with increasing temperature.   Both
isomers are insoluble in most common solvents, with the
exception of *N,N*-dimethylformamide.   Insolubility in nonpolar solvents has prevented dipole moment measurements.

Aqueous solutions of both isomers exhibit conductivities
characteristic of nonelectrolytes, but conductivities increase
with time because of hydrolysis.[8]   Concentrated sulfuric
acid does not attack either isomer.   Potassium hydroxide
solution dissolves the trans isomer without evolution of
ammonia.   When aqueous solutions of both compounds are
boiled for a long time with silver nitrate, all of the chlorine
is precipitated.

References

1. S. M. Jørgensen: *Z. anorg. u. allgem. Chem.*, **25**, 353 (1900).
2. C. Gerhardt: *Ann.*, **76**, 314 (1850); *Compt. rend.*, **31**, 241 (1850).
3. C. Grimm: *Ann.*, **99**, 85 (1856).
4. P. T. Cleve: *Acta Upsala*, **6**, 46 (1866); *Svenska Akad. Handl.*, **7**, 7 (1868); **10**, 9 (1872).
5. W. Odling: *Ber.* **3**, 682 (1870); *Chem. News*, **21**, 269, 289 (1870); *Proc. Roy. Inst. Gt. Brit.*, **6**, 176 (1872).
6. L. A. Chugaev and W. Chlopin: *Compt. rend.*, **161**, 699 (1915); *Z. anorg. u. allgem. Chem.*, **151**, 253 (1926).
7. J. W. Mellor: "A Comprehensive Treatise on Inorganic and Theo-retical Chemistry," Vol. XVI, pp. 307–308, Longmans, Green & Co., Ltd., London, 1937.
8. A. Werner and A. Miolati: *Z. physik. Chem.*, **12**, 54 (1893); **14**, 508 (1894).

* Values reported by checkers.

63. *cis-* AND *trans-*DICHLORODIAMMINE-PLATINUM(II)

SUBMITTED BY GEORGE B. KAUFFMAN* AND DWAINE O. COWAN*
CHECKED BY GEORGE SLUSARCZUK† AND STANLEY KIRSCHNER†

These two compounds, originally called Peyrone's salt[1] and Reiset's second chloride,[2] respectively, have long been known and have played an important role in the historical development of coordination theory. Werner's suggestion that these compounds are cis and trans isomers represents the earliest proposal of a planar configuration for bivalent platinum. He correctly identified these compounds by using his classical concept of "trans elimination."[3]

The cis isomer has been prepared by the action of aqueous ammonia on ammonium[4] or potassium[5] tetrachloroplatinate(II), while the trans isomer has been prepared by the action of heat[1,2,5] or concentrated hydrochloric acid[1] on tetraammineplatinum(II) chloride. These reactions are in accord with Peyrone's rule and Jørgensen's rule, respectively, both of which are included in Chernyaev's trans effect.

Other methods for the preparation of the cis isomer include heating the trans isomer[6] or tetraammineplatinum-(II) chloride[1] with aqueous ammonia and reaction of ammonium carbonate with tetrachloroplatinic(II) acid.[7] Other methods for the preparation of the trans isomer include the action of hydrochloric acid on dihydroxodiammineplatinum-(II)[6] and the thermal decompositions of ammonium tetrachloroplatinate(II),[8] tetraammineplatinum(II) chloride,[7] or tetraammineplatinum(II) tetrachloroplatinate(II) (Magnus' green salt).[9]

* Fresno State College, Fresno, Calif. Financial support of the Research Corporation and the National Science Foundation (Grant NSF-G11241) is gratefully acknowledged.

† Wayne State University, Detroit, Mich.

The preparations given here for the cis and trans isomers are modifications of the methods of Ramberg[5] and Peyrone,[1] respectively, and involve a minimum of side reactions. Both methods involve the preliminary preparation of potassium tetrachloroplatinate(II), which need not be isolated.

Procedure

A. POTASSIUM TETRACHLOROPLATINATE(II)*

$$2K_2[PtCl_6] + N_2H_4 \cdot 2HCl \rightarrow 2K_2[PtCl_4] + N_2 + 6HCl$$

To a suspension of 9.72 g. (0.02 mol) of potassium hexachloroplatinate(IV)† in 100 ml. of water contained in a 250-ml. beaker is added in small portions 1.0 g. (0.01 mol)‡ of hydrazine dihydrochloride.[10] The mixture is stirred mechanically while the temperature is raised to 50 to 65° over a period of 5 to 10 minutes. This temperature is maintained until only a small amount of yellow potassium hexachloroplatinate(IV) remains undissolved§ in the deep red solution (about 2 hours). The temperature is then raised to 80 to 90° to ensure completion of the reaction, and the mixture is cooled in an ice bath and filtered to remove unreacted potassium hexachloroplatinate(IV).‖ The latter is washed with several 10-ml. portions of ice water until the washings are colorless. The washings, combined with the deep red filtrate, contain pure potassium tetrachloroplatinate(II) and hydrochloric acid. This solution is divided

* An alternative method for the preparation of this compound has been described by R. N. Keller, INORGANIC SYNTHESES, **2**, 247 (1946).

† If it is desired to start with metallic platinum, sponge rather than wire is recommended, for reasons of economy and as a time-saver.

‡ Excess hydrazine dihydrochloride must be avoided to prevent formation of hydrazine complexes and reduction of potassium tetrachloroplatinate(II) to platinum when the solution is made basic with ammonia[11] (Procedure B).

§ An insoluble hexachloroplatinate(IV) is used to indicate when the reaction is complete.

‖ Use of excess potassium hexachloroplatinate(IV) prevents the reduction to metallic platinum noted by some workers.[11,12]

into two equal portions, one for use in Procedure B and one for Procedure C. *A solution containing 4.15 g. (0.01 mol) of potassium tetrachloroplatinate(II) and 2.5 ml. of concentrated hydrochloric acid in 75 ml. of water may be substituted for each of these portions.*

B. cis-DICHLORODIAMMINEPLATINUM(II)

$$K_2[PtCl_4] + 2NH_3 \xrightarrow{NH_4Cl} cis\text{-}[Pt(NH_3)_2Cl_2] + 2KCl$$

Three grams of ammonium chloride* is dissolved in one portion of the filtrate from Procedure A contained in a 150-ml. beaker. About 10 ml. of 3 M aqueous ammonia is cautiously added until the solution is neutral to litmus. Two one-hundredths mol of additional ammonia (6.75 ml. of 3 M solution) is then added.† The solution is refrigerated until the precipitation of the greenish yellow solid appears to be complete and the supernatant liquid has changed from deep red to light yellow (24 to 48 hours). The precipitate, consisting of the cis isomer containing a small amount of tetraammineplatinum(II) tetrachloroplatinate(II) (Magnus' green salt), is separated by suction filtration and washed free of soluble salts with several 10-ml. portions of ice water. The precipitate is then transferred to a 250-ml. Erlenmeyer flask, and 0.1 N hydrochloric acid‡ is added to bring the total volume to 150 ml. This mixture is heated to boiling and stirred until all the cis isomer dissolves, leaving a small residue of Magnus' green salt, which is removed by filtration. Crystallization of the isomer is prevented by use of a funnel heater or a jacketed Büchner funnel. The residue on the filter paper is washed with 10 to

---

* Use of an unbuffered solution may result in formation of hydroxo complexes.

† A slight excess of ammonia is not harmful. However, a large excess will markedly decrease the yield by formation of tetraammineplatinum(II) chloride.

‡ Dilute acid, rather than water, is used for recrystallization to prevent formation of aquo complexes (see Properties).

20 ml. of boiling 0.1 N hydrochloric acid and the washings are added to the filtrate. The latter is cooled in an ice bath until crystallization seems complete (1 to 2 hours). The yellow crystals are separated by suction filtration, washed with several 10-ml. portions of ice water, and air-dried. The yield is 1.80 g. (60%, based on potassium hexachloroplatinate(IV)*). *Anal.* Calcd. for $[Pt(NH_3)_2Cl_2]$: Pt, 65.02; N, 9.33; H, 2.01; Cl, 23.62. Found: Pt, 65.23; N, 9.62, 9.81;† H, 2.33;† Cl, 23.33.

C. *trans*-DICHLORODIAMMINEPLATINUM(II)

$$K_2[PtCl_4] + 4NH_3 \rightarrow [Pt(NH_3)_4]Cl_2 + 2KCl$$
$$[Pt(NH_3)_4]Cl_2 + 2HCl \xrightarrow{\Delta} trans\text{-}[Pt(NH_3)_2Cl_2] + 2NH_4Cl$$

In a 1-l. beaker, one portion of the filtrate from Procedure A is heated to boiling on a hot plate, and 10 ml. of concentrated aqueous ammonia is slowly added with swirling.‡ The resulting straw-colored solution is *cautiously* evaporated (*hood!*) to a volume of about 20 ml. (not to dryness), with continuous swirling during the latter stages in order to prevent spattering.§ Four hundred milliliters of 6 N hydrochloric acid is added to the resulting pale yellow residue of tetraammineplatinum(II) chloride, which may already contain some trans isomer, and the mixture is evaporated as above (*hood!*) to a volume of from 30 to 40 ml. (not to dryness).‖ As evaporation proceeds, the solution becomes turbid and then yellow. Finally, the trans isomer is

---

* The limiting reagent is actually hydrazine dihydrochloride; so the yield is really slightly higher.

† Values reported by the checkers.

‡ This technique converts potassium tetrachloroplatinate(II) directly to soluble tetraammineplatinum(II) chloride without precipitating insoluble Magnus' green salt, $[Pt(NH_3)_4][PtCl_4]$.

§ For this and all subsequent evaporations, an oscillating hot plate is convenient. Care must be taken to avoid decomposition by excessive heating. Use of a water bath is very time-consuming.

‖ The alternative procedure of heating the dry salt at 250° results in a much lower yield because of extensive decomposition to metallic platinum.

deposited as a fine yellow powder. After being cooled for about 15 minutes in an ice bath, the mixture, now the consistency of slush, is transferred to a 5-cm. sintered-glass funnel, drained by suction, washed with several 10-ml. portions of ice water, and air-dried. One or two more similar evaporations of the filtrate with 6 N hydrochloric acid followed by washing and drying as above are sufficient to produce a combined yield of about 2.7 g. (*ca.* 90%) of a product which is pure enough for most purposes. The trans isomer may be recrystallized from a *minimum* amount of boiling 0.1 N hydrochloric acid as was the cis isomer. The percentage recovery for this step is 80 to 90%. *Anal.* Calcd. for [Pt(NH$_3$)$_2$Cl$_2$]: Pt, 65.02; N, 9.33; H, 2.01; Cl, 23.62. Found: Pt, 65.28; N, 9.54, 9.54;* H, 2.44;* Cl, 23.39.

Properties[13]

Both the cis and trans compounds are yellow, the former possessing a somewhat deeper color than the latter. Both decompose at about 270°, yielding hydrogen chloride, ammonium chloride, nitrogen, and platinum. Both are only slightly soluble in cold water, the unsymmetrical cis form being the more soluble (cis, 0.253 g./100 g. at 25°; trans, 0.036 g./100 g. at 25°). The solubility of both compounds in water increases with increasing temperature.

In aqueous solution, the cis form slowly changes to the trans form. Solutions of both isomers exhibit very small conductivities, but the conductivities increase with time because of aquation:

$$[Pt(NH_3)_2Cl_2] + H_2O \rightleftharpoons [Pt(NH_3)_2(H_2O)Cl]^+ + Cl^-$$
$$[Pt(NH_3)_2(H_2O)Cl]^+ + H_2O \rightleftharpoons [Pt(NH_3)_2(H_2O)_2]^{++} + Cl^-$$

Both isomers are insoluble in most common solvents, with the exception of N,N-dimethylformamide. Insolubility in nonpolar solvents has prevented dipole moment measurements.

* Values reported by the checkers.

These compounds are convenient starting materials for the preparation of a wide variety of platinum(II) complexes. The chlorine atoms can be replaced by other negative groups such as bromide, iodide, hydroxide, nitrate, nitrite, and thiocyanate. The ammonia molecules can be replaced by other bases such as pyridine, arylamines, and quinoline. Oxidation with aqua regia or chlorine yields the corresponding isomers of tetrachlorodiammineplatinum(IV) (synthesis 62). A supposedly third (γ-) form has been shown to be a solid solution or mixture of the cis (β-) and trans (α-) isomers.

Several tests are available for distinguishing between the two isomers. They respond to the classical Kurnakov test:[14] in hot aqueous solution, the cis compound reacts with aqueous thiourea to give a deeper yellow solution from which yellow needles of tetrakis(thiourea)platinum(II) chloride deposit on cooling, while the trans compound gives a colorless solution from which snow-white needles of *trans*-bis(thiourea)diammineplatinum(II) deposit on cooling. An extremely sensitive test using oxydiphenylenetelluronium hydrogen sulfate [phenoxytellurine di(hydrogen sulfate)] permits detection of minute traces of cis isomer in large amounts of trans isomer. The reagent gives an intense violet color with the former but does not react with the latter.[15] Other tests using sodium sulfite,[16] sodium thiosulate,[17] and oxalic acid[18] require careful control of mol ratios.

References

1. M. Peyrone: *Ann.*, **51**, 15 (1845); **61**, 180 (1847); *Ann. chim. et phys.*, [3] **12**, 193 (1844); [3] **16**, 462 (1846).
2. J. Reiset: *Ann. chim. et phys.*, [3] **11**, 417 (1844); *Compt. rend.*, **18**, 1103 (1844).
3. A. Werner: *Z. anorg. Chem.*, **3**, 267 (1893).
4. E. Biilmann and A. C. Andersen: *Ber.*, **36**, 1570 (1903).
5. L. Ramberg: *ibid.*, **46**, 2362 (1913); *Z. anorg. Chem.*, **83**, 33 (1913).
6. W. Odling: *Ber.*, **3**, 682 (1870); *Chem. News*, **21**, 291 (1870); *Proc. Roy. Inst. Gt. Brit.*, **6**, 176 (1872).
7. H. Biltz and W. Biltz: "Laboratory Methods of Inorganic Chemistry," John Wiley & Sons, New York, 1909.

8. S. M. Jørgensen: *J. prakt. Chem.*, [2], **33**, 409 (1886); *Z. anorg. Chem.*, **24**, 153 (1900); **25**, 353 (1900).
9. L. A. Chugaev and N. K. Pshenicyn, *J. Russ. Phys. Chem. Soc.*, **52**, 47 (1920).
10. N. G. Klyuchnikov and R. N. Savelava, *Zhur. Neorg. Khim.*, **1**, 2764 (1956).
11. V. I. Goremykin: *Compt. rend. acad. sci. U. R. S. S.*, **33**, 227 (1941).
12. W. E. Cooley and D. H. Busch: Inorganic Syntheses, **5**, 208 (1957).
13. J. W. Mellor: "A Comprehensive Treatise on Inorganic and Theoretical Chemistry," Vol. XVI, pp. 261–266, Longmans, Green & Co., Ltd., London, 1937.
14. N. S. Kurnakov: *J. prakt. Chem.*, [2] **50**, 480 (1894); *J. Russ. Phys. Chem. Soc.*, **25**, 565 (1893).
15. H. D. K. Drew, F. W. Pinkard, W. Wardlaw, and E. G. Cox: *J. Chem. Soc.*, **1932**, 988.
16. M. M. Gurin: *Doklady Akad. Nauk S. S. S. R.*, **50**, 201 (1945).
17. D. I. Ryabchikov: *Compt. rend. acad. sci. U. R. S. S.*, **32**, 344 (1941).
18. A. A. Grinberg: *Ann. inst. platine U. S. S. R.*, **6**, 122 (1928).

64. cis- AND trans-DICHLOROBIS(TRI-n-BUTYLPHOSPHINE)PLATINUM(II)

$$K_2[PtCl_4] + 2(n\text{-}C_4H_9)_3P \rightarrow$$
$$cis\text{- and } trans\text{-}[PtCl_2\{(n\text{-}C_4H_9)_3P\}_2] + 2KCl$$

Submitted by George B. Kauffman* and Larry A. Teter*
Checked by James E. Huheey†

Coordination compounds of platinum(II) halides with tertiary alkylphosphines have long been known.[1,2]   Treatment of a potassium tetrachloroplatinate(II) solution with the stoichiometric amount of triethyl- or tri-n-propylphosphine yields a precipitate of [Pt(R₃P)₄][PtCl₄], which is transformed to the monomeric isomers, cis- and trans-[PtCl₂(R₃P)₂], on several weeks' standing, or more rapidly on heating.[3]   The stability of the ionic compound decreases

* Fresno State College, Fresno, Calif.   Financial support of the Research Corporation and the National Science Foundation (Grant NSF-G 11241) is gratefully acknowledged.
† Worcester Polytechnic Institute, Worcester, Mass.

from ethyl to propyl, whereas with tri-*n*-butyl-phosphine the molecular compound is formed directly. The monomeric isomers are all nonelectrolytes, have low melting points, and are soluble in organic solvents, the trans isomer more so than the cis. Solubility in organic solvents increases from the ethyl to the butyl compound. A modification of the method of Jensen[3] for the preparation of the tri-*n*-butyl compound is described in this synthesis.

Procedure

A. *cis*-DICHLOROBIS(TRI-*n*-BUTYLPHOSPHINE)PLATINUM(II)

A solution of 4.15 g. (0.01 mol) of potassium tetrachloroplatinate(II) in 50 ml. of water is shaken *vigorously* in a stoppered 250-ml. wide-mouth container* with 4.99 ml. (4.05 g.; 0.02 mol) of freshly distilled tri-*n*-butylphosphine[4] (density, 0.8118 g./ml.) until no further lightening of the color of the supernatant liquid occurs (about 3 hours).† The resulting waxy salmon-colored mass, containing predominantly cis isomer but also some trans isomer, is scraped from the sides of the container, washed with several 10-ml. portions of water, and dried in a vacuum oven at 30° for about one hour. Complete removal of occluded potassium chloride and tetrachloroplatinate(II) from the isomer mixture is difficult because of its waxy nature, but is effected by subsequent purification steps.

Since the trans isomer is quite soluble in *ice-cold low-boil-*

---

* A 250-ml. glass-stoppered Erlenmeyer flask is satisfactory, but removal of the product is facilitated by use of a wide-mouth vessel.

† The liquid is still orange because of unreacted potassium tetrachloroplatinate(II). Use of excess tri-*n*-butylphosphine causes the reaction to go to completion within a very short time, resulting in utilization of all the tetrachloroplatinate(II), but oily products are obtained rather than well-defined crystals. The checker reports that the unreacted potassium tetrachloroplatinate(II) can be recovered by concentrating the supernatant liquid on a steam bath to about one-half the original volume, stirring the solution into *ca.* 250 ml. of an acetone-ether (1:1) solution, washing the precipitated solid, first with acetone-ether solution, then with ether, followed by air-drying.[5]

ing petroleum ether, whereas the cis isomer is only very slightly soluble, the former is separated from the latter by repeatedly extracting the waxy mass with *ice-cold* petroleum ether (*b.p., 30 to 60°*).*   Not all of the trans isomer can be extracted in this manner since some of the cis isomer isomerizes to the trans isomer in petroleum ether.   The petroleum ether filtrate contains only a small amount of trans isomer, and it is suggested that this be evaporated to dryness and added to platinum residues.†

The yellowish white portion of the original waxy mass which was insoluble in petroleum ether consists mainly of cis isomer contaminated by a small amount of trans isomer. It is purified by adding 50 ml. of petroleum ether (*b.p., 30 to 60°*),‡ heating to boiling, and then adding 95% ethanol dropwise (about 1 ml.) with stirring until the solid just dissolves.   Upon cooling in an ice-salt bath for about half an hour, crystals of the cis isomer are deposited.   About four such recrystallizations, each of which is almost quantitative if carried out carefully, are generally necessary in order to obtain a pure product of snow-white crystals.   These are collected by suction filtration and air-dried.   The yield is 4.05 g. [60.3% based on potassium tetrachloroplatinate-(II)].   *Use of amounts smaller than those specified results in decreased yields.*

B. *trans-*DICHLOROBIS(TRI-*n*-BUTYLPHOSPHINE) PLATINUM(II)

The trans isomer is prepared by carefully heating a sample of the cis isomer in an evaporating dish on an oil-bath

---

* Six 10-ml. portions are recommended.   Extraction should be continued until the color of the light yellow filtrate remains constant.   *Low-boiling* petroleum ether should be used because the cis isomer is soluble in high-boiling petroleum ether.

† Since attempted crystallization of either isomer in the presence of impurities often results in oily substances and since the amount of trans isomer involved is quite small, recovery of the trans isomer seems inadvisable.   The purpose of the extraction is merely to remove most of the trans isomer from the cis isomer, rather than to prepare the trans isomer.

‡ If high-boiling petroleum ether is used, the cis isomer will fail to crystallize.

just above its melting point (about 144°), whereupon it melts to a yellow liquid. This temperature is maintained for about one hour.* The residue is dissolved in a *minimum* volume of warm 95% ethanol (*ca.* 5 ml. for each 1 g. of isomer) and the solution cooled for several minutes in an ice-salt bath. The resulting yellow crystals are collected by suction filtration, recrystallized again from warm ethanol, filtered by suction, and air-dried. The conversion is practically quantitative, but because of the high solubility of the trans isomer the yield is only 50% (based on the cis isomer).

Analysis

Ignition of the isomers appears to result in loss of platinum, whereas reduction with formic acid or hydrazine hydrate seems incomplete. The sample is therefore boiled with concentrated sulfuric acid until the supernatant liquid becomes clear and almost colorless (about 4 hours). The residual platinum is collected on a sintered-glass funnel, washed with water, ethanol, ether, and then air-dried. *Anal.* Calcd. for $[PtCl_2\{(C_4H_9)_3P\}_2]$: Pt, 29.10. Found: Pt, 29.00 (trans), 29.10 (cis).

Properties[3,6]

The cis isomer is snow-white, whereas the trans isomer is yellow. The melting points are 144 to 144.5° and 65 to 66°, respectively, and are greatly lowered by traces of impurities. The cis isomer is only slightly soluble in water, whereas the trans isomer is virtually insoluble. They are both soluble in water in the presence of tri-*n*-butylphosphine because of the reaction:

$$[PtCl_2\{(n\text{-}C_4H_9)_3P\}_2] + 2(n\text{-}C_4H_9)_3P \rightarrow [Pt\{(n\text{-}C_4H_9)_3P\}_4]^{++} + 2Cl^-$$

---

* Excessive heating (>155°) increases the efficiency of conversion but also decomposes the trans isomer formed.

The cis isomer is soluble in benzene, carbon disulfide, ethanol, and N,N-dimethylformamide, whereas the trans isomer is highly soluble in most organic solvents.

The dipole moments in benzene solution are 11.5 D. and 0 D., respectively. Such measurements were used by Jensen to prove unequivocally that the configuration of tetra-coordinate bivalent platinum is square planar. Conductivity measurements of their benzene solutions have shown them to be nonelectrolytes, but conductivity in alcoholic solutions increases with time because of alcoholysis. The conductivity of the cis isomer increases more rapidly than that of the trans. Aqueous and alcoholic solutions of the cis isomer give an immediate precipitate with silver nitrate, whereas those of the trans isomer react more slowly.

References

1. A. W. HOFMANN: *Ann.*, **103**, 357 (1857).
2. A. CAHOURS and H. GAL: *ibid.*, **155**, 223, 335 (1870); **156**, 302 (1870); *Compt. rend.*, **70**, 897, 1380 (1870); **71**, 208 (1870).
3. K. A. JENSEN: *Z. anorg u. allgem. Chem.*, **229**, 225 (1936).
4. G. B. KAUFFMAN and L. A. TETER: INORGANIC SYNTHESES, **6**, 87 (1960).
5. R. N. KELLER: *ibid.*, **2**, 247 (1946).
6. K. A. JENSEN: *Z. anorg. u. allgem. Chem.*, **229**, 252 (1936).

65. *cis-* AND *trans*-DICHLORO(DIPYRIDINE)-PLATINUM(II)

SUBMITTED BY GEORGE B. KAUFFMAN*
CHECKED BY RICHARD J. THOMPSON†

The two geometric isomers of dichloro(dipyridine) platinum(II) have been used by many investigators[1-7] in stereo-

* Fresno State College, Fresno, Calif. Financial support of the Research Corporation and the National Science Foundation (Grant NSF-G 11241) is gratefully acknowledged.
† North Texas State University, Denton, Tex.; present address, Texas Technical College, Lubbock, Tex.

chemical experiments designed to ascertain the configuration of tetracovalent platinum(II). These compounds are analogous to the corresponding dichloro diammine complexes in structure (square planar), reactions, and methods of synthesis. Their solubility in organic solvents, although limited, is greater than that of the dichloro diammines so that they are more suitable for such studies. The cis isomer can be prepared by treating aqueous potassium tetrachloroplatinate(II) with pyridine.[1,8] The trans isomer can be prepared, in accordance with Chernyaev's trans effect, by the action of heat or concentrated hydrochloric acid on tetrakis(pyridine)platinum(II) chloride[1,8] or of the dilute acid on *trans*-dihydroxobis(pyridine)platinum(II).[6]

Procedure

A. *cis*-DICHLORO(DIPYRIDINE)PLATINUM(II)

$$K_2[PtCl_4] + 2C_5H_5N \rightarrow cis\text{-}[Pt(C_5H_5N)_2Cl_2] + 2KCl$$

To a solution of 10.0 g. (0.0241 mol) of potassium tetrachloroplatinate(II)* in 100 ml. of water contained in a 400-ml. beaker is added with continuous mechanical stirring a solution of 3.90 ml. (3.84 g.; 0.0495 mol)† of pure pyridine (density, 0.982 g./ml.) in 25 ml. of water. In a few minutes, a sulfur-yellow precipitate begins to form. The stirring is continued for several hours; then the mixture is allowed to stand in a refrigerator until precipitation appears complete (about 24 hours). The precipitate is then separated from the very pale yellow supernatant liquid by means of a 5-cm. sintered-glass funnel, washed several times with ice water to remove potassium chloride, air-dried, and finally dried at 100° for one hour. The yield is 9.15 g. (89.4%). *Anal.* Calcd. for [Pt(C_5H_5N)_2Cl_2]: Pt, 46.01. Found: Pt, 45.83.

* This compound may be prepared according to the directions of R. N. Keller, INORGANIC SYNTHESES, **2**, 247 (1946) or as described in synthesis 63 in this volume.

† Excess pyridine should be avoided to prevent reduction in yield due to formation of soluble tetrapyridineplatinum(II) chloride.

B. *trans-*DICHLORO(DIPYRIDINE)PLATINUM(II)

$$cis\text{-}[Pt(C_5H_5N)_2Cl_2] + 2C_5H_5N \rightarrow [Pt(C_5H_5N)_4]Cl_2$$

$$[Pt(C_5H_5N)_4]Cl_2 + 2HCl \xrightarrow{\Delta}$$
$$trans\text{-}[Pt(C_5H_5N)_2Cl_2] + 2C_5H_5N\cdot HCl$$

To 5 g. (0.0118 mol) of *cis-*dichloro(dipyridine)platinum-(II) (Procedure A) contained in a 250-ml. evaporating dish is added a solution of 20 ml. of pure pyridine in 50 ml. of water. Stirring during heating on the steam bath helps to effect the ready dissolution of the yellow solid, yielding a clean colorless solution of tetrapyridineplatinum(II) chloride. After filtering, if necessary to remove any undissolved impurities, the solution is evaporated to dryness on the steam bath (about 1 to 2 hours). Fifty milliliters of concentrated hydrochloric acid is added to the white residue and the mixture is again evaporated to dryness on the steam bath (about 1 to 2 hours), resulting in a pale yellow residue. If any unchanged white tetrapyridineplatinum(II) chloride is still present, an additional 25 ml. of hydrochloric acid should be added and the evaporation repeated. The small pale yellow crystals are transferred to a 5-cm. sintered-glass funnel, washed with several portions of ice water in order to remove hydrochloric acid, and then washed with ethanol and ethyl ether. The yield of air-dried product is quantitative except for mechanical losses.

The product may be recrystallized by dissolving it with stirring in a minimum volume (*ca.* 325 ml.) of boiling chloroform contained in a 525-ml. evaporating dish (*hood!*), filtering if necessary, concentrating the solution on the water bath to one-half its original volume* and cooling in an ice bath for 10 minutes. The resulting yellow crystals are collected on a 5-cm. sintered-glass funnel, washed with ethyl ether, air-dried, and dried at 100° for one hour. The yield is 4.3 g. (86%). An additional crop of crystals

---

* A stream of air directed across the surface of the solution considerably reduces the time required for this process.

(0.35 g.; 7.0%) may be precipitated from the mother liquor by adding ether (*ca.* 50 ml.) with vigorous stirring. The combined yield is 4.65 g. (93%). *Anal.* Calcd. for $[Pt(C_5H_5N)_2Cl_2]$: Pt, 46.01. Found: Pt, 45.79.

Properties[1,8]

cis- and *trans*-Dichloro(dipyridine)platinum(II) are pale yellow microcrystalline powders, the latter generally somewhat darker in color than the former.* They are both virtually insoluble in cold water, the cis isomer being more soluble than the trans. In general, the cis isomer is less soluble in organic solvents than the trans. The trans isomer is soluble in chloroform, acetone, N,N-dimethylformamide, and benzene, while the cis isomer is soluble in the first three solvents mentioned. Both isomers dissolve in aqueous pyridine to yield tetrapyridineplatinum(II) chloride.

On heating, the cis isomer begins to decompose at 224°, whereas the trans isomer does not begin to decompose until 256°. In phenol solution, the freezing-point depression shows that both isomers are monomolecular.[5] Because of the limited solubility of both isomers in nonpolar solvents, dipole moments have not been determined.[9]

Several tests are available for distinguishing the two isomers. Oxyphenylenetelluronium hydrogen sulfate [phenoxytellurine di(hydrogen sulfate)] gives a red coloration with the cis isomer, while the reagent is without effect on the trans isomer.

Both isomers respond to Kurnakov's test.[3] In hot aqueous solution, the cis isomer reacts with saturated aqueous thiourea to give a bright yellow solution, from which yellow needles of tetrakis(thiourea)platinum(II) chloride deposit on cooling, while the trans isomer gives no visible reaction, but on cooling deposits snow-white needles of *trans*-dichlorobis(thiourea)platinum(II).

* The exact shade of yellow of any particular isomer probably varies with particle size.

A boiling saturated solution of the cis isomer reacts with hydrobromic acid to give a bright yellow precipitate. Similar treatment of the trans isomer yields a fine yellowish white precipitate.

Boiling the isomers with water and silver(I) oxide yields the corresponding isomers of dihydroxo(dipyridine)platinum(II). The cis isomer of this compound is a hygroscopic yellow glassy mass, which readily dissolves in water to give a strongly basic solution. The trans isomer consists of long white asbestos-like needles, which dissolve only sparingly in water to give a feebly basic solution.

References

1. S. M. JØRGENSEN: *J. prakt. Chem.*, [2], **33**, 409 (1886).
2. A. WERNER: *Z. anorg. Chem.*, **3**, 267 (1893).
3. N. S. KURNAKOV: *J. Russ. Phys. Chem. Soc.*, **25**, 565 (1893).
4. S. M. JØRGENSEN: *Z. anorg. Chem.*, **25**, 353 (1900); **48**, 374 (1906).
5. A. HANTZSCH: *Ber.*, **59**, 2761 (1926).
6. H. D. K. DREW, F. W. PINKARD, W. WARDLAW, and E. G. COX: *J. Chem. Soc.*, **1932**, 988, 1004.
7. J. P. MATHIEU: *J. chim. phys.*, **36**, 308 (1939).
8. S. G. HEDIN: *Acta Univ. Lundensis*, II, **22**, 1 (1887).
9. K. A. JENSEN: *Z. anorg. u. allgem. Chem.*, **229**, 225 (1936).

INDEX OF CONTRIBUTORS

SUBJECT INDEX

Names employed in the cumulative subject index for Volumes I to VII are based upon those adopted in Volume II (Appendix, page 257) with a few changes that have been standardized and approved since publication of Volume II. No major changes seemed to be required for general conformity with the "Definitive Rules for Nomenclature of Inorganic Chemistry," 1957 Report of the Commission on the Nomenclature of Inorganic Chemistry of the International Union of Pure and Applied Chemistry (*J. Am. Chem. Soc.*, **82**, 5523–44 (1960)).

Some of the general principles that have been followed in setting up the index are: (1) The Stock system, based on the use of Roman numerals to designate oxidation state, has been generally preferred; for example, *Iron(III) chloride*, rather than ferric chloride; *Potassium hexachlororhenate-(IV)* rather than potassium chlororhenite. (2) In the case of heteropoly acids, the structure-determining element is named last, as for instance, *12-Tungstophosphoric acid* instead of phosphotungstic acid. (3) General headings such as *Chromium(III) complex compounds* and *Ammines* are employed for grouping coordination compounds of similar types. In addition, entries are made under the specific names for individual compounds. (Halo and cyano complexes, however, have been entered only under their specific names.) (4) Numerical prefixes and prefixes such as "ortho-" and "meta-" (but not "hypo-" and "per-") have been dropped at the beginning of many names to form general headings covering classes of compounds, such as *Silicon chlorides* and *Phosphoric acids*, with some duplicate entries, as *Pyrophosphoric acid*. (5) Formulas for specific compounds are used under general headings. The Formula Index should also prove particularly helpful in troublesome cases. (6) Because of changes in practice since the appearance of Volume I, it has been deemed advisable to make extra entries or cross references under names that have been changed and under many specific names for compounds entered also under general headings. (7) Two entries are made for compounds having two cations. (8) Unsatisfactory names that have been retained for want of better ones are placed in quotation marks.

Inverted names are used only for derivatives of silanes (as *Silane, dibromo-;* and *Disilane, hexachloro-*), germanes, phosphine, and the like, and as duplicate entries for metal alkyls and aryls, for example, *Sodium, cyclopentadienyl-* in addition to *Cyclopentadienylsodium*, but not for the few organic compounds. For the nomenclature of some of these and other classes of compounds, see the heading *Nomenclature*.

Headings are alphabeted straight through, letter by letter, as in *Chemical Abstracts* indexes, not word by word. Roman numerals in Stock names are ignored in alphabeting unless two or more names are otherwise the same.

A

FORMULA INDEX

The chief aim of this formula index, like that of other formula indexes, is to help in locating specific compounds, or even groups of compounds, that might not be easily found in the Subject Index. To this end, formulas have been used wherever it seemed best in their usual form (*i.e.*, as used in the text) for easy recognition: PbO_2, $EuSO_4$, Si_2C_6, $ThOBr_2$. However, for compounds containing the more uncommon elements and groupings and also for complexes, the significant or central atom has been placed first in the formula in order to throw together as many related compounds as possible. This procedure usually involves placing the cation last (often of relatively minor interest, especially in the case of alkali and alkaline earth metals): $PtCl_4K_2$; $[Al(C_2O_4)_3]K_3 \cdot 3H_2O$; $(IO_6)_2Ba_3H_4$. The guiding principle in these cases has been the chapter in the text in which the preparation of a compound is described. Where there is likely to be almost equal interest in two or more parts of a formula, two or more entries have been made: $AgClO_3$ and ClO_3Ag; Al_2Se_3 and Se_3Al_2; SF_6 and F_6S (simple halides other than fluorides are entered only under the other elements in most cases); $NaNH_2$ and NH_2Na; NH_2SO_3H and SO_3HNH_2.

Formulas for organic compounds are structural or semistructural so far as possible: $CH_3COCH_2COCH_3$. Consideration has been given to probable interest for inorganic chemists, *i.e.*, any element other than carbon, hydrogen, or oxygen in an organic molecule is given priority in the formula if only one entry is made, or equal rating if more than one entry; $Zr(C_5H_7O_2)_4 \cdot 10H_2O$; $NaC \equiv CH$ and $CH \equiv CNa$.

The names used with the formulas are the preferred specific names of the text or Subject Index.

The formulas are listed alphabetically by atoms or by groups (considered as units) and then according to the number of each in turn in the formula rather than by total number of atoms of each element; formulas with special isotopes follow the usual ones. This system results in arrangements such as the following:

$NH_2SO_3NH_4$
$(NH_2)_2C_2H_4$ (instead of $N_2H_4C_2H_4$, $N_2H_8C_2$, or $C_2H_8N_2$)
NH_3

$Si(CH_3)Cl_3$	FH
$Si(CH_3)_3Cl$	$F^{18}H$
$Si(CH=CH_2)Cl_3$	FNa
$Si(C_2H_4Cl)Cl_6$	$F^{18}Na$

311

$Cr(CN)_6K_3$ (instead of $CrC_6N_6K_3$)
$Cr(C_2H_3O_2)_2$ (instead of $CrC_4H_6O_4$)
$[Cr(C_2O_4)_3]K_3 \cdot 3H_2O$ (instead of $CrC_6O_{12}K_3 \cdot H_6O_3$ or $CrC_6O_{15}K_3H_6$)
$[Cr(en)_2Cl_2]Cl \cdot H_2O$ ("en" and a few similar abbreviations are retained for simplicity and are alphabeted as such rather than as $C_2H_4(NH_2)_2$ or $(NH_2)_2C_2H_4$, etc.)

A

$[Ag(C_5H_5N)_2]ClO_4$ Dipyridine-silver(I) perchlorate, **6**:6
$[Ag(C_5H_5N)_2]NO_3$ Dipyridine-silver(I) nitrate, **7**:172
$[Ag(C_6H_{10}H_{16})_2](ClO_4)_3$ Ethylene-bisbiguanidesilver(III) per-chlorate, **6**:78
$[Ag(C_6N_{10}H_{16})_2](OH)_3$ Ethylene-bisbiguanidesilver(III) hydrox-ide, **6**:78
$[Ag(C_6N_{10}H_{16})_2](NO_3)_3$ Ethylene-bisbiguanidesilver(III) nitrate, **6**:78
$[Ag(C_6N_{10}H_{16})_2](SO_4)_3$ Ethylene-bisbiguanidesilver(III) sulfate, **6**:77
$AgCl$ Silver chloride, **1**:3
$AgClO_3$ Silver chlorate, **2**:4
AgF Silver(I) fluoride, **4**:136; **5**:19, 20
AgF_2 Silver(II) fluoride, **3**:176
$AgFeS_2$ Silver dithioferrate(III), **6**:171
AgI Silver iodide, **2**:6
AgO Silver(II) oxide, **4**:12
Ag_2CN_2 Silver cyanamide, **1**:98
Ag_2CO_3 Silver(I) carbonate, **5**:19
Ag_2F Disilver fluoride, **5**:18, 19
Ag_2PO_3F Silver monofluorophos-phate, **3**:109
$Ag_7O_8NO_3$ Silver oxynitrate, **4**:13
$AlBr_3$ Aluminum bromide, **3**:30, 33
$[Al(C_2O_4)_3]K_3 \cdot 3H_2O$ Potassium trioxalatoaluminate, **1**:36
$Al(C_5H_7O_2)_3$ Aluminum acetylace-tonate, **2**:25
$AlCl_3$ Aluminum chloride, **7**:167

$[AlCl_4]^-[SeCl_3]^+$ Aluminum chlo-ride, compound with selenium-(IV) chloride, **5**:127
$AlCs(SO_4)_2 \cdot 12H_2O$ Cesium alum, **4**:8
AlP Aluminum phosphide, **4**:23
Al_2I_6 Aluminum iodide, **4**:117
Al_2Se_3 Aluminum selenide, **2**:183, 184
$As(CH_3)Br_2$ Arsine, methyldi-bromo-, **7**:82
$As(CH_3)Cl_2$ Arsine, methyldi-chloro-, **7**:85
$As(CH_3)I_2$ Arsine, methyldiiodo-, **6**:113; **7**:85
$As(CH_3)_2Br$ Arsine, dimethyl-bromo-, **7**:82
$As(CH_3)_2Cl$ Arsine, dimethyl-chloro-, **7**:85
$As(CH_3)_2I$ Arsine, dimethyliodo-, **6**:116; **7**:85
$As(CH_3)_3$ Arsine, trimethyl-, **7**:84n.
$As(C_2H_5)Cl_2$ Arsine, ethyl-dichloro-, **7**:85
$As(C_2H_5)_2Cl$ Arsine, diethyl-chloro-, **7**:85
$As(C_6H_5)Br_2$ Arsine, phenyl-dibromo-, **7**:85
AsF_3 Arsenic(III) fluoride, **4**:137, 150
AsH_3 Arsine, **7**:34, 41
AsI_3 Arsenic(III) iodide, **1**:103
As_2H Arsenic hydrides, polymeric, **7**:42
$AuBr_4K$ Potassium tetrabromoau-rate(III), **4**:14, 16
$AuCl_4H$ Tetrachloroauric(III) acid, **4**:14, 15

B

C

CF$_4$ Carbon tetrafluoride, 1:34, 3:178

CH≡CH   Acetylene, 2:76

CH≡CNa   Monosodium acetylide, 2:75, 76, 79

(CH$_2$CO)$_2$NBr   *N*-Bromosuccinimide, 7:135*n*.

CH$_3$COCH$_2$COCH$_3$ Acetylacetone (2,4-pentanedione), 2:10

CH$_3$CO$_2$C$_3$H$_7$ Isopropyl acetate, 3:48

CH$_3$CO$_2$H   Acetic acid, 2:119

Cl$_4$ Carbon tetraiodide, 3:37

(CN)$_2$ Cyanogen, 5:43, 44

(CN)$_x$ Paracyanogen, 2:92*n*.

CNCl   Cyanogen chloride, 2:90, 93

(CN)$_2$Ni   Nickel cyanide, 2:228

C(=NH)(NH$_2$)NHCN   Dicyanodiamide, 3:43

[C(=NH)(NH$_2$)$_2$H]NO$_3$ Guanidonium nitrate, 1:94, 96, 97

[C(NH$_2$)$_2$(N$_2$H$_3$)]HCO$_3$ Aminoguanidonium hydrogen carbonate, 3:45

CN$_2$Ag$_2$ Silver cyanamide, 1:98

CN$_2$H$_2$ Cyanamide, 3:39, 41

CNa≡CNa   Disodium acetylide, 2:79, 80

CO   Carbon monoxide, 2:81; 6:157*n*.

COF$_2$ Carbonyl fluoride, 6:155

CO(N$_3$)$_2$ Carbonyl azide, 4:35

CO$_2$ Carbon dioxide, 5:44*n*.; 6:157*n*.

CS$_2$·(C$_4$H$_9$)$_3$P   Phosphine, tri-*n*-butyl, compound with carbon disulfide, 6:90

C$_3$N$_3$Cl$_3$ Cyanuric chloride, 2:94

C$_4$H$_4$O$_6$Ba   Barium *dextro*-tartrate, 6:184

C$_4$H$_4$O$_6$Co   Cobalt(II) *dextro*-tartrate, 6:187

(C$_5$H$_5$)$_2$Fe   Ferrocene, 6:11, 15

(C$_5$H$_5$)$_2$Mg   Bis(cyclopentadienyl)-magnesium, 6:11

C$_5$H$_6$ Cyclopentadiene, 6:11; 7:101

C$_6$H$_2$I$_3$OH   *sym*-Triiodophenol, 7:179

[C$_6$H$_4$(OH)CH=NCH$_2$]$_2$ *N,N'*-Disalicylalethylenediamine, 3:198

C$_7$H$_6$ Ditropyl, 7:106

C$_7$H$_7$Br   Tropylium bromide, 7:105

CaCO$_3$ Marble, 2:49

CaCl$_2$ Calcium chloride, 6:20*n*.

CaF$_2$ Calcium fluoride, 4:137

CaHPO$_4$ Calcium hydrogen orthophosphate, 4:19, 22; 6:16–17; 2-hydrate, 4:19, 20

Ca(H$_2$PO$_4$)$_2$·H$_2$O   Calcium dihydrogen orthophosphate 1-hydrate, 4:18

Ca(OCl)$_2$ Calcium hypochlorite, 5:161, 165

Ca$_3$(PO$_4$)$_2$ Whitlockite, 6:17

Ca$_5$(OH)(PO$_4$)$_3$ or Ca$_{10}$(OH)$_2$-(PO$_4$)$_6$ Calcium orthophosphate, basic, 6:16; 7:63

CdCl$_2$ Cadmium chloride, 5:154; 7:168

Ce(NO$_3$)$_3$ Cerium(III) nitrate, 2:51

2Ce(NO$_3$)$_3$·3Mg(NO$_3$)$_2$·24H$_2$O   Cerium(III) magnesium nitrate, 2:57

Cl^{36}D   Deuterium chloride(Cl^{36}), 7:155

ClH   Hydrogen chloride, 1:147; 2:72; 3:14, 131; 4:57, 58; 5:25*n*.; 6:55

ClNH$_2$ Chloramide, 1:59, 62; 5:92

ClNO   Nitrosyl chloride, 1:55, 57; 4:48

ClNO$_2$ Nitryl chloride, 4:52

ClOH   Hypochlorous acid, 5:160, 164; 2-hydrate, 5:161

ClONa   Sodium hypochlorite, 1:90; 5:159*n*.

(ClO)$_2$Ca   Calcium hypochlorite, 5:161, 165

ClO$_2$ Chlorine(IV) oxide, 4:152; 8-hydrate, 4:158

ClO$_2$Na   Sodium chlorite, 4:156

D

DCl^{36} Deuterium chloride, **7**:155

D$_2$SO$_4$ Deuterosulfuric acid, **6**:21; **7**:155

D$_3$PO$_4$ Deuterophosphoric acid, **6**:81

E

EuCO$_3$ Europium(II) carbonate, **2**:69, 71

Eu(C$_2$H$_3$O$_2$)$_2$ Europium(II) acetate, **2**:68

Eu(C$_2$H$_3$O$_2$)$_3$ Europium(III) acetate, **2**:66

EuCl$_2$ Europium(II) chloride, **2**:68, 69, 71

EuSO$_4$ Europium(II) sulfate, **2**:69, 70

Eu$_2$(C$_2$O$_4$)$_3$·10H$_2$O   Europium(III) oxalate, **2**:66

Eu$_2$O$_3$ Europium(III) oxide, **2**:66

Eu$_3$Hg$_2$ Europium amalgam, **2**:68n.

F

FAg   Silver(I) fluoride, **4**:136; **5**:19, 20

FAg$_2$ Disilver fluoride, **5**:18

FBr   Bromine(I) fluoride, **3**:185

FH   Hydrogen fluoride, **1**:134; **3**:112; **4**:136; **7**:123

F^{18}H   Hydrogen fluoride(F^{18}), **7**:154

FHg   Mercury(I) fluoride, **4**:136

FNa   Sodium fluoride, **7**:120n.

F^{18}Na   Sodium fluoride(F^{18}), **7**:150

FPOCl(CH$_3$)   Methyl chlorofluorophosphite, **4**:141

FPO$_3$Ag$_2$ Silver monofluorophosphate, **3**:109

FPO$_3$K$_2$ Potassium monofluorophosphate, **3**:109

FPO$_3$(NH$_4$)$_2$ Ammonium monofluorophosphate, **2**:155

FPO$_3$Na$_2$ Sodium monofluorophosphate, **3**:106, 108

FSO$_3$H   Fluorosulfuric acid, **7**:127

F$_2$Ag   Silver(II) fluoride, **3**:176

F$_2$CO   Carbonyl fluoride, **6**:155

F$_2$Ca   Calcium fluoride, **4**:137

F$_2$Hg   Mercury(II) fluoride, **4**:136

F$_2$KH   Potassium hydrogen fluoride, **1**:140

F$_2$Ni   Nickel(II) fluoride, **3**:173

F$_2$O   Oxygen fluoride, **1**:109

F$_2$PO(CH$_3$)   Methyl difluorophosphite, **4**:141

F$_2$PO$_2$NH$_4$ Ammonium difluorophosphate, **2**:157

F$_2$SO   Thionyl fluoride, **6**:162; **7**:123

F$_2$SO$_2$ Sulfuryl fluoride, **6**:158

F$_2$S$_2$O$_6$ Peroxydisulfuryl difluoride, **7**:124

F$_2$V   Vanadium(II) fluoride, **7**:91

F$_3$As   Arsenic(III) fluoride, **4**:137, 150

F$_3$B   Boron fluoride, **1**:21, 23; compound with hexamethyldisilazane, **5**:58

F$_3$B·(CH$_3$)$_3$N   Boron fluoride–trimethylamine, **5**:26

F$_3$Br   Bromine(III) fluoride, **3**:184

(F$_3$C)$_2$O$_2$ Perfluorodimethyl peroxide, **6**:157

F$_3$Co   Cobalt(III) fluoride, **3**:175

F$_3$P   Phosphorus(III) fluoride, **4**:149; **5**:95

F$_3$Sb   Antimony(III) fluoride, **4**:134

F$_3$V   Vanadium(III) fluoride, **7**:87, 90

F$_4$C   Carbon tetrafluoride, **1**:34; **3**:178

F$_4$Ge   Germanium(IV) fluoride, **4**:147

F$_4$S   Sulfur(IV) fluoride, **7**:119

F$_4$Si   Silicon tetrafluoride, **4**:145

F$_5$Br   Bromine(V) fluoride, **3**:185

F$_5$Nb   Niobium(V) fluoride, **3**:179

F$_5$Ta   Tantalum(V) fluoride, **3**:179

O

(OCN)K Potassium cyanate, 2:87
(OCN)Na Sodium cyanate, 2:88
OF₂ Oxygen fluoride, 1:109
[OsBr₆](NH₄)₂ Ammonium hexa-
   bromoosmate(IV), 5:204
OsCl₅NH₂K₂ Potassium penta-
   chloroamidoosmate(IV), 6:207
OsCl₅NK₂ Potassium penta-
   chloronitridoosmate(IV), 6:206
[OsCl₆](NH₄)₂ Ammonium hexa-
   chloroosmate(IV), 5:206
OsO₂ Osmium(IV) oxide, 5:206
OsO₃NC(CH₃)₃ Trioxo(t-butyl-
   nitrido)osmium(VIII), 6:207
OsO₃NK Potassium nidridoos-
   mate(VIII), 6:204
OsO₄ Osmium(VIII) oxide, 5:205

P

PAl Aluminum phosphide, 4:23
PBr₃ Phosphorus(III) bromide,
   2:147
P(CH₃)Br₂ Phosphine, methyl-
   dibromo-, 7:85
P(CH₃)Cl₂ Phosphine, methyl-
   dichloro-, 7:85
P(CH₃)₂Br Phosphine, dimethyl-
   bromo-, 7:85
P(CH₃)₂Cl Phosphine, dimethyl-
   chloro-, 7:85
P(CH₃)₃ Phosphine, trimethyl-,
   7:85
P(CN)₃ Phosphorus(III) cyanide,
   6:84
P(C₂H₅)Br₂ Phosphine, ethyl-
   dibromo-, 7:85
P(C₂H₅)₂Br Phosphine, diethyl-
   bromo-, 7:85
P(C₄H₉)₃ Phosphine, tri-n-butyl-,
   6:87; compounds with CS₂ and
   HgCl₂, 6:90
[P(C₄H₉)₃NH₂]Cl (Tri-n-butyl)-
   aminophosphonium chloride,
   7:67

[P(C₆H₅)(C₄H₈)NH₂]Cl Phenyl-
   (cyclotetramethylene)amino-
   phosphonium chloride, 7:67
[P(C₆H₅)(C₅H₁₀)NH₂]Cl Phenyl-
   (cyclopentamethylene)amino-
   phosphonium chloride, 7:67
[P(C₆H₅)₃NH₂]Cl (Triphenyl)-
   aminophosphonium chloride,
   7:67; other salts, 7:69
PCl₃ Phosphorus(III) chloride,
   2:145
(PCl₃)₄Ni Tetrakis[phosphorus-
   (III) chloride]nickel, 6:201
PCl₃³⁶ Phosphorus(III) chloride-
   (Cl³⁶), 7:160
PCl₅ Phosphorus(V) chloride, 1:99
PCl₅·BCl₃ Phosphorus(V) chloride,
   compound with boron chloride,
   7:79
PCl₅·GaCl₃ Phosphorus(V) chlo-
   ride, compound with gallium-
   (III) chloride, 7:81
PF₃ Phosphorus(III) fluoride,
   4:149; 5:95
PF₆K Potassium hexafluorophos-
   phate, 3:111, 115
PF₆Na Sodium hexafluorophos-
   phate, 3:111, 115
PF₆NH₄ Ammonium hexafluoro-
   phosphate, 3:111, 114
PH₄I Phosphonium iodide, 2:141,
   143; 6:91
PNBr₂·PBr_n Phosphonitrile bro-
   mide compound, with phos-
   phorus(V) bromide, 7:77
(PNBr₂)₃ Phosphonitrile bromide,
   trimeric, 7:76
(PNBr₂)₄ Phosphonitrile bromide,
   tetrameric, 7:76
(PNCl₂)₃ Phosphonitrile chloride,
   trimeric, 6:94
(PNCl₂)₄ Phosphonitrile chloride,
   tetrameric, 6:94
P(NHC₆H₅)₃ Phosphine, triani-
   lino-, 5:61
P(=NH)OC₂H₅ Ethyl phosphen-
   imidate, 4:65

WCl$_6$ Tungsten(VI) chloride,
  3:163; **7**:167
WF$_6$ Tungsten(VI) fluoride, **3**:181
WO$_4$K$_2$ Potassium tungstate(VI),
  6:149
W$_2$Cl$_9$K$_3$ Potassium enneachloro-
  ditungstate(III), **5**:139; **6**:149,
  150; **7**:143
W$_3$Cl$_{14}$K$_5$ Pentapotassium tetra-
  decachlorotritungstate(III),
  6:149, 153

Y

Y(NO$_3$)$_3$ Yttrium nitrate, **5**:41

Z

ZnCl$_2$ Zinc chloride, **5**:154; **7**:168
ZrBr$_4$ Zirconium bromide, **1**:49
Zr(C$_5$H$_7$O$_2$)$_4$ Zirconium acetyl-
  acetonate, **2**:121; 10-hydrate,
  2:121
ZrCl$_4$ Zirconium chloride, **4**:121;
  7:167
ZrI$_4$ Zirconium(IV) iodide, **7**:52
ZrOBr$_2$ Zirconium oxybromide,
  1:51
ZrOCl$_2$ Zirconium oxychloride,
  3:76
ZrOCl$_2$·8H$_2$O Zirconium oxychlo-
  ride 8-hydrate, **2**:121
ZrO$_2$ Zirconium oxide, **3**:76